Christian Praise

THE TYNDALE PRESS

39 BEDFORD SQUARE LONDON WC1

First published 1957

Printed in Great Britain by
Lowe & Brydone (Printers) Limited, London, N.W.10

PREFACE

Christian Praise has been compiled in order to fill a gap which has long been evident. All the Christian Communions possess their own hymnals for use in public worship. Other large collections exist for mission services, Sunday Schools and clubs. This book is designed to meet the need of student fellowships, schools, church weekday meetings, Bible classes, Young People's Fellowships and the like for a fully representative hymnal of moderate size. Its basis is inter-denominational and it is hoped that through it some who are acquainted only with the hymn book of their own church may be introduced to a wider range of hymns and tunes.

In making the selection for *Christian Praise* two ideals have continually influenced the decisions of the compilers: first, that the terms in which the hymns set forth the praise of almighty God and express the gospel should be biblical; second, that in their form both of words and music, they should be of the highest possible standard. Nothing less seems demanded if the praise of God is to be worthily attempted and the worshippers influenced for good. Hymns expressing unreal sentiments and hymns which are intellectually unworthy cannot but be injurious in the long run. Only in what were regarded as ' border-line ' cases was present popularity or long custom allowed to influence choice.

In the production of the book many sources have been drawn upon. The ancient hymnody of the Church is represented. The Reformation and immediate post-Reformation period provide a number of metrical Psalms. From the 17th century come hymns by George Herbert (1593-1632), John Bunyan (1628-88) and Bishop Thomas Ken (1637-1711). It was not until the 18th century, however, that a hymn book in the modern sense was produced, when in 1707 (exactly 250 years ago) Isaac Watts published his *Hymns and Spiritual Songs* containing 150 hymns. Belonging to this period are four of the greatest names in English hymnody—those of Isaac Watts (1674-1748), Charles Wesley (1707-88), John Newton (1725-1807) and William Cowper (1731-1800). To these four writers alone we owe more than seventy hymns in our book, including one or two not now so well known such as Charles Wesley's ' Open Lord my inward ear ' and Newton's ' Let us love, and sing, and wonder.'

During the 19th century there was a flood of new hymns. Several poets— for example Reginald Heber (1783-1826)—published their own collections.

Other hymns, now well known, first appeared in magazines or in private collections of religious verse. Under the influence of the Oxford Movement a large number of early Greek and Latin hymns were translated by John Mason Neale (1818-66) and others. In 1861 came the publication of the first edition of *Hymns Ancient and Modern* followed by its second edition in 1875. This book brought into common use a great number of new hymns and is an important source to which subsequent compilers have been much indebted.

Although some of the hymns of this period were of poor quality, being marred by sentimental writing and an extravagant use of pious phraseology which now falls strangely on our ears, many others were of lasting worth and an examination of the Index of Authors and Translators will show that the great majority of the hymns in this book come from authors who lived during the 19th century.

The last fifty years have seen the publication of *The English Hymnal* (1906), *Songs of Praise* (1925), *The Church Hymnary* (1927), *The Methodist Hymn Book* (1933), *The Baptist Church Hymnal (Revised)* (1933), *The B.B.C. Hymn Book* (1950), *Ancient and Modern Revised* (1950) and *Congregational Praise* (1951). As the list of acknowledgments will show, from each of these books hymns have been selected for the present collection. The compilers have also drawn on other recent sources, and in addition have been able to include several hymns not previously published.

A special feature of the book is the inclusion of a fairly extensive group of Carols. Many of these are simple choir settings such as may be sung in the services of Lessons and Carols which are now in annual use in many churches and fellowships. For the same purpose a number of the Christmas hymns have been provided with descants.

As some will be aware, the wording of many hymns varies considerably from book to book. As far as possible the compilers have consulted the original text of the hymns, even though, in most cases, they have chosen the more modern version. In a very few instances they have made slight emendations of their own. An example is the hymn, ' Art thou weary, art thou languid ? ' which appears as ' Art thou weary, heavy laden ? ' Where the text has been comparatively recently modified the fact is indicated by the sign † following the author's name.

The music comes from many periods, including our own: some has been specially composed for *Christian Praise*. The aim has been to supply a wide variety of honest and singable tunes, and to exclude as far as possible those that are either mawkish or dull. This ideal has not always been achieved (for the music is not the only ingredient to be considered); but for the most part the compilers have taken a bold course, and trusted the users of the book to do likewise. A good tune can be relied on to drive out a bad one, if it is given a favourable introduction (for example, through its repeated use in voluntaries, or through a congregational practice) and a fair trial. The effort is worth making, for a poor tune is not only emotionally enervating: it offers what is shoddy in the service of God.

One musical feature of the book deserves particular mention. In the Metrical Index a facsimile of the first line of the music accompanies the name of each tune. It has too long been assumed that all organists can identify all tunes by their names. The metre and tune of each hymn are also named in the Index of First Lines, so that by recourse to the Metrical Index all the tunes available for any particular hymn can be quickly examined. Further, in the body of the book there are numerous cross-references to alternative tunes.

The preparation of any hymn book is a considerable undertaking and *Christian Praise* has been no exception to this general rule. The publishers take this opportunity of expressing their thanks to the many helpers who assisted them when the project was first launched by providing lists of hymns for consideration. In its later stages the work of selecting the hymns and tunes has been the responsibility of a small Editorial and Music Committee consisting of the Rev. F. D. Kidner (Chairman), the Rev. R. G. G. Hooper, Mr. Brian Howard, F.R.C.O., and Mr. Ronald Inchley. The publishers acknowledge with considerable gratitude the help received from this Committee. They join with them in expressing the hope that where the gospel of the grace of God is proclaimed this book may help to inspire saving faith in Jesus Christ, and that through this collection the spiritual life of those who believe may be deepened. May it be used by almighty God in His service and, in spite of the imperfection of human effort, bring glory to His name.

ACKNOWLEDGMENTS

Permission to use copyright hymns and music has been granted as listed below

HYMNS

Author	By Permission of	No. of Hymn
BARING-GOULD, S.	Messrs. J. Curwen & Sons Ltd.	272
„ „	Messrs. E. H. Freeman, Ltd.	385
Bennett, L. A.	Mr. Robert M. Bennett	218
Bevan, E. F.	Exors. of the late Dr. Bevan	198
Bridges, R.	The Clarendon Press, Oxford	51 (from *The Yattendon Hymnal* edited by Robert Bridges).
Butler, H. M.	The Exors. of the late E. M. Butler	16
Butler, M. E.	Messrs. Novello & Co. Ltd.	384
Byrne, M. E.	The Exors. of the late Miss E. H. Hull and Messrs. Chatto & Windus	317
CAIRD, G. B.	The Congregational Union of England and Wales	388
Campbell, J. D. Sutherland, ninth Duke of Argyll	His Grace, the Duke of Argyll	242
Clarkson, E. M.	The Inter-Varsity Christian Fellowship, U.S.A.	108
DEARMER, P.	The Oxford University Press	162, 303, 386
Deck, H. L. R.	Miss Elsie Deck	289
Draper, W. H.	Messrs. J. Curwen & Sons Ltd.	4
Fox, H. E.	The Church Missionary Society	167
Francis, S. T.	Messrs. Pickering & Inglis, Ltd.	15, 116
Fullerton, W. Y.	The Carey-Kingsgate Press	87
GRIMES, E. M.	Messrs. Marshall, Morgan & Scott, Ltd.	184
„ „	The South Africa General Mission	269
HARDY, H. E.	Messrs. A. R. Mowbray & Co. Ltd.	320
Head, B. P.	The Rev. A. Hanbury Head	133
Holland, H. S.	The Oxford University Press	165
Houghton, F.	The Author	89, 168, 182, 390
„ „	The Inter-Varsity Fellowship	284
Hoyle, R. B.	Mrs. Norah Mitchell	71
Hull, E. H.	The Exors. of the late Miss E. H. Hull and Messrs. Chatto & Windus	317
Humphreys, C. W.	The Oxford University Press	162

ACKNOWLEDGMENTS

Author	*By Permission of*	*No. of Hymn*
JENKINS, W. V.	The Rev. F. C. Vaughan Jenkins	302
KELLY, K. A. M.	The National Young Life Campaign	61
MacBEAN, L.	The Fifeshire Advertiser, Ltd.	395
Maude, M. F.	The Oxford University Press	259
Midlane, A.	Mr. W. J. R. Midlane	178
Monod, T.	Messrs. Marshall, Morgan & Scott, Ltd.	349
Moule, H. C. G.	Mrs. Isabel de Vere	342
PENN, W. J.	Miss E. J. Penn	193
Pierpoint, F. S.	The Oxford University Press	32
Pott, F.	The Proprietors of Hymns Ancient and Modern	17, 67
RALEIGH, A.	Messrs. Novello & Co. Ltd.	381
Ramsey, B. M.	Mr. George Taylor and Miss L. F. Ramsey	353
Rawley, F. H.	Messrs. Marshall, Morgan & Scott, Ltd.	253
Rees, T.	The Proprietors of Hymns Ancient and Modern	171
Roberts, K. E.	The Oxford University Press	387
SALMON, A. L.	The Exors. of the late Arthur L. Salmon	382
Smith, W. C.	The Oxford University Press	33
Stewart, A.	Messrs. Pickering & Inglis, Ltd.	159
TUCKER, F. B.	The Author	91
VINE, A. H.	Miss S. M. Vine	132
WILKINSON, K. B.	Miss E. W. Gould	348

MUSIC

Composer	*By Permission of*	*No. of Tune*
ALLEN, C. J.	The Composer	331
Armes, P.	The Proprietors of Hymns Ancient and Modern	81 (ii)
BAKER, F. G.	Miss C. Morley Horder	46
Barham-Gould, A. C.	Miss E. W. Gould	348
Baring-Gould, S.	Messrs. J. Curwen & Sons, Ltd.	209 (i)
Bell, J. M.	Mrs. M. H. Anderson	160
Blair, H.	The Church Society	200
Booth, J.	The Oxford University Press	181
Brown, A. H.	The Oxford University Press	122, 203, 345 (i)
Buck, P. C.	Mr. A. F. Buck	103 (ii)
,, ,,	The Oxford University Press	148 (ii)

ACKNOWLEDGMENTS

Composer	By Permission of	No. of Tune
Button, H. E.	Messrs. Novello & Co. Ltd.	10 (ii)
Dale, R. F.	The Exors. of the late Miss M. Pickersgill-Cunliffe	195
Davies, H. Walford	Miss C. Morley Horder	392
,, ,,	The Exors. of the late Sir H. Walford Davies	382 (published by Novello & Co.)
Duckworth, F.	Mr. F. C. Duckworth	28 (ii)
Elliott, J. W.	Messrs. Novello & Co. Ltd.	74 (ii), 366
Evans, D. E.	The Union of Welsh Independents	231
Farrer, J. D.	The Oxford University Press	369
Ferguson, W. H.	The Oxford University Press	93 (ii), 112
,, ,,	The Royal School of Church Music	90 (ii)
Finlay, K. G.	The Composer	5, 34 (ii), 43 (ii), 140 (i), 192, 281, 319, 320
Francis, S. T.	Messrs. Pickering & Inglis, Ltd.	15
Greatorex, W.	The Oxford University Press	16
Green, H.	The South Africa General Mission	269
Hammond, M. J.	The Composer	133
Harris, W. H.	The Composer	84
,, ,,	The Oxford University Press	242
Harwood, B.	The Exors. of the late Dr. Basil Harwood	10 (i), 47, 78, 257, 318 (ii), 336
Holmes, H. J. E.	Miss M. J. Holmes	275 (ii)
Holst, G.	The Exors. of the late Gustav Holst	397
Hughes, J.	Mrs. Hannah M. Hughes	283 (ii)
Hunt, J. E.	The Composer	119 (i), 335 (ii)
Ireland, J.	The Composer	46 (i)
James, F.	The Methodist Publishing House	32
Jenkins, D.	Messrs. Snell & Sons, Ltd., Swansea.	238
Kelly, K. A. M.	The National Young Life Campaign	61
Kidner, F. D.	The Composer	168
Lahee, H.	Miss C. Morley Horder	98
Langran, J.	Messrs. Novello & Co. Ltd.	152 (ii)
Ley, H. G.	Messrs. A. & C. Black Ltd.	293 (i)
MacLagan, W. D.	The Oxford University Press	259
Maker, F. C.	The Psalms & Hymns Trust	59, 257 (ii), 339 (ii)
Mann, A. H.	Dr. F. R. Goodliffe	268

Composer	By Permission of	No. of Tune
Martin, G. C.	The Proprietors of Hymns Ancient and Modern	283 (i)
Matthews, T. R.	Messrs. Novello & Co. Ltd.	45
Morley, H. K.	Mrs. Evelyn H. Manwell	340
Mountain, J.	Messrs. Marshall, Morgan & Scott, Ltd.	334
NAYLOR, E. W.	Mr. Bernard Naylor	299 (ii)
PALMER, P. S.	The Congregational Union of England and Wales	106
,, ,,	The Inter-Varsity Fellowship	184, 300, 349
Parry, C. H. H.	Messrs. Novello & Co. Ltd.	9, 339
Peace, A. L.	Messrs. Novello & Co. Ltd.	347
Poole, C. W.	Miss C. Morley Horder	188
Prout, E.	The Congregational Union of England and Wales	222
RAMSEY, B. M.	Mr. George Taylor	353
Roberts, R. E.	The Oxford University Press	74, 367
Routley, E.	The Congregational Union of England and Wales	235 (i), 243
Rowlands, W. P.	Mr. T. H. Rowlands	271
SANKEY, I. D.	Messrs. Marshall, Morgan & Scott, Ltd.	345 (ii)
Scott-Gatty, A.	The Abbot of Downside	206, 342
Shaw, M.	Messrs. J. Curwen & Sons Ltd.	180, 272
,, ,,	The Royal School of Church Music	362 (ii)
Slater, G.	The Oxford University Press	193
Smith, A. B.	The Congregational Union of England and Wales	236
Somervell, A.	The Exors. of the late Sir Arthur Somervell	101
Stanford, C. V.	Messrs. Stainer & Bell, Ltd.	91
Stanton, W. K.	The Oxford University Press	167, 284
Stebbins, G.	The Charles Alexander Copyright Trust	365 (from *Alexander's Hymns* No. 3)
TAYLOR, C. V.	The Oxford University Press	143, 335 (i)
Thiman, E. H.	The Composer	199
,, ,,	The Congregational Union of England and Wales	295 (i)
Thorne, E. H.	The Proprietors of Hymns Ancient and Modern	314
UNIVERSITY OF WALES	The Oxford University Press	179 (i)
VAUGHAN WILLIAMS, R.	The Oxford University Press	118, 147
WARRELL, A. S.	The Oxford University Press	237, 368
Williams, T. J.	Messrs. W. Gwenlyn Evans & Son	116
Wilson, F. R. D.	The Composer	261 (i)
Winn, C.	The Composer	111 (ii)
Wood, T.	The Oxford University Press	302

ACKNOWLEDGMENTS

Thanks are also due to the following who have kindly allowed the inclusion of versions, harmonizations and arrangements of traditional and other melodies. An asterisk after the number of the tune denotes that the acknowledgment concerns a descant or fa-burden arrangement only.

Messrs. A. & C. Black, Ltd., 89, 390

The Congregational Union of England and Wales, 114 (ii), 198, 316, 317, 381, 387

Messrs. J. Curwen and Sons, Ltd., 396

The Faith Press, Ltd., (reprinted from *The Tenor Tune Book*), 19*, 25*, 248*

E. H. Freeman, Ltd., 385

Messrs. Novello & Co. Ltd., 39, 40*, 391*, 394*

The Oxford University Press, 1*, 3, 4, 22, 29, 38, 53(i), 57(ii), 67(ii), 69, 124, 171, 174, 177, 197, 202(i), 202(ii), 215(ii), 218, 223, 252, 253, 262, 266, 273, 279, 291(i), 291(ii), 303, 370(ii), 386, 400

Miss Peggy Spencer Palmer, 106*

The Proprietors of Hymns Ancient and Modern, 130, 372

Messrs. Stainer & Bell, Ltd., 277(i), 389

The pointing of the *Te Deum, Magnificat* and *Nunc Dimittis* is taken from *The Parish Psalter* and is reprinted by permission of The Faith Press, Ltd.

The Rev. F. Derek Kidner has harmonized or adapted the following tunes: 41*, 54, 87*, 140, 152(ii), 249, 395, 398*

Mr. Brian S. Howard has harmonized or adapted the following tunes: 15, 37*, 142, 250, 251, 340, 343.

Although every effort has been made to trace the holders of copyright, in the following instances it has so far proved impossible to get into touch with the present owner or to establish whether copyright does in fact still exist. If for either of these reasons or through inadvertence, any rights still surviving have not been acknowledged, the Publishers tender their apologies to those concerned and express their willingness to make any necessary corrections in subsequent reprints.

HYMNS: 22, 185, 200, 238; TUNES: 178, 251(ii).

CONTENTS

To enable hymns to be found quickly their numbers are printed at the top right or left hand corners of the pages as well as above the music.

INDEXES

THE GODHEAD

PRAISE AND ADORATION

1

CARLISLE (S.M.)   CHARLES LOCKHART (1745-1815)
Descant for verses 3 and 5 by SYDNEY HUGO NICHOLSON (1875-1947)

This hymn may also be sung to the tune QUINTA, No. 179(i)

Based on Nehemiah ix. 5

S TAND up, and bless the Lord,
Ye people of His choice;
Stand up, and bless the Lord your God
With heart and soul and voice.

2 Though high above all praise,
Above all blessing high,
Who would not fear His holy name,
And praise and magnify?

3 O for the living flame
From His own altar brought,
To touch our lips, our minds inspire,
And wing to heaven our thought!

4 God is our strength and song,
And His salvation ours;
Then be His love in Christ proclaimed
With all our ransomed powers.

5 Stand up, and bless the Lord,
The Lord your God adore;
Stand up, and bless His glorious name
Henceforth for evermore.

JAMES MONTGOMERY (1771-1854)

13

2

OLD 100TH   (L.M.)   From the *Genevan Psalter* (1551)

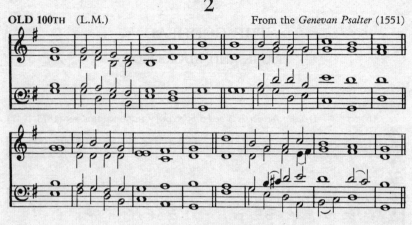

ALTERNATIVE VERSION

Verse 3: Melody in the Tenor   Fa-burden by JOHN DOWLAND (1562-1626)

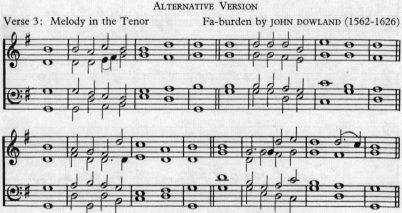

Based on Psalm c

ALL people that on earth do dwell,
    Sing to the Lord with cheerful voice.
Him serve with fear, His praise forth tell;
    Come ye before Him and rejoice.

2 The Lord, ye know, is God indeed;
    Without our aid He did us make;
We are His folk, He doth us feed,
    And for His sheep He doth us take.

3 O enter then His gates with praise,
    Approach with joy His courts unto;
Praise, laud, and bless His name always,
    For it is seemly so to do.

4 For why, the Lord our God is good;
    His mercy is for ever sure;
His truth at all times firmly stood,
    And shall from age to age endure.

WILLIAM KETHE (d. 1594); in Day's *Psalter* (1561)

3

ANDERNACH (L.M.) *Andernach Gesangbuch* (1608)

Based on Psalm c

BEFORE Jehovah's aweful throne,
Ye nations, bow with sacred joy;
Know that the Lord is God alone;
He can create, and He destroy.

His sovereign power, without our aid,
Made us of clay, and formed us men;
And, when like wandering sheep we strayed,
He brought us to His fold again.

3 We are His people, we His care,—
Our souls and all our mortal frame:
What lasting honours shall we rear,
Almighty Maker, to Thy name?

4 We'll crowd Thy gates with thankful songs,
High as the heavens our voices raise;
And earth, with her ten thousand tongues,
Shall fill Thy courts with sounding praise.

5 Wide as the world is Thy command,
Vast as eternity Thy love;
Firm as a rock Thy truth shall stand,
When rolling years shall cease to move.

ISAAC WATTS (1674-1748);
alt. JOHN WESLEY (1703-91)

4

LASST UNS ERFREUEN (8 8. 4 4. 8 8 and Hallelujah)

Melody from *Geistliche Kirchengesang* (Cologne, 1623)

LAUDATO SIA DIO MIO SIGNORE

O give thanks unto the Lord; for he is good: for his mercy endureth for ever (Psalm cxxxvi. 1)

ALL creatures of our God and King,
  Lift up your voice and with us sing:
    Hallelujah, Hallelujah!
  Thou burning sun with golden beam,
  Thou silver moon with softer gleam:

O praise Him, O praise Him,
Hallelujah, Hallelujah, Hallelujah!

2 Thou rushing wind that art so strong,
    Ye clouds that sail in heaven along,
      O praise Him, Hallelujah!
    Thou rising morn, in praise rejoice,
    Ye lights of evening, find a voice:

3 Thou flowing water, pure and clear,
    Make music for thy Lord to hear,
      Hallelujah, Hallelujah!
    Thou fire so masterful and bright,
    That givest man both warmth and light:

4 Dear mother earth, who day by day
    Unfoldest blessings on our way,
      O praise Him, Hallelujah!
    The flowers and fruits that in thee grow,
    Let them His glory also show:

5 And all ye men of tender heart,
    Forgiving others, take your part,
      O sing ye, Hallelujah!
    Ye who long pain and sorrow bear,
    Praise God and on Him cast your care:

6 And thou, most kind and gentle death,
   Waiting to hush our latest breath,
     O praise Him, Hallelujah!
   Thou leadest home the child of God,
   And Christ our Lord the way hath trod:

7 Let all things their Creator bless,
   And worship Him in humbleness,
     O praise Him, Hallelujah!
   Praise, praise the Father, praise the Son,
   And praise the Spirit, Three in One:

WILLIAM HENRY DRAPER (1855-1933);
based on *The Sun Song* by FRANCIS OF ASSISI (1182-1226)

5

GARELOCHSIDE (S.M.)   KENNETH GEORGE FINLAY (1882-)

This hymn may also be sung to the tune VENICE, No. 178

Based on Psalm ciii. 1-7

*O BLESS the Lord, my soul!
   Let all within me join,
And aid my tongue to bless His name
   Whose favours are divine.

2 O bless the Lord, my soul!
   Nor let His mercies lie
Forgotten in unthankfulness,
   And without praises die.

3 'Tis He forgives thy sins,
   'Tis He relieves thy pain,
'Tis He that heals thy sicknesses,
   And makes thee young again.

4 He crowns thy life with love,
   When ransomed from the grave;
He that redeemed my soul from hell
   Hath sovereign power to save.

5 He fills the poor with good,
   He gives the sufferers rest;
The Lord hath judgments for the proud,
   And justice for the oppressed.

6 His wondrous works and ways
   He made by Moses known;
But sent the world His truth and grace
   By His belovèd Son.

ISAAC WATTS (1674-1748)

*If desired, this verse may be repeated after verse 6

6

WESTMINSTER (C.M.)   JAMES TURLE (1802-82)

This nymn may also be sung to the tune ST. FULBERT, No. 326

The high and lofty One that inhabiteth eternity, whose name is Holy (Isaiah lvii. 15)

MY God, how wonderful Thou art,
    Thy majesty how bright,
How beautiful Thy mercy-seat,
    In depths of burning light!

2 How dread are Thine eternal years,
    O everlasting Lord,
By prostrate spirits day and night
    Incessantly adored!

3 Oh, how I fear Thee, living God,
    With deepest, tenderest fears,
And worship Thee with trembling hope
    And penitential tears!

4 Yet I may love Thee too, O Lord,
    Almighty as Thou art,
For Thou hast stooped to ask of me
    The love of my poor heart.

5 No earthly father loves like Thee;
    No mother, e'er so mild,
Bears and forbears as Thou hast done
    With me, Thy sinful child.

6 How wonderful, how beautiful,
    The sight of Thee must be,
Thine endless wisdom, boundless power,
    And aweful purity!

FREDERICK WILLIAM FABER (1814-63)

7

GERONTIUS (C.M.)   JOHN BACCHUS DYKES (1823-76)

This hymn may also be sung to the tunes CHORUS ANGELORUM, No. 101, and RICHMOND, No. 248

The second man is the Lord from heaven (1 Corinthians xv. 47)

* PRAISE to the Holiest in the height,
    And in the depth be praise,—
In all His words most wonderful,
    Most sure in all His ways.

2 O loving wisdom of our God!
    When all was sin and shame,
A second Adam to the fight
    And to the rescue came.

3 O wisest love! that flesh and blood,
    Which did in Adam fail,
Should strive afresh against the foe,
    Should strive and should prevail;

4 And that a higher gift than grace
    Should flesh and blood refine,
God's presence, and His very self
    And essence all-divine.

5 O generous love! that He who smote
    In Man for man, the foe,
The double agony in Man,
    For man, should undergo.

6 And in the garden secretly,
    And on the cross on high,
Should teach His brethren, and inspire
    To suffer and to die.

JOHN HENRY NEWMAN (1801-90)

*If desired, this verse may be repeated after verse 6

19

8

PRAISE, MY SOUL   (8 7. 8 7. 8 7.)   JOHN GOSS (1800-80)

Unison

1. PRAISE, my soul, the King of hea - ven, To His feet thy tri-bute bring;

Ran-somed, healed, re-stored, for - giv - en, Who like thee His praise should sing?

Praise Him! Praise Him! Praise Him! Praise Him! Praise the ev - er - last-ing King.

Harmony

2. Praise Him for His grace and fa - vour To our fa-thers in dis - tress;

Praise Him, still the same for ev - er, Slow to chide and swift to bless:

Praise Him! Praise Him! Praise Him! Praise Him! Glo-rious in His faith-ful - ness.

Trebles only

3. Fa-ther-like He tends and spares us; Well our fee-ble frame He knows;

In His hands He gen-tly bears us, Res-cues us from all our foes:

Praise Him! Praise Him! Praise Him! Praise Him! Wide-ly as His mer-cy flows.

Based on Psalm ciii

HENRY FRANCIS LYTE (1793-1847)

9

LAUDATE DOMINUM (5 5. 5 5. 6 5. 6 5.)

CHARLES HUBERT HASTINGS PARRY (1848-1918)

Let every thing that hath breath praise the Lord (Psalm cl. 6)

O PRAISE ye the Lord!
   Praise Him in the height;
Rejoice in His Word,
   Ye angels of light;
Ye heavens, adore Him
   By whom ye were made,
And worship before Him,
   In brightness arrayed.

2 O praise ye the Lord!
   Praise Him upon earth,
In tuneful accord,
   Ye sons of new birth;
Praise Him who hath brought you
   His grace from above,
Praise Him who hath taught you
   To sing of His love.

3 O praise ye the Lord,
   All things that give sound;
Each jubilant chord,
   Re-echo around;
Loud organs, His glory
   Forth tell in deep tone,
And sweet harp, the story
   Of what He hath done.

4 O praise ye the Lord!
   Thanksgiving and song
To Him be outpoured
   All ages along;
For love in creation,
   For heaven restored,
For grace of salvation
   O praise ye the Lord!

HENRY WILLIAMS BAKER (1821-77)

10

LUCKINGTON   (10 4. 6 6. 6 6. 10 4.)   BASIL HARWOOD (1859-1949)

All the earth shall worship thee, and shall sing unto thee (Psalm lxvi. 4)

LET all the world in every corner sing,
    ' My God and King!'
The heavens are not too high,
His praise may thither fly:
The earth is not too low,
His praises there may grow.
Let all the world in every corner sing,
    ' My God and King!'

2 Let all the world in every corner sing,
    'My God and King!'
The Church with psalms must shout,
No door can keep them out:
But, above all, the heart
Must bear the longest part.
Let all the world in every corner sing,
    'My God and King!'

GEORGE HERBERT (1593-1633)

ALTERNATIVE TUNE

WILTON (10 4. 6 6. 6 6. 10 4.)   H. ELLIOT BUTTON (1861-1925)

GEORGE HERBERT (1593-1633)

11

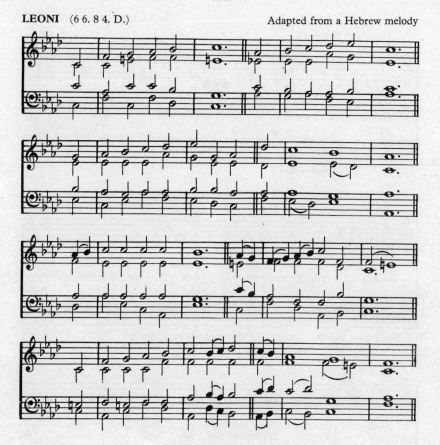

LEONI (6 6. 8 4. D.)   Adapted from a Hebrew melody

My praise shall be continually of thee (Psalm lxxi. 6)

THE God of Abraham praise,
    Who reigns enthroned above,
Ancient of everlasting days,
    And God of love.
Jehovah, great I AM!
By earth and heaven confessed,
I bow, and bless the sacred name,
    For ever blest.

2   The God of Abraham praise,
        At whose supreme command
From earth I rise, and seek the joys
        At His right hand.
    I all on earth forsake,
    Its wisdom, fame, and power;
And Him my only portion make,
        My shield and tower.

3   He by Himself hath sworn,
    I on His oath depend:
I shall, on eagle's wings upborne,
    To heaven ascend;
    I shall behold His face,
    I shall His power adore,
And sing the wonders of His grace
    For evermore.

4   There dwells the Lord our King,
    The Lord our Righteousness,
Triumphant o'er the world and sin,
    The Prince of Peace.
    On Zion's sacred height
    His kingdom He maintains,
And glorious with His saints in light
    For ever reigns.

5   The whole triumphant host
    Give thanks to God on high;
'Hail, Father, Son and Holy Ghost!'
    They ever cry.
Hail, Abraham's God, and mine!
    (I join the heavenly lays),
All might and majesty are Thine,
    And endless praise.

THOMAS OLIVERS (1725-99); based on the Hebrew *Yigdal*

12

MONKLAND   (7 7. 7 7.)   Melody from *Hymn Tunes of the United Brethren* (1824)
Arr. by JOHN BERNARD WILKES (1785-1869)

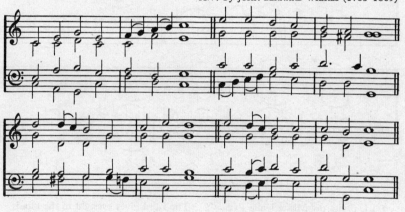

Based on Psalm cxxxvi

LET us with a gladsome mind
Praise the Lord, for He is kind:

For His mercies shall endure,
Ever faithful, ever sure.

2 He, with all-commanding might,
Filled the new-made world with light:

3 All things living He doth feed;
His full hand supplies their need:

4 He His chosen race did bless
In the wasteful wilderness:

5 He hath with a piteous eye
Looked upon our misery:

6 Let us then with gladsome mind
Praise the Lord, for He is kind:

JOHN MILTON (1608-74)

13

MONMOUTH (8 8 8. D.)   GABRIEL DAVIS (*c.* 1768-1824)

Paraphrase of Psalm cxlvi

I'LL praise my Maker while I've
    breath;
And when my voice is lost in death,
    Praise shall employ my nobler powers;
My days of praise shall ne'er be past,
While life, and thought, and being last,
    Or immortality endures.

2 Happy the man whose hopes rely
On Israel's God! He made the sky,
    And earth, and sea, with all their train:
His truth for ever stands secure;
He saves the oppressed, He feeds the poor,
    And none shall find His promise vain.

3 The Lord gives eyesight to the blind;
The Lord supports the fainting mind;
    He sends the labouring conscience
        peace;
He helps the stranger in distress,
The widow and the fatherless,
    And grants the prisoner sweet release.

4 I'll praise Him while He lends me breath;
And when my voice is lost in death,
    Praise shall employ my nobler powers;
My days of praise shall ne'er be past,
While life, and thought, and being last,
    Or immortality endures.

ISAAC WATTS (1674-1748)†

14

GWALCHMAI (7 4. 7 4. D.)   JOSEPH DAVID JONES (1827-70)

Let such as love thy salvation say continually, Let God be magnified (Psalm lxx. 4)

KING of glory, King of peace,
  I will love Thee;
And that love may never cease,
  I will move Thee.
Thou hast granted my request,
  Thou hast heard me;
Thou didst note my working breast,
  Thou hast spared me.

2 Wherefore with my utmost art
    I will sing Thee,
  And the cream of all my heart
    I will bring Thee.
  Though my sins against me cried,
    Thou didst clear me;
  And alone, when they replied,
    Thou didst hear me.

3 Seven whole days, not one in seven,
    I will praise Thee;
  In my heart, though not in heaven,
    I can raise Thee.
  Small it is, in this poor sort
    To enrol Thee:
  E'en eternity's too short,
    To extol Thee.

GEORGE HERBERT (1593-1633)

15

WORSHIP   (7 7 7. 6.)   SAMUEL TREVOR FRANCIS (1834-1925)

By him therefore let us offer the sacrifice of praise to God continually (Hebrews xiii. 15)

Gracious God, we worship Thee,
Reverently we bow the knee;
Jesus Christ our only plea:
Father, we adore Thee.

2 Vast Thy love, how deep, how wide,
In the gift of Him who died;
Righteous claims all satisfied:
Father, we adore Thee.

3 Low we bow before Thy face,
Sons of God, O wondrous place;
Great the riches of Thy grace:
Father, we adore Thee.

4 By Thy Spirit grant that we
Worshippers in truth may be;
Praise, as incense sweet to Thee:
Father, we adore Thee.

5 Yet again our song we raise,
Note of deep adoring praise;
Now, and soon through endless days:
Father, we adore Thee.

SAMUEL TREVOR FRANCIS (1834-1925)

16

WOODLANDS   (10 10. 10 10.)   WALTER GREATOREX (1877-1949)

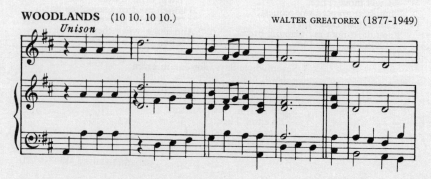

This hymn may also be sung to the tune JULIUS, No. 362 (ii)

Let us lift up our heart with our hands unto God in the heavens (Lamentations iii. 41)

'LIFT up your hearts!' We lift them, Lord, to Thee;
Here at thy feet none other may we see:
'Lift up your hearts!' E'en so, with one accord,
We lift them up, we lift them to the Lord.

2 Above the level of the former years,
The mire of sin, the slough of guilty fears,
The mist of doubt, the blight of love's decay,
O Lord of Light, lift all our hearts today!

3 Above the swamps of subterfuge and shame,
The deeds, the thoughts, that honour may not name,
The halting tongue that dares not tell the whole,
O Lord of Truth, lift every Christian soul!

4 Lift every gift that Thou Thyself hast given;
Low lies the best till lifted up to heaven:
Low lie the bounding heart, the teeming brain,
Till, sent from God, they mount to God again.

5 Then, as the trumpet-call in after years,
'Lift up your hearts!' rings pealing in our ears,
Still shall those hearts respond with full accord,
'We lift them up, we lift them to the Lord!'

HENRY MONTAGUE BUTLER (1833-1918)

17

ANGEL-VOICES   (8 5. 8 5. 8 4 3.)   EDWIN GEORGE MONK (1819-1900)

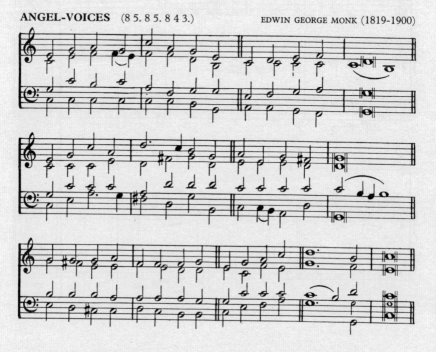

Praise God in his sanctuary (Psalm cl. 1)

ANGEL voices, ever singing
Round Thy throne of light,
Angel harps, for ever ringing,
Rest not day nor night;
Thousands only live to bless Thee,
And confess Thee
Lord of might.

2 Thou who art beyond the farthest
Mortal eye can scan,
Can it be that Thou regardest
Songs of sinful man?
Can we know that Thou art near us
And wilt hear us?
Yea, we can.

3 Yea, we know that Thou rejoicest
O'er each work of Thine;
Thou didst ears and hands and voices
For Thy praise design;
Craftsman's art and music's measure
For Thy pleasure
All combine.

4 In Thy house, great God, we offer
Of Thine own to Thee,
And for Thine acceptance proffer,
All unworthily,
Hearts and minds and hands and voices,
In our choicest
Psalmody.

5 Honour, glory, might, and merit
Thine shall ever be,
Father, Son, and Holy Spirit,
Blessèd Trinity.
Of the best that Thou hast given,
Earth and heaven
Render Thee.

FRANCIS POTT (1832-1909)

18

LAUS DEO (8 7. 8 7.)   RICHARD REDHEAD (1820-1901)

Based on Isaiah vi. 1-3

BRIGHT the vision that delighted
Once the sight of Judah's seer;
Sweet the countless tongues united
To entrance the prophet's ear.

2 Round the Lord in glory seated,
Cherubim and seraphim
Filled His temple, and repeated
Each to each the alternate hymn:

3 'Lord Thy glory fills the heaven;
Earth is with its fullness stored;
Unto Thee be glory given,
Holy, Holy, Holy, Lord.'

4 Heaven is still with glory ringing,
Earth takes up the angels' cry,
'Holy, Holy, Holy,'—singing,
'Lord of hosts, The Lord most high '

5 With His seraph train before Him,
With His holy Church below,
Thus unite we to adore Him,
Bid we thus our anthem flow:

6 'Lord, Thy glory fills the heaven;
Earth is with its fullness stored;
Unto Thee be glory given,
Holy, Holy, Holy, Lord.'

            RICHARD MANT (1776-1848)

19

DARWALL'S 148TH   (6 6. 6 6. 4 4. 4 4.)   JOHN DARWALL (1731-89)

ALTERNATIVE VERSION

Verse 4: Melody in the Tenor   Fa-burden by MARTIN SHAW (1875-)

(When this setting is sung in four-part harmony, omit the small notes.)

Sing unto the Lord, bless his name; shew forth his salvation from day to day (Psalm xcvi. 2)

YE holy angels bright,
　Who wait at God's right hand,
Or through the realms of light
Fly at your Lord's command,
　Assist our song,
　　Or else the theme
　　Too high doth seem
　For mortal tongue.

2 Ye blessèd souls at rest,
　Who ran this earthly race,
And now, from sin released,
Behold the Saviour's face,
　His praises sound,
　　As in His light
　　With sweet delight
　Ye do abound.

3 Ye saints, who toil below,
　Adore your heavenly King,
And onward as ye go,
　Some joyful anthem sing;
　Take what He gives,
　　And praise Him still,
　　Through good or ill,
　Who ever lives.

4 My soul, bear thou thy part,
　Triumph in God above,
And with a well-tuned heart
Sing thou the songs of love.
　Let all thy days
　　Till life shall end,
　　Whate'er He send,
　Be filled with praise.

RICHARD BAXTER (1615-91) and others

20

AUSTRIA (8 7. 8 7. D.)　　　　　FRANZ JOSEF HAYDN (1732-1809)

Based on Psalm cxlviii

PRAISE the Lord! ye heavens,
　adore Him;
　Praise Him, angels, in the height;
Sun and moon, rejoice before Him,
　Praise Him, all ye stars and light.
Praise the Lord! for He hath spoken:
　Worlds His mighty voice obeyed;
Laws, which never shall be broken,
　For their guidance He hath made.

2 Praise the Lord! for He is glorious;
　Never shall His promise fail;
God hath made His saints victorious,
　Sin and death shall not prevail.
Praise the God of our salvation;
　Hosts on high, His power proclaim;
Heaven and earth and all creation,
　Laud and magnify His name.

Printed separately and pasted into copies of
The Foundling Hospital Collection (1796)

21

NICAEA (11 12. 12 10.)   JOHN BACCHUS DYKES (1823-76)

Based on Revelation iv. 8-11

HOLY, holy, holy, Lord God Almighty!
Early in the morning our song shall rise to Thee:
Holy, holy, holy, merciful and mighty,
God in Three Persons, blessèd Trinity!

2 Holy, holy, holy! all the saints adore Thee,
Casting down their golden crowns around the glassy sea,
Cherubim and seraphim falling down before Thee,
Which wert, and art, and evermore shalt be.

3 Holy, holy, holy! though the darkness hide Thee,
Though the eye of sinful man Thy glory may not see,
Only Thou art holy, there is none beside Thee,
Perfect in power, in love, and purity.

4 Holy, holy, holy, Lord God Almighty!
All Thy works shall praise Thy name in earth and sky and sea;
Holy, holy, holy, merciful and mighty,
God in Three Persons, blessèd Trinity!

REGINALD HEBER (1783-1826)

22

CHRISTE SANCTORUM (11 11 11. 5.)

Melody by FRANÇOIS DE LA FEILLÉE (1808)

O PATER SANCTE

Let every thing that hath breath praise the Lord (Psalm cl. 6)

FATHER most holy, merciful and loving,
Jesus, Redeemer, ever to be worshipped,
Life-giving Spirit, Comforter most gracious,
God everlasting;

2 Three in a wondrous unity unbroken,
One perfect Godhead, love that never faileth,
Light of the angels, succour of the needy,
Hope of all living;

3 All Thy creation serveth its Creator;
Thee every creature praiseth without ceasing;
We too would sing Thee psalms of true devotion;
Hear, we beseech Thee.

4 Lord God Almighty, unto Thee be glory,
One in Three Persons, over all exalted;
Thine, as is meet, be honour, praise, and blessing,
Now and for ever.

Latin (*c.* 10th century); tr. ALFRED EDWARD ALSTON (1862-1927)

See also the section THE SON OF GOD: HIS GLORY, NAME AND PRAISE, Nos. 89-117.
The following hymns also refer to this theme:

CREATION AND PROVIDENCE

23

CULBACH (7 7. 7 7.)   From a Chorale in SCHEFFLER's *Heilige Seelenlust* (1657)

My heart greatly rejoiceth; and with my song will I praise him (Psalm xxviii. 7)

SONGS of praise the angels sang,
Heaven with hallelujahs rang,
When creation was begun,
When God spake, and it was done.

2 Songs of praise awoke the morn
When the Prince of Peace was born;
Songs of praise arose when He
Captive led captivity.

3 Heaven and earth must pass away,
Songs of praise shall crown that day;
God will make new heavens and earth,
Songs of praise shall hail their birth.

4 And shall man alone be dumb
Till that glorious kingdom come?
No! the Church delights to raise
Psalms and hymns and songs of praise.

5 Saints below, with heart and voice,
Still in songs of praise rejoice,
Learning here, by faith and love,
Songs of praise to sing above.

JAMES MONTGOMERY (1771-1854)

24

LOBE DEN HERREN (14 14. 4. 7. 8.)   Later form of melody in *Stralsund*
Gesangbuch (1665) (as given in *The Chorale Book for England*, 1863)

LOBE DEN HERREN

Based on Psalms ciii and cl

PRAISE to the Lord, the Almighty,
    the King of creation!
O my soul, praise Him, for He is thy
    health and salvation:
        Come, ye who hear,
        Brothers and sisters, draw near,
Praise Him in glad adoration!

2 Praise to the Lord, who o'er all things
    so wondrously reigneth!
Shelters thee under His wings, yea, so
    gently sustaineth:
        Hast thou not seen?
        All that is needful hath been
Granted in what He ordaineth.

3 Praise to the Lord, who doth prosper
    thy work and defend thee!
Surely His goodness and mercy here
    daily attend thee:
        Ponder anew
        What the Almighty can do,
He who with love doth befriend thee.

4 Praise to the Lord! O let all that is in
    me adore Him!
All that hath life and breath come now
    with praises before Him!
        Let the amen
        Sound from His people again:
Gladly for aye we adore Him!

JOACHIM NEANDER (1650-80);
tr. CATHERINE WINKWORTH (1829-78) and others

25

HANOVER (5 5. 5 5. 6 5. 6 5.)   Probably by WILLIAM CROFT (1678-1727)

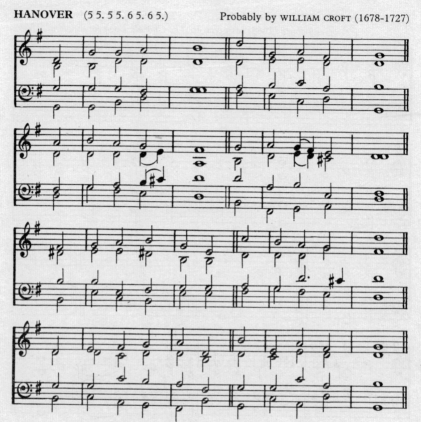

For alternative version with Fa-burden see following page

Based on Psalm civ

O WORSHIP the King,
   All glorious above;
O gratefully sing
   His power and His love;
Our Shield and Defender,
   The Ancient of Days,
Pavilioned in splendour,
   And girded with praise.

2 O tell of His might,
   O sing of His grace,
Whose robe is the light,
   Whose canopy space;
His chariots of wrath
   The deep thunder-clouds form,
And dark is His path
   On the wings of the storm.

3 The earth, with its store
   Of wonders untold,
Almighty, Thy power
   Hath founded of old;
Hath stablished it fast
   By a changeless decree,
And round it hath cast,
   Like a mantle, the sea.

ALTERNATIVE VERSION

Verses 4 and 6: Melody in the Tenor   Fa-burden by HARVEY GRACE (1874-   )

This hymn may also be sung to the tune LAUDATE DOMINUM, No. 9

4 Thy bountiful care
    What tongue can recite?
It breathes in the air,
    It shines in the light;
It streams from the hills,
    It descends to the plain,
And sweetly distils
    In the dew and the rain.

5 Frail children of dust,
    And feeble as frail,
In Thee do we trust,
    Nor find Thee to fail;
Thy mercies how tender,
    How firm to the end,
Our Maker, Defender,
    Redeemer, and Friend!

6 O measureless Might!
    Ineffable Love!
While angels delight
    To hymn Thee above,
Thy humbler creation,
    Though feeble their lays,
With true adoration
    Shall sing to Thy praise.

ROBERT GRANT (1779-1838)

41

26

NUN DANKET (6 7. 6 7. 6 6. 6 6.)   JOHANN CRÜGER (1598-1662)

NUN DANKET ALLE GOTT

O clap your hands, all ye people; shout unto God with the voice of triumph (Psalm xlvii. 1)

NOW thank we all our God,
  With hearts and hands and voices,
Who wondrous things hath done,
  In whom His world rejoices,—
Who, from our mothers' arms,
  Hath blessed us on our way
With countless gifts of love,
  And still is ours today.

2 O may this bounteous God
  Through all our life be near us,
With ever-joyful hearts
  And blessèd peace to cheer us,
And keep us in His grace,
  And guide us when perplexed,
And free us from all ills
  In this world and the next.

3 All praise and thanks to God
  The Father now be given,
The Son, and Him who reigns
  With them in highest heaven,—
The one, eternal God,
  Whom earth and heaven adore;
For thus it was, is now,
  And shall be evermore.

MARTIN RINKART (1586-1649);
tr. CATHERINE WINKWORTH (1829-78)

27

ST. ANNE (C.M.)   WILLIAM CROFT (1678-1727)

Based on Psalm xc

O GOD, our help in ages past,
    Our hope for years to come,
Our shelter from the stormy blast,
    And our eternal home!

2 Under the shadow of Thy throne
    Thy saints have dwelt secure;
Sufficient is Thine arm alone,
    And our defence is sure.

3 Before the hills in order stood,
    Or earth received her frame,
From everlasting Thou art God,
    To endless years the same.

4 A thousand ages in Thy sight
    Are like an evening gone;
Short as the watch that ends the night
    Before the rising sun.

5 Time, like an ever-rolling stream,
    Bears all its sons away;
They fly, forgotten, as a dream
    Dies at the opening day.

6 O God, our help in ages past,
    Our hope for years to come,
Be Thou our guard while troubles last,
    And our eternal home.

ISAAC WATTS (1674-1748)

28

ANTWERP (L.M.)   WILLIAM SMALLWOOD (1831-97)

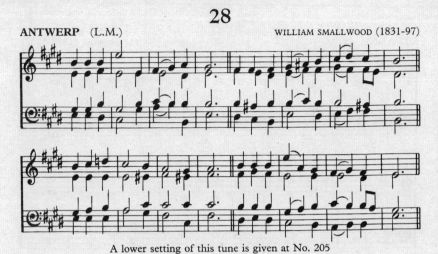

A lower setting of this tune is given at No. 205

ALTERNATIVE TUNE

RIMINGTON (L.M.)   FRANCIS DUCKWORTH (1862-1941)

Paraphrase of Psalm cxxxvi

GIVE to our God immortal praise,
Mercy and truth are all His ways;
Wonders of grace to God belong,
Repeat His mercies in your song.

2 Give to the Lord of lords renown;
The King of kings with glory crown:
His mercies ever shall endure,
When lords and kings are known no
more.

3 He built the earth, He spread the sky,
And fixed the starry lights on high:
Wonders of grace to God belong,
Repeat His mercies in your song.

4 He fills the sun with morning light,
He bids the moon direct the night:
His mercies ever shall endure,
When suns and moons shall shine no
more.

5 He sent His son with power to save
From guilt and darkness and the grave:
Wonders of grace to God belong,
Repeat His mercies in your song.

6 Through this vain world He guides
our feet,
And leads us to His heavenly seat:
His mercies ever shall endure,
When this vain world shall be no more.

ISAAC WATTS (1674-1748)

29

BIRLING (L.M.)

From an early 19th century MS.,
adapted by GEOFFREY SHAW (1879-1943)

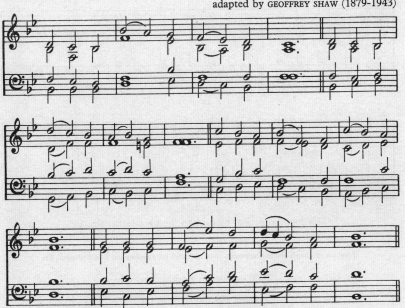

This hymn may also be sung to the tune OMBERSLEY, No. 191

God is light, and in him is no darkness at all (1 John i. 5)

LORD of all being, throned afar,
Thy glory flames from sun and star;
Centre and soul of every sphere,
Yet to each loving heart how near!

2 Sun of our life, Thy quickening ray
Sheds on our path the glow of day;
Star of our hope, Thy softened light
Cheers the long watches of the night.

3 Our midnight is Thy smile withdrawn,
Our noontide is Thy gracious dawn,
Our rainbow arch Thy mercy's sign;
All, save the clouds of sin, are Thine.

4 Lord of all life, below, above,
Whose light is truth, whose warmth is love,
Before Thy ever-blazing throne
We ask no lustre of our own.

5 Grant us Thy truth to make us free,
And kindling hearts that burn for Thee,
Till all Thy living altars claim
One holy light, one heavenly flame.

OLIVER WENDELL HOLMES (1809-94)

30

LONDON NEW (C.M.)   Adapted from *Scottish Psalter* (1635)

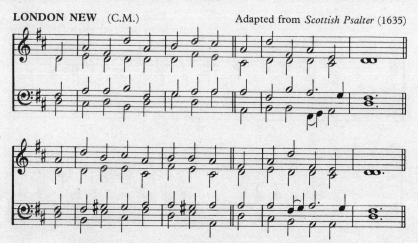

This hymn may also be sung to the tune IRISH, No. 125

How unsearchable are his judgments, and his ways past finding out ! (Romans xi. 33)

GOD moves in a mysterious way,
His wonders to perform;
He plants His footsteps in the sea,
And rides upon the storm.

2 Deep in unfathomable mines
Of never-failing skill
He treasures up His bright designs,
And works His sovereign will.

3 Ye fearful saints, fresh courage take;
The clouds ye so much dread
Are big with mercy, and shall break
In blessings on your head.

4 Judge not the Lord by feeble sense,
But trust Him for His grace;
Behind a frowning providence
He hides a smiling face.

5 His purposes will ripen fast,
Unfolding every hour;
The bud may have a bitter taste,
But sweet will be the flower.

6 Blind unbelief is sure to err,
And scan His work in vain;
God is His own interpreter,
And He will make it plain.

WILLIAM COWPER (1731-1800)

46

31

DUNFERMLINE (C.M.) *Scottish Psalter* (1615)

This hymn may also be sung to the tune SENNEN COVE, No. 84

I will sing unto the Lord as long as I live (Psalm civ. 33)

I SING the almighty power of God
That made the mountains rise,
That spread the flowing seas abroad,
And built the lofty skies.

2 I sing the wisdom that ordained
The sun to rule the day;
The moon shines full at His command,
And all the stars obey.

3 I sing the goodness of the Lord,
That filled the earth with food;
He formed the creatures with His word,
And then pronounced them good.

4 Lord, how Thy wonders are displayed
Where'er I turn mine eye,
If I survey the ground I tread,
Or gaze upon the sky;

5 There's not a plant or flower below
But makes Thy glories known,
And clouds arise and tempests blow
By order from Thy throne.

6 God's hand is my perpetual guard,
He guides me with His eye;
Why should I then forget the Lord,
Whose love is ever nigh?

ISAAC WATTS (1674-1748)

32

NORICUM   (7 7. 7 7. 7 7.)   FREDERICK JAMES (1858-1922)

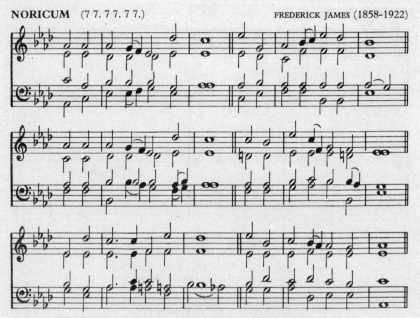

This hymn may also be sung to the tune HEATHLANDS, No. 169

Every good gift and every perfect gift is from above (James i. 17)

FOR the beauty of the earth,
    For the beauty of the skies,
For the love which from our birth
    Over and around us lies:

> *Christ, our God, to Thee we raise*
> *This our sacrifice of praise.*

2 For the beauty of each hour
    Of the day and of the night,
Hill and vale, and tree and flower,
    Sun and moon and stars of light:

3 For the joy of ear and eye,
    For the heart and mind's delight,
For the mystic harmony
    Linking sense to sound and sight:

4 For the joy of human love,
    Brother, sister, parent, child,
Friends on earth and friends above,
    Pleasures pure and undefiled:

5 For each perfect gift of Thine
    To our race so freely given
Graces human and divine,
    Flowers of earth and buds of heaven:

FOLLIOTT SANDFORD PIERPOINT (1835-1917)

33

ST. DENIO (11 11. 11 11.)   Welsh Hymn Melody

Based on 1 Timothy i. 17

IMMORTAL, invisible, God only wise,
In light inaccessible hid from our eyes,
Most blessèd, most glorious, the Ancient of Days,
Almighty, victorious, Thy great name we praise.

2 Unresting, unhasting, and silent as light,
Nor wanting, nor wasting, Thou rulest in might;
Thy justice like mountains high soaring above
Thy clouds which are fountains of goodness and love.

3 To all, life Thou givest—to both great and small;
In all life Thou livest, the true life of all;
We blossom and flourish as leaves on the tree,
And wither and perish—but nought changeth Thee.

4 Great Father of glory, pure Father of light
Thine angels adore Thee, all veiling their sight;
All laud we would render: O help us to see
'Tis only the splendour of light hideth Thee.

WALTER CHALMERS SMITH (1824-1908)

The following hymns also refer to this theme:

246   When all Thy mercies, O my God
257   My God, I thank Thee, who hast made
258   O Lord of heaven and earth and sea

THE SON OF GOD
HIS INCARNATION
34

BRISTOL (C.M.)

RAVENSCROFT'S *Psalter* (1621)

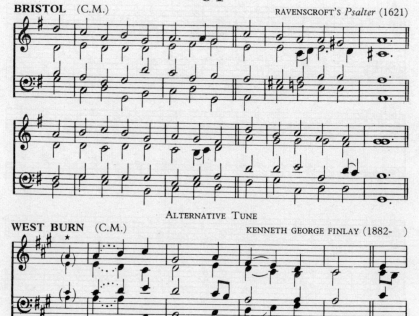

ALTERNATIVE TUNE

WEST BURN (C.M.)

KENNETH GEORGE FINLAY (1882-   )

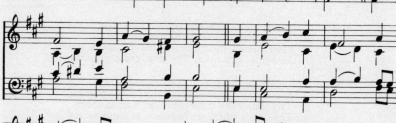

★*Small notes and dotted slurs for verses 2, 3 and 4*

Based on Luke iv. 18, 19

HARK, the glad sound, the Saviour
       comes,
 The Saviour promised long!
Let every heart prepare a throne,
 And every voice a song.

2 He comes the prisoners to release
 In Satan's bondage held;
The gates of brass before Him burst,
 The iron fetters yield.

3 He comes the broken heart to bind,
 The bleeding soul to cure,
And with the treasures of His grace
 To enrich the humble poor.

4 Our glad hosannas, Prince of Peace,
 Thy welcome shall proclaim,
And heaven's eternal arches ring
 With Thy beloved name.

PHILIP DODDRIDGE (1702-51)

35

CORDE NATUS (8 7. 8 7. 8 7 7.) *Piae Cantiones* (1582)

CORDE NATUS EX PARENTIS

That every tongue should confess that Jesus Christ is Lord (Philippians ii. 11)

OF the Father's love begotten
Ere the worlds began to be,
He is Alpha, He is Omega,
He the source, the ending He,
Of the things that are, that have been,
And that future years shall see,
Evermore and evermore.

2 This is He whom seers in old time
Chanted of with one accord,
Whom the voices of the prophets
Promised in their faithful word;
Now He shines, the long-expected;
Let creation praise its Lord,
Evermore and evermore.

3 Oh ye heights of heaven, adore Him;
Angel hosts, His praises sing;
All dominions, bow before Him,
And extol our God and King;
Let no tongue on earth be silent,
Every voice in concert ring,
Evermore and evermore.

4 Christ, to Thee, with God the Father,
And, O Holy Ghost, to Thee,
Hymn, and chant, and high thanks-
And unwearied praises be, [giving,
Honour, glory, and dominion,
And eternal victory,
Evermore and evermore.

AURELIUS CLEMENS PRUDENTIUS (348-*c*. 410);
tr. JOHN MASON NEALE (1818-66)

36

PLEADING SAVIOUR   (8 7. 8 7. D.)   *Plymouth Collection* (U.S.A.,1855)

There was no room for them in the inn (Luke ii. 7)

CRADLED in a manger, meanly
   Laid the Son of Man His head;
Sleeping His first earthly slumber
   Where the oxen had been fed.
Happy were those shepherds listening
   To the holy angel's word;
Happy they within that stable,
   Worshipping their infant Lord.

2 Happy all who hear the message
   Of His coming from above;
Happier still who hail His coming,
   And with praises greet His love.
Blessèd Saviour, Christ most holy,
   In a manger Thou didst rest;
Canst Thou stoop again, yet lower,
   And abide within my breast?

3 Evil things are there before Thee;
   In the heart, where they have fed,
Wilt Thou pitifully enter,
   Son of Man, and lay Thy head?
Enter, then, O Christ most holy;
   Make a Christmas in my heart;
Make a heaven of my manger:
   It is heaven where Thou art.

4 And to those who never listened
   To the message of Thy birth,
Who have winter, but no Christmas
   Bringing them Thy peace on earth,
Send to these the joyful tidings;
   By all people, in each home,
Be there heard the Christmas anth'em:
   Praise to God, the Christ has come!

GEORGE STRINGER ROWE (1830-1913)

37

WINCHESTER OLD (C.M.)   ESTE'S *Psalter* (1592)

Descant for verses 2 and 5 by BRIAN STANLEY HOWARD (1930-)

Based on Luke ii. 8-14

WHILE shepherds watched their flocks by night,
   All seated on the ground,
The angel of the Lord came down,
   And glory shone around.

2 'Fear not,' said he (for mighty dread
      Had seized their troubled mind);
   'Glad tidings of great joy I bring
      To you and all mankind.

3 'To you in David's town this day
      Is born, of David's line,
   A Saviour, who is Christ the Lord;
      And this shall be the sign:

4 'The heavenly Babe you there shall find
      To human view displayed,
   All meanly wrapped in swathing bands,
      And in a manger laid.'

5 Thus spake the seraph; and forthwith
      Appeared a shining throng
   Of angels praising God, and thus
      Addressed their joyful song;

6 'All glory be to God on high,
      And to the earth be peace;
   Good will henceforth from heaven to men
      Begin and never cease!'

NAHUM TATE (1652-1715)

38

IRIS (8 7. 8 7. and refrain)   French Carol Melody

This hymn may also be sung to the tune REGENT SQUARE, No. 63

We . . . are come to worship him (Matthew ii. 2)

ANGELS from the realms of glory,
  Wing your flight o'er all the earth;
Ye who sang creation's story,
  Now proclaim Messiah's birth;
    Come and worship,
    Worship Christ, the new-born King.

2 Shepherds, in the fields abiding,
  Watching o'er your flocks by night,
God with man is now residing,
  Yonder shines the infant light;

3 Sages, leave your contemplations;
  Brighter visions beam afar;
Seek the great desire of nations;
  Ye have seen His natal star;

4 Saints, before the altar bending,
  Watching long in hope and fear,
Suddenly the Lord, descending,
  In His temple shall appear;

JAMES MONTGOMERY (1771-1854)

39

MENDELSSOHN   (7 7. 7 7. D. and refrain)

Adapted by WILLIAM HAYMAN CUMMINGS (1831-1915) from
a chorus of FELIX MENDELSSOHN-BARTHOLDY (1809-47)

Organ

Glory to God in the highest (Luke ii. 14)

HARK, the herald angels sing,
'Glory to the new-born King,
Peace on earth, and mercy mild,
God and sinners reconciled!'
Joyful, all ye nations, rise,
Join the triumph of the skies,
With the angelic host proclaim,
'Christ is born in Bethlehem'.

Hark, the herald angels sing,
'Glory to the new-born King'.

2 Christ, by highest heaven adored,
Christ, the everlasting Lord,
Late in time behold Him come,
Offspring of a virgin's womb.
Veiled in flesh the Godhead see;
Hail, the incarnate Deity,
Pleased as Man with man to dwell,
Jesus, our Immanuel!

3 Hail, the heaven-born Prince of Peace
Hail, the Sun of Righteousness!
Light and life to all He brings,
Risen with healing in His wings.
Mild He lays His glory by,
Born that man no more may die,
Born to raise the sons of earth,
Born to give them second birth:

CHARLES WESLEY (1707-88), GEORGE WHITEFIELD (1714-70),
MARTIN MADAN (1726-90) and others

40

ADESTE FIDELES (Irregular)   English melody (18th century)

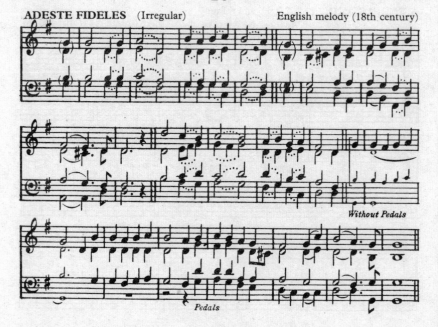

Without Pedals

Pedals

ADESTE FIDELES

Let us now go even unto Bethlehem, and see this thing which is come to pass (Luke ii. 15)

O COME, all ye faithful,
  Joyful and triumphant,
O come ye, O come ye to Bethlehem:
Come and behold Him,
Born the King of angels:

   O come, let us adore Him,
   O come, let us adore Him,
  O come, let us adore Him, Christ the Lord!

2 God of God,
  Light of light,
Lo, He abhors not the Virgin's womb;
  Very God,
  Begotten not created:

3 See how the shepherds,
  Summoned to his cradle,
Leaving their flocks, draw nigh with
  We too will thither   [lowly fear;
  Bend our joyful footsteps:

4 Lo, star-led chieftains,
  Wise men, Christ adoring,
Offer him incense, gold, and myrrh;
  We to the Christ-child
  Bring our hearts' oblations:

5 Child, for us sinners
  Poor and in the manger,
Fain we embrace thee, with awe and love;
  Who would not love thee,
  Loving us so dearly?

*6 Sing, choirs of angels,
  Sing in exultation,
Sing, all ye citizens of heaven above;
  Glory to God
  In the highest:

7 Yea, Lord, we greet thee,
  Born this happy morning,
Jesu, to thee be glory given;
  Word of the Father,
  Now in flesh appearing:

Latin (before 18th century); tr. FREDERICK OAKELEY (1802-80) and others
It is suggested that, except on Christmas day, the hymn should conclude with this verse.

ALTERNATIVE ARRANGEMENT FOR VERSE SIX

Descant by HERBERT ARTHUR CHAMBERS (1880-)

41

IRBY (8 7 8 7. 7 7.)

HENRY JOHN GAUNTLETT (1805-76)

ALTERNATIVE VERSION

Verse 3 Unaccompanied: Melody in the Tenor. Fa-burden by F. DEREK KIDNER (1913-)

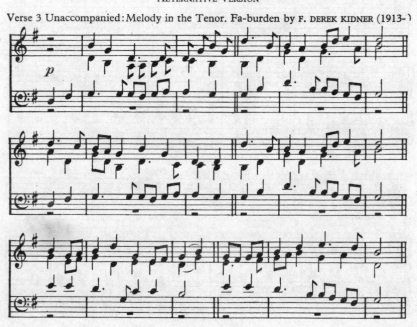

The Word was made flesh, and dwelt among us (John i. 14)

ONCE in royal David's city
  Stood a lowly cattle-shed,
Where a mother laid her baby,
  In a manger for His bed.
Mary was that mother mild,
Jesus Christ her little child.

2 He came down to earth from heaven
  Who is God and Lord of all,
And His shelter was a stable,
  And His cradle was a stall.
With the poor and mean and lowly
Lived on earth our Saviour holy.

3 And through all His wondrous child-
  He would honour and obey,   [hood
Love, and watch the lowly mother
  In whose gentle arms He lay.
Christian children all must be
Mild, obedient, good as He.

4 For He is our childhood's pattern:
  Day by day like us He grew;
He was little, weak, and helpless;
  Tears and smiles like us He knew;
And He feeleth for our sadness,
And He shareth in our gladness.

5 And our eyes at last shall see Him,
  Through His own redeeming love;
For that child so dear and gentle
  Is our Lord in heaven above;
And He leads His children on
To the place where He is gone.

6 Not in that poor lowly stable,
  With the oxen standing by,
We shall see Him, but in heaven,
  Set at God's right hand on high,
When, like stars, His children crowned,
All in white shall wait around.

CECIL FRANCES ALEXANDER (1818-95)

42

STUTTGART   (8 7 8 7.)   CHRISTIAN FRIEDRICH WITT (1660-1716)

O SOLA MAGNARUM URBIUM

He sent them to Bethlehem (Matthew ii. 8)

EARTH has many a noble city;
  Bethlehem, thou dost all excel:
Out of thee the Lord from heaven
  Came to rule His Israel.

2 Fairer than the sun at morning
  Was the star that told His birth,
To the world its God announcing,
  Seen in fleshly form on earth.

3 Eastern sages at His cradle
  Make oblations rich and rare;
See them give, in deep devotion,
  Gold, and frankincense, and myrrh.

4 Sacred gifts of mystic meaning;
  Incense doth their God disclose,
Gold the King of kings proclaimeth,
  Myrrh His sepulchre foreshows.

5 Jesu, whom the Gentiles worshipped
  At Thy glad Epiphany,
Unto Thee, with God the Father
  And the Spirit, glory be.

AURELIUS CLEMENS PRUDENTIUS (348-c. 410);
tr. EDWARD CASWALL (1814-78) and others

43

EPIPHANY   (11 10. 11 10. Dactylic)   JOSEPH FRANCIS THRUPP (1827-67)

ALTERNATIVE TUNE

FORT WILLIAM   (11 10. 11 10. Dactylic)   KENNETH GEORGE FINLAY (1882-)

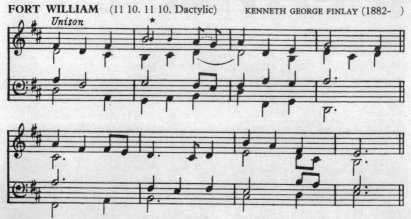

Small notes and dotted slur for verses 2, 3 and 4

We . . . are come to worship him (Matthew ii., 2)

BRIGHTEST and best of the sons of the morning,
    Dawn on our darkness, and lend us thine aid;
Star of the east, the horizon adorning,
    Guide where our infant Redeemer is laid.

2 Cold on His cradle the dew-drops are shining;
    Low lies His head with the beasts of the stall;
Angels adore Him in slumber reclining,
    Maker and monarch and Saviour of all.

3 Say, shall we yield Him, in costly devotion
    Odours of Edom, and offerings divine,
Gems of the mountain and pearls of the ocean,
    Myrrh from the forest or gold from the mine?

4 Vainly we offer each ample oblation,
    Vainly with gifts would His favour secure;
Richer by far is the heart's adoration;
    Dearer to God are the prayers of the poor.

5 Brightest and best of the sons of the morning,
    Dawn on our darkness, and lend us thine aid,
Star of the east, the horizon adorning,
    Guide where our infant Redeemer is laid.

REGINALD HEBER (1783-1826)

44

DIX (7 7. 7 7. 7 7.) CONRAD KOCHER (1786-1872)

When they saw the star, they rejoiced with exceeding great joy (Matthew ii. 10)

AS with gladness men of old
Did the guiding star behold,
As with joy they hailed its light,
Leading onward, beaming bright,—
So, most gracious Lord, may we
Evermore be led to Thee.

2 As with joyful steps they sped,
Saviour, to Thy lowly bed,
There to bend the knee before
Thee, whom heaven and earth adore,—
So may we with willing feet
Ever seek Thy mercy-seat.

3 As they offered gifts most rare
At Thy cradle rude and bare,—
So may we with holy joy,
Pure, and free from sin's alloy,
All our costliest treasures bring,
Christ, to Thee, our heavenly King.

4 Holy Jesus, every day
Keep us in the narrow way;
And, when earthly things are past,
Bring our ransomed souls at last
Where they need no star to guide,
Where no clouds Thy glory hide.

5 In the heavenly country bright
Need they no created light;
Thou its light, its joy, its crown,
Thou its sun which goes not down;
There for ever may we sing
Hallelujahs to our King.

WILLIAM CHATTERTON DIX (1837-98)

See also the section CHRISTMAS CAROLS, NOS. 381-399

45

MARGARET (Irregular)   TIMOTHY RICHARD MATTHEWS (1826-1910)

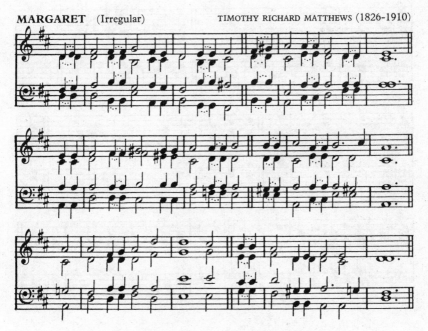

He came unto his own, and his own received him not (John i. 11)

THOU didst leave Thy throne
And Thy kingly crown
When Thou camest to earth for me;
But in Bethlehem's home
Was there found no room
For Thy holy nativity:
O come to my heart, Lord Jesus;
There is room in my heart for Thee.

2 Heaven's arches rang
When the angels sang,
Proclaiming Thy royal degree;
But of lowly birth
Cam'st Thou, Lord, on earth,
And in great humility;
O come to my heart, Lord Jesus;
There is room in my heart for Thee.

3 The foxes found rest,
And the birds their nest,
In the shade of the cedar tree;
But Thy couch was the sod,
O Thou Son of God,
In the deserts of Galilee:
O come to my heart, Lord Jesus;
There is room in my heart for Thee.

4 Thou camest, O Lord,
With the living word
That should set Thy people free;
But, with mocking scorn,
And with crown of thorn,
They bore to Thee to Calvary:
O come to my heart, Lord Jesus;
Thy cross is my only plea.

5 When heaven's arches ring,
And her choirs shall sing,
At Thy coming to victory,
Let Thy voice call me home,
Saying, 'Yet there is room,
There is room at My side for thee!'
And my heart shall rejoice, Lord Jesus,
When Thou comest and callest for me.

EMILY ELIZABETH STEELE ELLIOTT (1836-97)

46

LOVE UNKNOWN   (6 6. 6 6. 4 4. 4 4.)   JOHN IRELAND (1879-)

Unison

The Son of God, who loved me, and gave himself for me (Galatians ii. 20)

MY song is love unknown,
　My Saviour's love to me,
Love to the loveless shown,
That they might lovely be.
　O who am I,
　　That for my sake
　My Lord should take
Frail flesh, and die?

2 He came from His blest throne,
　Salvation to bestow;
But men made strange, and none
　The longed-for Christ would know.
　But O, my Friend,
　　My Friend indeed,
　Who at my need
His life did spend!

3 Sometimes they strew His way,
　And His sweet praises sing;
Resounding all the day
　Hosannas to their King.
　Then: 'Crucify!'
　　Is all their breath,
　And for His death
They thirst and cry.

ALTERNATIVE TUNE

ST. JOHN (6 6. 6 6. 4 4. 4 4.)   JOHN BAPTISTE CALKIN (1827-1905)

*4 Why, what hath my Lord done?
 What makes this rage and spite?
He made the lame to run,
 He gave the blind their sight.
  Sweet injuries!
   Yet they at these
  Themselves displease,
   And 'gainst Him rise.

*6 In life, no house, no home
 My Lord on earth might have;
In death, no friendly tomb
 But what a stranger gave.
  What may I say?
   Heaven was His home;
  But mine the tomb
   Wherein He lay.

5 They rise, and needs will have
 My dear Lord made away;
A murderer they save,
 The Prince of Life they slay.
  Yet cheerful He
   To suffering goes,
  That He His foes
   From thence might free.

7 Here might I stay and sing,
 No story so divine;
Never was love, dear King,
 Never was grief like Thine.
  This is my Friend,
   In whose sweet praise
  I all my days
   Could gladly spend.

SAMUEL CROSSMAN (c. 1624-83)

*If desired, verses 4 and 6 may be omitted

47

ST. AUDREY NEW (8 7. 8 7. D.)   BASIL HARWOOD (1859-1949)

This hymn may also be sung to the tune BETHANY, No. 75

(He) became obedient unto death . . . Wherefore God also hath highly exalted him (Philippians ii. 8, 9)

WHO is this, so weak and helpless,
   Child of lowly Hebrew maid,
Rudely in a stable sheltered,
   Coldly in a manger laid?
'Tis the Lord of all creation,
   Who this wondrous path hath trod;
He is God from everlasting,
   And to everlasting God.

2 Who is this, a Man of Sorrows,
   Walking sadly life's hard way,
Homeless, weary, sighing, weeping
   Over sin and Satan's sway?
'Tis our God, our glorious Saviour,
   Who above the starry sky
Now for us a place prepareth,
   Where no tear can dim the eye.

3 Who is this? behold Him shedding
   Drops of blood upon the ground!
Who is this, despised, rejected,
   Mocked, insulted, beaten, bound?
'Tis our God, who gifts and graces
   Poureth on His Church below,
Now, in royal might victorious,
   Triumphing o'er every foe.

4 Who is this that hangeth dying
   While the rude world scoffs and
      scorns,
Numbered with the malefactors,
   Pierced with nails, and crowned with
'Tis the God who ever liveth [thorns?
   'Mid the shining ones on high,
In the glorious golden city
   Reigning everlastingly.

WILLIAM WALSHAM HOW (1823-97)

48

BISHOPTHORPE (C.M.) Attributed to JEREMIAH CLARK (*c.* 1670-1707)

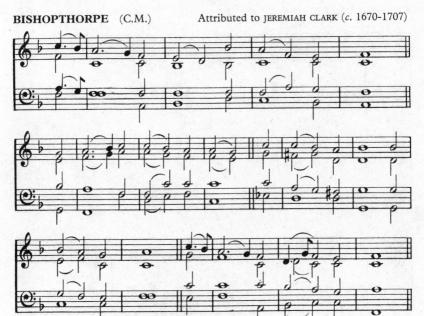

One is your Master, even Christ (Matthew xxiii. 8)

IMMORTAL love, for ever full,
For ever flowing free,
For ever shared, for ever whole,
A never-ebbing sea!

2 Our outward lips confess the Name
All other names above;
Love only knoweth whence it came,
And comprehendeth love.

3 And warm, sweet, tender, even yet
A present help is He;
And faith has still its Olivet,
And love its Galilee.

4 The healing of His seamless dress
Is by our beds of pain;
We touch Him in life's throng and press,
And we are whole again.

5 Through Him the first fond prayers are said
Our lips of childhood frame,
The last low whispers of our dead
Are burdened with His name.

6 O Lord and Master of us all,
Whate'er our name or sign,
We own Thy sway, we hear Thy call,
We test our lives by Thine.

JOHN GREENLEAF WHITTIER (1807-92)

49

ST. THEODULPH (7 6. 7 6. D.)   MELCHIOR TESCHNER (*c.* 1615)

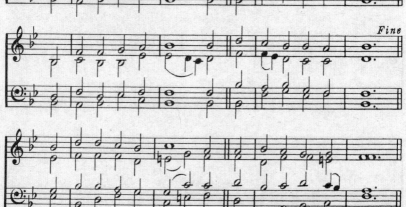

GLORIA, LAUS ET HONOR

Rejoice greatly . . . behold, thy King cometh unto thee (Zechariah ix. 9)

All glory, laud and honour
To Thee, Redeemer King,
To whom the lips of children
Made sweet hosannas ring !

2 Thou art the King of Israel,
Thou David's royal Son,
Who in the Lord's name comest,
The King and blessèd one.
All glory—

3 The company of angels
Are praising Thee on high,
And mortal men and all things
Created make reply.
All glory—

4 The people of the Hebrews
With palms before Thee went;
Our praise and prayer and anthems
Before Thee we present.
All glory—

5 To Thee before Thy passion
They sang their hymns of praise;
To Thee now high exalted
Our melody we raise.
All glory—

6 Thou didst accept their praises;
Accept the prayers we bring,
Who in all good delightest,
Thou good and gracious King.
All glory—

THEODULPH OF ORLEANS (*c.* 821);
tr. JOHN MASON NEALE (1818-66)

50

ST. DROSTANE (L.M.)   JOHN BACCHUS DYKES (1823-76)

This hymn may also be sung to the tune WINCHESTER NEW, No. 77

Blessed is he that cometh in the name of the Lord (Matthew xxi. 9)

RIDE on! ride on in majesty!
 Hark, all the tribes 'Hosanna' cry;
O Saviour meek, pursue Thy road
With palms and scattered garments strowed.

2 Ride on! ride on in majesty!
 In lowly pomp ride on to die;
O Christ, Thy triumphs now begin
O'er captive death and conquered sin.

3 Ride on! ride on in majesty!
 The angel armies of the sky
Look down with sad and wondering eyes
To see the approaching sacrifice.

4 Ride on! ride on in majesty!
 Thy last and fiercest strife is nigh;
The Father on His sapphire throne
Awaits His own anointed Son.

5 Ride on! ride on in majesty!
 In lowly pomp ride on to die;
Bow Thy meek head to mortal pain,
Then take, O God, Thy power, and reign.

HENRY HART MILMAN (1791-1868)

51

HERZLIEBSTER JESU (11 11. 11 5.)

Later form of melody by JOHANN CRÜGER (1598-1662)

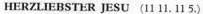

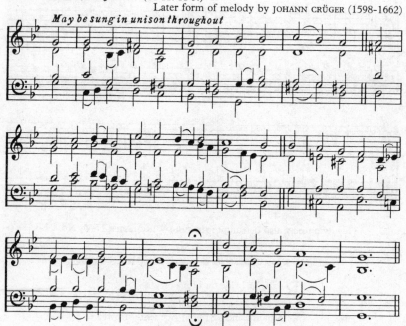

HERZLIEBSTER JESU, WAS HAST DU VERBROCHEN

Who his own self bare our sins in his own body on the tree (1 Peter ii. 24)

AH, holy Jesu, how hast Thou offended,
  That man to judge Thee hath in hate pretended?
By foes derided, by Thine own rejected,
    O most afflicted.

2 Who was the guilty? Who brought this upon Thee?
Alas, my treason, Jesu, hath undone Thee;
'Twas I, Lord Jesu, I it was denied Thee:
    I crucified Thee.

3 Lo, the good Shepherd for the sheep is offered;
The slave hath sinnèd, and the Son hath suffered;
For man's atonement, while he nothing heedeth,
    God intercedeth.

4 For me, kind Jesu, was Thy incarnation,
Thy mortal sorrow, and Thy life's oblation;
Thy death of anguish and Thy bitter passion,
    For my salvation.

5 Therefore, kind Jesu, since I cannot pay Thee,
I do adore Thee, and will ever pray Thee,
Think on Thy pity and Thy love unswerving,
    Not my deserving.

JOHANN HEERMANN (1585-1647);
par. ROBERT BRIDGES (1844-1930)

52

PASSION CHORALE (7 6. 7 6. D.) Melody by HANS LEO HASSLER (1564-1612)
Adapted and harmonized by JOHANN SEBASTIAN BACH (1685-1750)

O HAUPT VOLL BLUT UND WUNDEN

He was wounded for our transgressions (Isaiah liii. 5)

O SACRED Head, sore wounded,
  With grief and shame weighed down!
O kingly Head, surrounded
  With thorns, Thine only crown!
How pale art Thou with anguish,
  With sore abuse and scorn!
How does that visage languish,
  Which once was bright as morn!

2 O Lord of life and glory,
  What bliss till now was Thine!
I read the wondrous story;
  I joy to call Thee mine.
Thy grief and bitter passion
  Were all for sinners' gain;
Mine, mine was the transgression,
  But Thine the deadly pain.

3 What language shall I borrow
  To praise Thee, heavenly Friend,
For this Thy dying sorrow,
  Thy pity without end?
Lord, make me Thine for ever,
  Nor let me faithless prove;
O let me never, never
  Abuse such dying love.

PAUL GERHARDT (1607-76); based on *Salve caput cruentatum;*
tr. JAMES WADDELL ALEXANDER (1804-59

71

53

HERONGATE (L.M.)   English Traditional Melody

ALTERNATIVE TUNE

GIDEON (L.M.)   THOMAS B. SOUTHGATE (1814-68)

We love him, because he first loved us (1 John iv. 19)

IT is a thing most wonderful,
  Almost too wonderful to be,
That God's own Son should come from heaven,
  And die to save a child like me.

2 And yet I know that it is true;
  He chose a poor and humble lot,
And wept, and toiled, and mourned, and died,
  For love of those who loved Him not.

3 I sometimes think about the cross,
  And shut my eyes, and try to see
The cruel nails, and crown of thorns,
  And Jesus crucified for me.

4 But even could I see Him die,
  I could but see a little part
Of that great love, which, like a fire,
  Is always burning in His heart.

5 It is most wonderful to know
    His love for me so free and sure;
But 'tis more wonderful to see
    My love for Him so faint and poor.

6 And yet I want to love Thee, Lord;
    O light the flame within my heart,
And I will love Thee more and more,
    Until I see Thee as Thou art.

WILLIAM WALSHAM HOW (1823-97)

54

BODLEY (L.M.)   Melody from *Eighty-four Church Tunes* (1857)

This hymn may also be sung to the tune CHURCH TRIUMPHANT, No. 74 (ii)

God forbid that I should glory, save in the cross of our Lord Jesus Christ (Galatians vi. 14)

WE sing the praise of Him who died,
    Of Him who died upon the cross;
The sinner's hope let men deride,
    For this we count the world but loss.

2 Inscribed upon the cross we see
    In shining letters, 'God is Love';
He bears our sins upon the tree;
    He brings us mercy from above.

3 The cross! it takes our guilt away;
    It holds the fainting spirit up;
It cheers with hope the gloomy day,
    And sweetens every bitter cup.

4 It makes the coward spirit brave,
    And nerves the feeble arm for fight;
It takes its terror from the grave,
    And gilds the bed of death with light;

5 The balm of life, the cure of woe,
    The measure and the pledge of love,
The sinners' refuge here below,
    The angels' theme in heaven above.

THOMAS KELLY (1769-1854)

THE SON OF GOD

55

ROCKINGHAM (L.M.)   Adapted by EDWARD MILLER (1731-1807)

Based on Galatians vi. 14

WHEN I survey the wondrous cross
   On which the Prince of glory died,
My richest gain I count but loss,
   And pour contempt on all my pride.

2 Forbid it, Lord, that I should boast
   Save in the cross of Christ my God;
All the vain things that charm me most,
   I sacrifice them to His blood.

3 See, from His head, His hands, His feet,
   Sorrow and love flow mingled down;
Did e'er such love and sorrow meet,
   Or thorns compose so rich a crown?

4 Were the whole realm of nature mine,
   That were an offering far too small;
Love so amazing, so divine,
   Demands my soul, my life, my all.

ISAAC WATTS (1674-1748)

56

CASWALL (6 5. 6 5.)   FRIEDRICH FILITZ (1804-76)

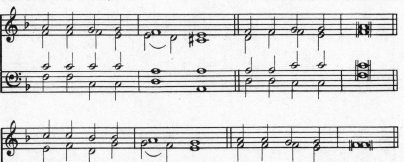

VIVA! VIVA! GESÙ

The precious blood of Christ (1 Peter i. 19)

GLORY be to Jesus,
Who in bitter pains
Poured for me the life-blood
From His sacred veins.

2 Grace and life eternal
    In that blood I find;
Blest be His compassion,
    Infinitely kind!

3 Blest through endless ages
    Be the precious stream,
Which from endless torments
    Did the world redeem.

4 Abel's blood for vengeance
    Pleaded to the skies;
But the blood of Jesus
    For our pardon cries.

5 Oft as earth exulting
    Wafts its praise on high,
Angel-hosts rejoicing
    Make their glad reply.

6 Lift ye then your voices;
    Swell the mighty flood;
Louder still and louder
    Praise the precious blood.

Italian (18th century); tr. EDWARD CASWALL (1814-78)

57

HORSLEY (C.M.)   WILLIAM HORSLEY (1774-1858)

ALTERNATIVE TUNE

THIS ENDRIS NYGHT (C.M.)   English Carol (15th century)

While we were yet sinners, Christ died for us (Romans v. 8)

THERE is a green hill far away,
　Without a city wall,
Where the dear Lord was crucified,
　Who died to save us all.

2 We may not know, we cannot tell,
　What pains He had to bear;
But we believe it was for us
　He hung and suffered there.

3 He died that we might be forgiven,
　He died to make us good,
That we might go at last to heaven,
　Saved by His precious blood.

4 There was no other good enough
   To pay the price of sin;
He only could unlock the gate
   Of heaven, and let us in.

5 O dearly, dearly has He loved,
   And we must love Him too,
And trust in His redeeming blood,
   And try His works to do.

CECIL FRANCES ALEXANDER (1818-95)

58

WALSALL (C.M.)   WILLIAM ANCHORS *A Choice Collection of Psalm Tunes* (c.1721)

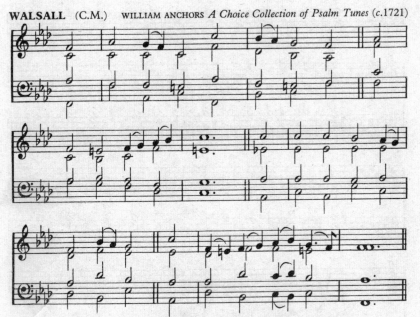

This hymn may also be sung to the tune ST. FLAVIAN, No. 354

For he hath made him to be sin for us, who knew no sin (2 Corinthians v. 21)

ALAS! and did my Saviour bleed?
   And did my Sovereign die?
Would He devote that sacred head
   For sinners such as I?

2 Was it for sins that I had done
   He groaned upon the tree?
Amazing pity! Grace unknown!
   And love beyond degree!

3 Well might the sun in darkness hide,
   And shut his glories in,
When Christ, the mighty Maker, died
   For man, the creature's sin.

4 Thus might I hide my blushing face
   While His dear cross appears,
Dissolve my heart in thankfulness,
   And melt mine eyes to tears.

5 But drops of grief can ne'er repay
   The debt of love I owe;
Here, Lord, I give myself away:
   'Tis all that I can do.

ISAAC WATTS (1674-1748)

59

ST. CHRISTOPHER (7 6. 8 6. 8 6. 8 6.)   FREDERICK CHARLES MAKER (1844-1927)

A man shall be as an hiding place . . . as the shadow of a great rock in a weary land (Isaiah xxxii. 2)

BENEATH the cross of Jesus
    I fain would take my stand—
The shadow of a mighty rock
    Within a weary land;
A home within a wilderness,
    A rest upon the way,
From the burning of the noontide heat
    And the burden of the day.

2 O safe and happy shelter,
    O refuge tried and sweet,
O trysting-place, where heaven's love
    And heaven's justice meet!
As to the exiled patriarch
    That wondrous dream was given,
So seems my Saviour's cross to me—
    A ladder up to heaven.

3 Upon that cross of Jesus,
    Mine eye at times can see
The very dying form of One
    Who suffered there for me;
And from my stricken heart, with tears,
    Two wonders I confess—
The wonders of redeeming love,
    And my own worthlessness.

4 I take, O cross, thy shadow,
    For my abiding-place;
I ask no other sunshine than
    The sunshine of His face;
Content to let the world go by,
    To know no gain nor loss—
My sinful self my only shame,
    My glory all, the cross.

ELIZABETH CECILIA CLEPHANE (1830-69)

60

ST. GEORGE (S.M.)   HENRY JOHN GAUNTLETT (1805-76)

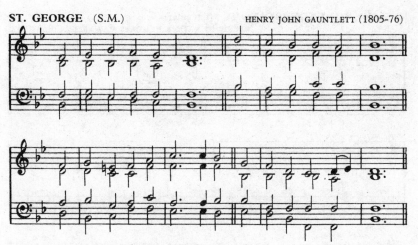

Christ was once offered to bear the sins of many (Hebrews ix. 28)

NOT all the blood of beasts
   On Jewish altars slain
Could give the guilty conscience peace
   Or wash away the stain.

2 But Christ, the heavenly Lamb,
   Takes all our sins away;
A sacrifice of nobler Name,
   And richer blood, than they.

3 My faith would lay her hand
   On that dear head of Thine,
While like a penitent I stand,
   And there confess my sin.

4 My soul looks back to see
   The burdens Thou didst bear
When hanging on the accursèd tree,
   And knows her guilt was there.

5 Believing, we rejoice
   To see the curse remove;
We bless the Lamb with cheerful voice,
   And sing His wondrous love.

ISAAC WATTS (1674-1748)

61

O MAKE ME UNDERSTAND IT (Irregular)

Melody by KATHERINE AGNES MAY KELLY (1869-1942)

Refrain

The Son of God, who loved me, and gave himself for me (Galatians ii. 20)

G IVE me a sight, O Saviour,
Of Thy wondrous love to me,
Of the love that brought Thee down to
     To die on Calvary.   [earth,

> *O make me understand it,*
> *Help me to take it in,*
> *What it meant to Thee, the Holy One,*
> *To bear away my sin.*

2 Was it the nails, O Saviour,
     That bound Thee to the tree?
Nay, 'twas Thine everlasting love,
     Thy love for me, for me.

3 O wonder of all wonders,
     That through Thy death for me,
My open sins, my secret sins,
     Can all forgiven be!

4 Then melt my heart, O Saviour,
     Bend me, yes, break me down,
Until I own Thee Conqueror,
     And Lord and Sovereign crown.

KATHERINE AGNES MAY KELLY (1869-1942)

62

MAN OF SORROWS (7 7 7. 8.)   PHILIPP BLISS (1838-76)

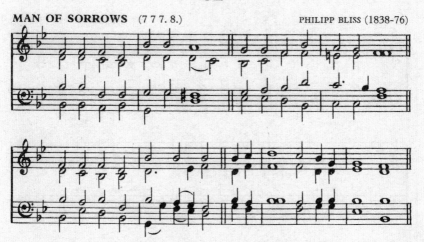

He is despised and rejected of men; a man of sorrows, and acquainted with grief (Isaiah liii. 3)

MAN of Sorrows! what a name
For the Son of God. who came
Ruined sinners to reclaim!
    Hallelujah! What a Saviour!

2 Bearing shame and scoffing rude,
In my place condemned He stood,
Sealed my pardon with His blood:
    Hallelujah! What a Saviour!

3 Guilty, vile, and helpless, we;
Spotless Lamb of God was He:
Full atonement,—can it be?
    Hallelujah! What a Saviour!

4 Lifted up was He to die,
'It is finished' was His cry;
Now in heaven exalted high:
    Hallelujah! What a Saviour!

5 When He comes, our glorious King,
All His ransomed home to bring,
Then anew this song we'll sing,
    'Hallelujah! What a Saviour!'

PHILIPP BLISS (1838-76)

63

REGENT SQUARE (8 7. 8 7. 8 7.)　　　　　HENRY SMART (1813-79)

It is finished (John xix. 30)

HARK! the voice of love and mercy
　Sounds aloud from Calvary;
See! it rends the rocks asunder,
　Shakes the earth, and veils the sky:
　　'It is finished!'
　Hear the dying Saviour cry.

2 'It is finished!' What assurance
　　Do the wondrous words afford!
　Heavenly blessings without measure
　　Flow to us from Christ the Lord:
　　　'It is finished!'
　　Saints the dying words record!

3 Finished all the types and shadows
　　Of the ceremonial law,
　Finished all that God had promised;
　　Death and hell no more shall awe:
　　　'It is finished!'
　　Saints, from hence your comfort draw.

4 Saints and angels shout His praises,
　　His great finished work proclaim;
　All on earth and all in heaven
　　Join to bless Immanuel's name:
　　　Hallelujah!
　　Endless glory to the Lamb!

JONATHAN EVANS (*c.* 1748-1809)†

64

ALL FOR JESUS (8 7. 8 7.) JOHN STAINER (1840-1901)

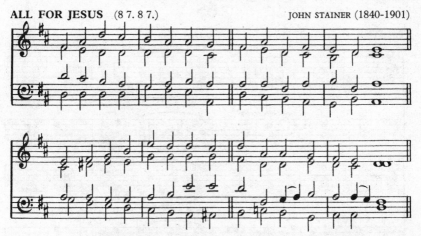

This hymn may also be sung to the tune STUTTGART, No. 42

God forbid that I should glory, save in the cross of our Lord Jesus Christ (Galatians vi. 14)

* IN the cross of Christ I glory,
    Towering o'er the wrecks of time;
All the light of sacred story
    Gathers round its head sublime.

2 When the woes of life o'ertake me,
    Hopes deceive, and fears annoy,
Never shall the cross forsake me;
    Lo! it glows with peace and joy.

3 When the sun of bliss is beaming
    Light and love upon my way,
From the cross the radiance streaming
    Adds more lustre to the day.

4 Bane and blessing, pain and pleasure,
    By the cross are sanctified;
Peace is there that knows no measure,
    Joys that through all time abide.

JOHN BOWRING (1792-1872)

*If desired, this verse may be repeated after verse 4

See also the section THE CHURCH OF GOD: WORSHIP AND THE LORD'S SUPPER, NOS.
151-163. *The following hymns also refer to this theme:*

320 O dearest Lord, Thy sacred head
351 Thy life was given for me

EASTER HYMN (7 7. 7 7. and Hallelujahs)

Altered from melody in *Lyra Davidica* (1708)

The Lord is risen indeed (Luke xxiv. 34)

JESUS Christ is risen today,
   Hallelujah !
Our triumphant holy day,
Who did once, upon the cross,
Suffer to redeem our loss.

2 Hymns of praise, then, let us sing
Unto Christ, our heavenly King,
Who endured the cross and grave,
Sinners to redeem and save.

3 But the anguish He endured
Our salvation hath procured;
Now above the sky He's King,
Where the angels ever sing.

LYRA DAVIDICA (1708);
and *Supplement to the New Version* (*c.* 1816)

66

LUX EOI (8 7. 8 7. D.)   ARTHUR SEYMOUR SULLIVAN (1842-1900)

This hymn may also be sung to the tune HYFRYDOL, No. 171

God . . . hath quickened us together with Christ (Ephesians ii. 5)

HALLELUJAH! Hallelujah!
    Hearts to heaven and voices raise;
Sing to God a hymn of gladness,
    Sing to God a hymn of praise;
He who on the cross a victim
    For the world's salvation bled,
Jesus Christ, the King of glory,
    Now is risen from the dead.

2 Now the iron bars are broken,
    Christ from death to life is born,
Glorious life, and life immortal,
    On this holy Easter morn.
Christ has triumphed, and we conquer
    By His mighty enterprise,
We with Him to life eternal
    By His resurrection rise.

3 Christ is risen, Christ the first-fruits
    Of the holy harvest field,
Which will all its full abundance
    At His second coming yield;
Then the golden ears of harvest
    Will their heads before Him wave,
Ripened by His glorious sunshine,
    From the furrows of the grave.

4 Christ is risen, we are risen;
    Shed upon us heavenly grace,
Rain and dew and gleams of glory
    From the brightness of Thy face;
That, with hearts in heaven dwelling,
    We on earth may fruitful be,
And by angel hands be gathered,
    And be ever, Lord, with Thee.

CHRISTOPHER WORDSWORTH (1807-85) and others

67

VICTORY (8 8 8. 4.)   First three lines adapted from GIOVANNI PIERLUIGI DA PALESTRINA (1525-94).   Hallelujah by WILLIAM HENRY MONK (1823-89)

Hal - le - lu - jah!

ALTERNATIVE TUNE

VULPIUS (8 8 8. 4.)   Melody by MELCHIOR VULPIUS (c. 1560-1616)

Unison

Harmony

Hal - le - lu - jah! Hal - le - lu - jah! Hal-le-lu - jah!

FINITA JAM SUNT PROELIA

Death is swallowed up in victory (1 Corinthians xv. 54)

THE strife is o'er, the battle done;
Now is the Victor's triumph won;
O let the song of praise be sung:
         Hallelujah!

2 Death's mightiest powers have done
    their worst,
And Jesus hath His foes dispersed;
Let shouts of praise and joy outburst:

3 On the third morn He rose again
Glorious in majesty to reign;
O let us swell the joyful strain:

4 He broke the age-bound chains of hell;
The bars from heaven's high portals
    fell;
Let hymns of praise His triumph tell:

5 Lord, by the stripes which wounded
    Thee,
From death's dread sting Thy servants
    free,
That we may live, and sing to Thee:

From *Symphonia Sirenum* (Cologne, 1695);
tr. FRANCIS POTT (1832-1909)

68

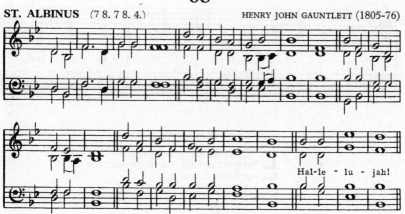

ST. ALBINUS (7 8. 7 8. 4.)   HENRY JOHN GAUNTLETT (1805-76)

Hal-le - lu - jah!

JESUS LEBT

I am he that liveth (Revelation i. 18)

JESUS lives! thy terrors now
Can, O death, no more appal us;
Jesus lives! by this we know
Thou, O grave, canst not enthral us:
        Hallelujah!

2 Jesus lives! henceforth is death
    But the gate of life immortal;
This shall calm our trembling breath
When we pass its gloomy portal:

3 Jesus lives! for us He died;
    Then, alone to Jesus living,
Pure in heart may we abide,
Glory to our Saviour giving:

4 Jesus lives! our hearts know well
    Nought from us His love shall sever;
Life, nor death, nor powers of hell
Tear us from His keeping ever:

5 Jesus lives! to Him the throne
Over all the world is given;
May we go where He is gone,
Rest and reign with Him in heaven:

CHRISTIAN FÜRCHTEGOTT GELLERT (1715-69);
tr. FRANCES ELIZABETH COX (1812-97) and others

69

ORIENTIS PARTIBUS (7 7. 7 7. 4.)   Later form of Medieval French Melody

Hal - le - lu - jah!

I am the resurrection, and the life (John xi. 25)

LOVE'S redeeming work is done;
  Fought the fight, the battle won:
Lo, our Sun's eclipse is o'er!
Lo, He sets in blood no more!
                    Hallelujah!

2 Vain the stone, the watch, the seal!
  Christ has burst the gates of hell;
  Death in vain forbids His rise;
  Christ has opened Paradise.

3 Lives again our glorious King;
  Where, O death, is now thy sting?
  Dying once, He all doth save;
  Where thy victory, O grave?

4 Soar we now where Christ has led,
  Following our exalted Head;
  Made like Him, like Him we rise;
  Ours the cross, the grave, the skies.

5 Hail the Lord of earth and heaven!
  Praise to Thee by both be given:
  Thee we greet triumphant now;
  Hail, the Resurrection Thou!

CHARLES WESLEY (1707-88)

ASCENSION (7 7. 7 7. and Hallelujahs) WILLIAM HENRY MONK (1823-89)

While he blessed them, he was . . . carried up into heaven (Luke xxiv. 51)

HAIL the day that sees Him rise,
     Hallelujah!
To His throne above the skies;
Christ, awhile to mortals given,
Enters now the highest heaven:

2 There for Him high triumph waits:
Lift your heads, eternal gates;
Christ hath conquered death and sin;
Take the King of glory in:

3 Lo, the heaven its Lord receives,
Yet He loves the earth He leaves;
Though returning to His throne,
Still He calls mankind His own:

4 See, He lifts His hands above;
See, He shows the prints of love;
Hark, His gracious lips bestow
Blessings on His Church below:

5 Still for us He intercedes,
His prevailing death He pleads,
Near Himself prepares our place,
He the first-fruits of our race:

6 Lord, though parted from our sight,
Far above the starry height,
Grant our hearts may thither rise,
Seeking Thee above the skies:

CHARLES WESLEY (1707-88),
THOMAS COTTERILL (1779-1823) and others

71

MACCABAEUS (10 11. 11 11. and refrain)   From *Judas Maccabaeus*,
GEORGE FREDERICK HANDEL (1685-1759)

À TOI LA GLOIRE, O RESSUSCITÉ

Thanks be to God, which giveth us the victory through our Lord Jesus Christ (1 Corinthians xv. 57)

THINE be the glory, risen, conquering Son,
   Endless is the victory Thou o'er death hast won;
Angels in bright raiment rolled the stone away,
Kept the folded grave-clothes, where Thy body lay.

   Thine be the glory, risen, conquering Son,
   Endless is the victory Thou o'er death hast won.

2 Lo! Jesus meets us, risen from the tomb;
   Lovingly He greets us, scatters fear and gloom;
   Let the Church with gladness, hymns of triumph sing,
   For her Lord now liveth, death hath lost its sting.

3 No more we doubt Thee, glorious Prince of life;
   Life is nought without Thee: aid us in our strife;
   Make us more than conquerors, through Thy deathless love;
   Bring us safe through Jordan to Thy home above.

                              EDMOND LOUIS BUDRY (1854-1932);
                              tr. RICHARD BIRCH HOYLE (1875-1939)

DIADEMATA (D.S.M.)   GEORGE JOB ELVEY (1816-93)

On his head were many crowns (Revelation xix. 12)

CROWN Him with many crowns,
    The Lamb upon His throne:
Hark how the heavenly anthem drowns
    All music but its own.
Awake, my soul, and sing
    Of Him who died for thee,
And hail Him as thy matchless King
    Through all eternity.

2 Crown Him the Lord of life,
    Who triumphed o'er the grave,
And rose victorious in the strife
    For those He came to save.
His glories now we sing
    Who died and rose on high,
Who died eternal life to bring,
    And lives that death may die.

3 Crown Him the Lord of peace,
    Whose power a sceptre sways
From pole to pole, that wars may cease,
    And all be prayer and praise.
His reign shall know no end;
    And round His piercèd feet
Fair flowers of Paradise extend
    Their fragrance ever sweet.

4 Crown Him the Lord of love;
    Behold His hands and side,
Those wounds yet visible above,
    In beauty glorified.
All hail, Redeemer, hail!
    For Thou hast died for me:
Thy praise shall never, never fail
    Throughout eternity.

MATTHEW BRIDGES (1800-94)
and GODFREY THRING (1823-1903)

73

TRIUMPH (8 7. 8 7. 8 7.)   HENRY JOHN GAUNTLETT (1805-76)

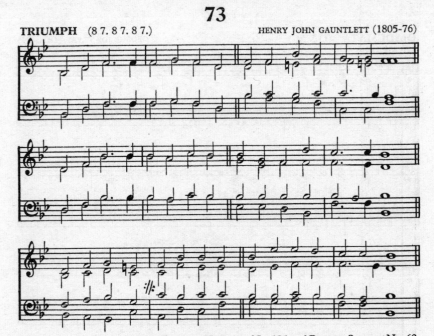

This hymn may also be sung to the tunes NEANDER, No. 186 and REGENT SQUARE, No. 63

Our Lord Jesus Christ . . . the King of kings, and Lord of lords (1 Timothy vi. 14, 15)

LOOK, ye saints! the sight is glorious;
　　See the Man of Sorrows now,
From the fight returned victorious,
　　Every knee to Him shall bow:
　　　Crown Him! crown Him!
　　Crowns become the Victor's brow.

2 Crown the Saviour! angels, crown Him!
　　Rich the trophies Jesus brings;
In the seat of power enthrone Him,
　　While the vault of heaven rings:
　　　Crown Him! crown Him!
　　Crown the Saviour King of kings!

3 Sinners in derision crowned Him,
　　Mocking thus the Saviour's claim;
Saints and angels crowd around Him,
　　Own His title, praise His name:
　　　Crown Him! crown Him!
　　Spread abroad the Victor's fame.

4 Hark, those bursts of acclamation!
　　Hark, those loud triumphant chords!
Jesus takes the highest station:
　　O what jòy the sight affords!
　　　Crown Him! crown Him
　　King of kings, and Lord of lords!

THOMAS KELLY (1769-1854)

See also the sections THE SON OF GOD: HIS PRIESTHOOD AND INTERCESSION, Nos. 74–79;
THE LORD'S DAY, Nos. 366-372. *The following hymn also refers to this theme:*
343   Thou whose name is callèd Jesus.

74

PHILIPPINE (L.M.)   ROBERT EDWIN ROBERTS (1878-1940)

ALTERNATIVE TUNE

CHURCH TRIUMPHANT (L.M.)   JAMES WILLIAM ELLIOTT (1833-1915)

This hymn, with Hallelujahs, may also be sung to the tune LASST UNS ERFREUEN, No. 4

I know that my redeemer liveth (Job xix. 25)

I KNOW that my Redeemer lives:
What comfort this sweet sentence gives!
He lives, He lives, who once was dead:
He lives, my everlasting Head.

2 He lives, triumphant from the grave;
He lives, eternally to save;
He lives, all glorious in the sky;
He lives, exalted there on high.

3 He lives, to bless me with His love,
And still He pleads for me above;
He lives to raise me from the grave,
And me eternally to save.

4 He lives, my kind, wise, constant Friend;
Who still will keep me to the end;
He lives, and while He lives I'll sing,
Jesus, my Prophet, Priest, and King.

5 He lives my mansion to prepare;
And He will bring me safely there;
He lives, all glory to His Name!
Jesus, unchangeably the same!

SAMUEL MEDLEY (1738-99)

75

BETHANY (8 7. 8 7. D.)   HENRY SMART (1813-79)

Worthy is the Lamb that was slain (Revelation v. 12)

HAIL, Thou once despisèd Jesus!
　　Hail, Thou Galilean King!
Thou didst suffer to release us;
　　Thou didst free salvation bring.
Hail, Thou agonizing Saviour,
　　Bearer of our sin and shame!
By Thy merits we find favour;
　　Life is given through Thy name.

2 Paschal Lamb by God appointed,
　　All our sins on Thee were laid;
By almighty love anointed,
　　Thou hast full atonement made:
All Thy people are forgiven
　　Through the virtue of Thy blood;
Opened is the gate of heaven;
　　Peace is made 'twixt man and God.

3 Jesus, hail! enthroned in glory,
　　There for ever to abide;
All the heavenly host adore Thee,
　　Seated at Thy Father's side:
There for sinners Thou art pleading,
　　There Thou dost our place prepare,
Ever for us interceding,
　　Till in glory we appear.

4 Worship, honour, power, and blessing,
　　Thou art worthy to receive;
Loudest praises without ceasing,
　　Meet it is for us to give.
Help, ye bright, angelic spirits!
　　Bring your sweetest, noblest lays;
Help to sing our Saviour's merits,
　　Help to chant Immanuel's praise!

JOHN BAKEWELL (1721-1819) and others

76

FESTUS (L.M.)   Adapted from a melody in FREYLINGHAUSEN'S *Gesangbuch*, 1704

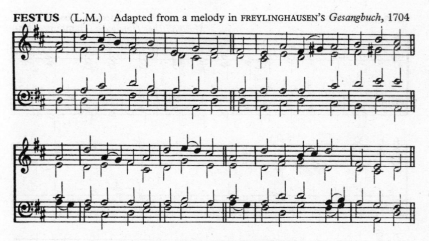

He ever liveth to make intercession for them (Hebrews vii. 25)

BEFORE the throne of God above
I have a strong, a perfect plea;
A great High Priest, whose name is Love,
Who ever lives and pleads for me.

2 My name is graven on His hands,
   My name is written on His heart;
I know that while in heaven He stands
   No tongue can bid me thence depart.

3 When Satan tempts me to despair,
   And tells me of the guilt within,
Upward I look, and see Him there
   Who made an end of all my sin.

4 Because the sinless Saviour died,
   My sinful soul is counted free;
For God, the Just, is satisfied
   To look on Him and pardon me.

5 Behold Him there! the risen Lamb!
   My perfect, spotless Righteousness,
The great unchangeable I AM,
   The King of glory and of grace!

6 One with Himself, I cannot die;
   My soul is purchased by His blood;
My life is hid with Christ on high,
   With Christ, my Saviour and my God.

CHARITIE LEES BANCROFT (1841- ?)

77

WINCHESTER NEW (L.M.) Adapted from a Chorale in the
Musikalisches Handbuch (Hamburg, 1690)

Based on Hebrews iv. 14-16

WHERE high the heavenly temple stands,
The house of God not made with hands,
A great High Priest our nature wears,
The Guardian of mankind appears.

2 He who for men their surety stood,
And poured on earth His precious blood,
Pursues in heaven His mighty plan,
The Saviour and the Friend of man.

3 Though now ascended up on high,
He bends on earth a brother's eye;
Partaker of the human name,
He knows the frailty of our frame.

4 Our Fellow-sufferer yet retains
A fellow-feeling of our pains;
And still remembers in the skies
His tears, His agonies, and cries.

5 In every pang that rends the heart,
The Man of Sorrows had a part;
He sympathizes with our grief,
And to the sufferer sends relief.

6 With boldness, therefore, at the throne
Let us make all our sorrows known;
And ask the aid of heavenly power
To help us in the evil hour.

Scottish Paraphrases (1781)

78

O AMOR QUAM EXSTATICUS (L.M.) Old French Melody (?). Mode I.
Set by BASIL HARWOOD (1859-1949)

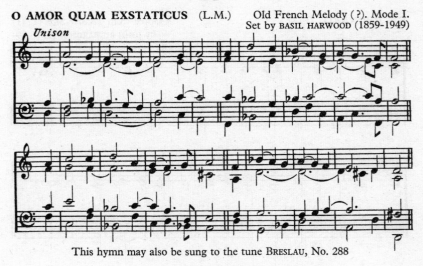

This hymn may also be sung to the tune BRESLAU, No. 288

Based on Micah vi. 6-8

WHEREWITH, O God, shall I draw near,
And bow myself before Thy face?
How in Thy purer eyes appear?
What shall I bring to gain Thy grace?

2 Whoe'er to Thee themselves approve
Must take the path Thy Word hath showed,
Justice pursue, and mercy love,
And humbly walk by faith with God.

3 But though my life henceforth be Thine,
Present for past can ne'er atone;
Though I to Thee the whole resign,
I only give Thee back Thine own.

4 What have I then wherein to trust?
I nothing have, I nothing am;
Excluded is my every boast,
My glory swallowed up in shame.

5 Guilty I stand before Thy face,
On me I feel Thy wrath abide;
'Tis just the sentence should take place;
'Tis just—but O Thy Son hath died!

6 Jesus, the Lamb of God, hath bled,
He bore our sins upon the tree;
Beneath our curse He bowed His head;
'Tis finished! He hath died for me!

7 See where before the throne He stands,
And pours the all-prevailing prayer,
Points to His side, and lifts His hands,
And shows that I am graven there.

8 He ever lives for me to pray;
He prays that I with Him may reign:
Amen to what my Lord doth say!
Jesus, Thou canst not pray in vain.

CHARLES WESLEY (1707-88)

79

ST. BERNARD (C.M.)

Adapted from *Tochter Sion* (1741)
by JOHN RICHARDSON (1816-79)

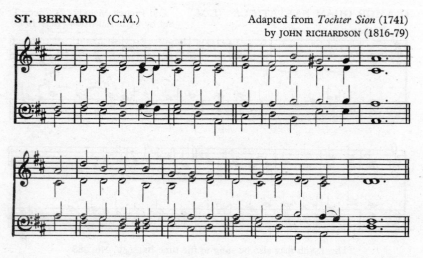

We have not an high priest which cannot be touched with the feeling of our infirmities (Hebrews iv. 15)

WITH joy we meditate the grace
    Of our High Priest above;
His heart is made of tenderness,
    And ever yearns with love.

2 Touched with a sympathy within,
    He knows our feeble frame;
He knows what sore temptations mean,
    For He hath felt the same.

3 He in the days of feeble flesh
    Poured out His cries and tears;
And, though exalted, feels afresh
    What every member bears.

4 He'll never quench the smoking flax,
    But raise it to a flame;
The bruisèd reed He never breaks,
    Nor scorns the meanest name.

5 Then let our humble faith address
    His mercy and His power:
We shall obtain delivering grace
    In the distressing hour.

ISAAC WATTS (1674-1748)

The following hymns also refer to this theme:

  94   Brethren, let us join to bless
107   Join all the glorious names
110   Let us love, and sing, and wonder
237   Now I have found the ground wherein

80

GOPSAL (6 6. 6 6. 8 8.) GEORGE FREDERICK HANDEL (1685-1759)

Rejoice in the Lord alway (Philippians iv. 4)

REJOICE, the Lord is King!
Your Lord and King adore;
Mortals, give thanks and sing,
And triumph evermore:
Lift up your heart, lift up your voice;
Rejoice, again I say, rejoice.

2 Jesus, the Saviour, reigns,
The God of truth and love;
When He had purged our stains,
He took His seat above:

3 His Kingdom cannot fail;
His rules o'er earth and heaven;
The keys of death and hell
Are to our Jesus given:

4 He sits at God's right hand
Till all His foes submit,
And bow to His command,
And fall beneath His feet:

5 Rejoice in glorious hope;
Jesus the Judge shall come,
And take His servants up
To their eternal home:
We soon shall hear the archangel's voice;
The trump of God shall sound, Rejoice!

CHARLES WESLEY (1707-88)

99

81

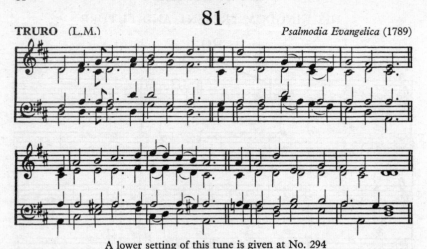

TRURO　(L.M.)　　　　　　　　　　　　　*Psalmodia Evangelica* (1789)

A lower setting of this tune is given at No. 294

ALTERNATIVE TUNE

GALILEE　(L.M.)　　　　　　　　　　　PHILIP ARMES (1836-1908)

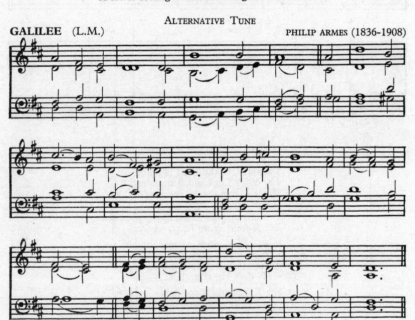

This hymn may also be sung to the tune RIMINGTON, No. 28 (ii)

All nations shall serve him (Psalm lxxii. 11)

JESUS shall reign where'er the sun
　　Does his successive journeys run;
His kingdom stretch from shore to shore,
Till moons shall wax and wane no more.

2 People and realms of every tongue
　Dwell on His love with sweetest song,
　And infant voices shall proclaim
　Their early blessings on His name.

3 Blessings abound where'er He reigns;
　The prisoner leaps to lose his chains;
　The weary find eternal rest,
　And all the sons of want are blest.

4 Let every creature rise and bring
　Peculiar honours to our King,
　Angels descend with songs again,
　And earth repeat the loud Amen.

ISAAC WATTS (1674-1748)

82

CRÜGER (7 6. 7 6. D.)   JOHANN CRÜGER (1598-1662)

Based on Psalm lxxii

HAIL to the Lord's Anointed,
    Great David's greater Son!
Hail, in the time appointed,
    His reign on earth begun!
He comes to break oppression,
    To set the captive free:
To take away transgression,
    And rule in equity.

2 He shall come down like showers
    Upon the fruitful earth,
And love, joy, hope, like flowers,
    Spring in His path to birth;
Before Him on the mountains
    Shall peace the herald go;
And righteousness in fountains
    From hill to valley flow.

3 Kings shall fall down before Him,
    And gold and incense bring;
All nations shall adore Him,
    His praise all people sing;
To Him shall prayer unceasing
    And daily vows ascend;
His kingdom still increasing,
    A kingdom without end.

4 O'er every foe victorious,
    He on His throne shall rest,
From age to age more glorious,
    All-blessing and all-blest:
The tide of time shall never
    His covenant remove;
His name shall stand for ever;
    His changeless name of Love.

JAMES MONTGOMERY (1771-1854)

83

GLASGOW (C.M.)   MOORE'S *Psalm-Singer's Pocket Companion* (1756)

Paraphrase of Isaiah ii. 2-5

BEHOLD! the mountain of the Lord
  In latter days shall rise
On mountain-tops above the hills,
  And draw the wondering eyes.

2 To this the joyful nations round,
  All tribes and tongues, shall flow;
Up to the hill of God, they'll say,
  And to His house we'll go.

3 The beam that shines from Zion's hill
  Shall lighten every land;
The King who reigns in Salem's towers
  Shall all the world command.

4 Among the nations He shall judge;
  His judgments truth shall guide;
His sceptre shall protect the just,
  And quell the sinner's pride.

5 No strife shall rage, nor hostile feuds
  Disturb those peaceful years;
To ploughshares men shall beat their swords,
  To pruning forks their spears.

6 Come then, O house of Jacob! come
  To worship at His shrine;
And, walking in the light of God,
  With holy beauties shine.

Scottish Paraphrases (1781)

84

SENNEN COVE (C.M.)   WILLIAM H. HARRIS (1883-

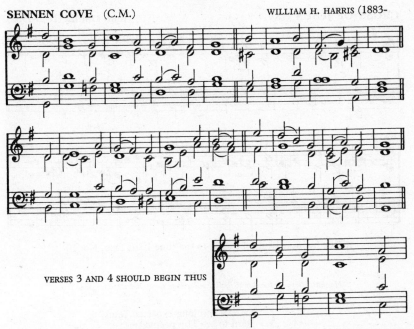

VERSES 3 AND 4 SHOULD BEGIN THUS

This hymn may also be sung to the tunes BEATITUDO, No. 267, and IRISH, No. 125

Based on Revelation vii. 13-17

HOW bright these glorious spirits shine!
 Whence all their white array?
How came they to the blissful seats
 Of everlasting day?

2 Lo! these are they, from sufferings great,
 Who came to realms of light,
And in the blood of Christ have washed
 Those robes which shine so bright.

3 Now, with triumphal palms, they stand
 Before the throne on high,
And serve the God they love, amidst
 The glories of the sky.

4 Hunger and thirst are felt no more,
 Nor suns with scorching ray;
God is their Sun, whose cheering beams
 Diffuse eternal day.

5 The Lamb which dwells amidst the throne
 Shall o'er them still preside;
Feed them with nourishment divine,
 And all their footsteps guide.

6 'Midst pastures green He'll lead His flock,
 Where living streams appear;
And God the Lord from every eye
 Shall wipe off every tear.

ISAAC WATTS (1674-1748) and (?) WILLIAM CAMERON
(1751-1811), as in *Scottish Paraphrases* (1781)

103

85

CROSS OF JESUS (8 7. 8 7.)   JOHN STAINER (1840-1901)

This hymn may also be sung to the tune LAUS DEO, No. 18

He that sitteth on the throne shall dwell among them (Revelation vii. 15)

COME, Thou long-expected Jesus,
   Born to set Thy people free;
From our fears and sins release us;
   Let us find our rest in Thee.

2 Israel's strength and consolation,
   Hope of all the earth Thou art,
Dear desire of every nation,
   Joy of every longing heart.

3 Born Thy people to deliver,
   Born a child and yet a king.
Born to reign in us for ever,
   Now Thy gracious kingdom bring.

4 By Thine own eternal Spirit
   Rule in all our hearts alone;
By Thine all-sufficient merit
   Raise us to Thy glorious throne.

CHARLES WESLEY (1707-88)

86

VENI IMMANUEL   (8 8. 8 8. 8 8.)

Melody adapted by THOMAS HELMORE
(1811-90) from a French Missal

Unison

VENI, VENI, IMMANUEL

They shall see the Son of man coming in the clouds of heaven with power and great glory (Matthew xxiv. 30)

O COME, O come, Immanuel,
  And ransom captive Israel,
That mourns in lonely exile here,
Until the Son of God appear.

Rejoice, rejoice ! Immanuel
Shall come to thee, O Israel.

2 O come, O come, Thou Lord of might
Who to Thy tribes, on Sinai's height,
In ancient times didst give the law
In cloud and majesty and awe:

3 O come, Thou Rod of Jesse, free
Thine own from Satan's tyranny;
From depths of hell Thy people save,
And give them victory o'er the grave:

4 O come, Thou Dayspring, come and cheer
Our spirits by Thine advent here;
Disperse the gloomy clouds of night,
And death's dark shadows put to flight:

5 O come, Thou Key of David, come
And open wide our heavenly home;
Make safe the way that leads on high,
And close the path to misery:

From the *Great O Antiphons* (12th-13th centuries);
tr. JOHN MASON NEALE (1818-66)

87

LONDONDERRY AIR (11 10. 11 10. D.)   Irish Traditional Melody
Descant: last verse   Arranged by F. DEREK KIDNER (1913-   )

I can-not tell how   all shall wor-ship,   When ev'ry storm is—

Unison: all verses

stilled,   Or who can say how   great   the joy,   When hearts of

men with love are filled.   The skies will thrill with rap - ture,

And my-riad hu-man   voi - ces sing,   And heav'n will ans - wer

earth: At last the Sa-viour of the world is King.

When the fulness of the time was come, God sent forth his Son . . . to redeem them that were under the law.
(Galatians iv. 4, 5)

I CANNOT tell why He, whom angels worship,
    Should set His love upon the sons of men,
Or why, as Shepherd, He should seek the wanderers,
    To bring them back, they know not how or when.
But this I know, that He was born of Mary
    When Bethlehem's manger was His only home,
And that He lived at Nazareth and laboured,
    And so the Saviour, Saviour of the world, is come.

2 I cannot tell how silently He suffered,
    As with His peace He graced this place of tears,
Or how His heart upon the cross was broken,
    The crown of pain to three and thirty years.
But this I know, He heals the broken-hearted,
    And stays our sin, and calms our lurking fear,
And lifts the burden from the heavy laden,
    For yet the Saviour, Saviour of the world, is here.

3 I cannot tell how He will win the nations,
    How He will claim His earthly heritage,
How satisfy the needs and aspirations
    Of East and West, of sinner and of sage.
But this I know, all flesh shall see His glory,
    And He shall reap the harvest He has sown,
And some glad day His sun shall shine in splendour
    When He the Saviour, Saviour of the world, is known.

4 I cannot tell how all the lands shall worship,
    When, at His bidding, every storm is stilled,
Or who can say how great the jubilation
    When all the hearts of men with love are filled.
But this I know, the skies will thrill with rapture,
    And myriad, myriad human voices sing,
And earth to heaven, and heaven to earth, will answer:
    At last the Saviour, Saviour of the world, is King!

WILLIAM YOUNG FULLERTON (1857-1932)

88

HELMSLEY (8 7. 8 7. 8 7.)　　　　　　　English Melody (18th century)

Every eye shall see him (Revelation i. 7)

LO! He comes, with clouds descending,
　Once for favoured sinners slain;
Thousand thousand saints attending
　Swell the triumph of His train;
　　Hallelujah!
　Christ appears on earth to reign.

2 Every eye shall now behold Him,
　Robed in dreadful majesty;
Those who set at naught and sold Him,
　Pierced, and nailed Him to the tree,
　　Deeply wailing,
　Shall the true Messiah see.

3 Now redemption, long expected,
　See in solemn pomp appear;
All His saints, by man rejected,
　Now shall meet Him in the air.
　　Hallelujah!
　See the day of God appear!

4 Yea, Amen! let all adore Thee,
　High on Thine eternal throne;
Saviour, take the power and glory,
　Claim the kingdom for Thine own;
　　Hallelujah!
　O come quickly; come, Lord, come!

JOHN CENNICK (1718-55), CHARLES WESLEY (1707-88)
and MARTIN MADAN (1726-90)

The following hymns also refer to this theme:

163　Thou art coming, O my Saviour　　170　Lord, her watch Thy Church is keeping
173　Thy kingdom come, O God

89

FRAGRANCE (9 8. 9 8. 9 8.)

French Carol Melody
Harmonized by CHARLES HERBERT KITSON (1874-1944)

A Choir setting of this melody in a higher key is given at No. 390

He humbled himself (Philippians ii. 8)

THOU who wast rich beyond all splendour,
  All for love's sake becamest poor;
Thrones for a manger didst surrender,
  Sapphire-paved courts for stable floor.
Thou who wast rich beyond all splendour,
  All for love's sake becamest poor.

2 Thou who art God beyond all praising,
    All for love's sake becamest Man;
  Stooping so low, but sinners raising
    Heavenwards by Thine eternal plan.
  Thou who art God beyond all praising,
    All for love's sake becamest Man.

3 Thou who art love beyond all telling,
    Saviour and King, we worship Thee.
  Immanuel, within us dwelling,
    Make us what Thou wouldst have us be.
  Thou who art love, beyond all telling,
    Saviour and King, we worship Thee.

FRANK HOUGHTON (1894-)

90

MILES LANE (C.M.)   WILLIAM SHRUBSOLE (1760-1806)

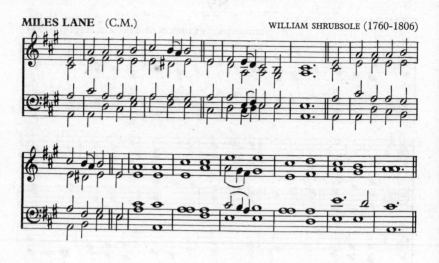

ALTERNATIVE TUNE

LADYWELL (D.C.M.)   WILLIAM HAROLD FERGUSON (1874-1950)
(Unison: verses 1,2,5,6)

This hymn may also be sung to the tune LYDIA, No. 102

And he hath . . . a name written, KING OF KINGS, AND LORD OF LORDS (Revelation xix. 16)

ALL hail the power of Jesus' name!
Let angels prostrate fall;
Bring forth the royal diadem,
To crown Him Lord of all.

2 Crown Him, ye martyrs of your God,
Who from His altar call;
Extol Him in whose path ye trod,
And crown Him Lord of all.

3 Ye seed of Israel's chosen race,
Ye ransomed of the fall,
Hail Him who saves you by His grace,
And crown Him Lord of all.

4 Sinners, whose love can ne'er forget
The wormwood and the gall,
Go, spread your trophies at His feet,
And crown Him Lord of all.

5 Let every kindred, every tribe
On this terrestrial ball,
To Him all majesty ascribe,
And crown Him Lord of all.

6 O that, with yonder sacred throng,
We at His feet may fall,
Join in the everlasting song,
And crown Him Lord of all!

EDWARD PERRONET (1726-92);
revised by JOHN RIPPON (1751-1836)

91

This hymn may also be sung to the tune SINE NOMINE, No. 147

Based on Philippians ii. 5-11

ALL praise to Thee, for Thou, O King divine,
Didst yield the glory that of right was Thine,
That in our darkened hearts Thy grace might shine:
    Hallelujah!

2 Thou cam'st to us in lowliness of thought;
By Thee the outcast and the poor were sought,
And by Thy death was God's salvation wrought:
    Hallelujah!

3 Let this mind be in us which was in Thee,
Who wast a servant that we might be free,
Humbling Thyself to death on Calvary:
    Hallelujah!

4 Wherefore, by God's eternal purpose, Thou
Art high exalted o'er all creatures now,
And given the name to which all knees shall bow:
    Hallelujah!

5 Let every tongue confess with one accord,
In heaven and earth, that Jesus Christ is Lord;
And God the Father be by all adored:
    Hallelujah!

FRANCIS BLAND TUCKER (1895-   )

92

CELESTE   (8 8. 8 8. Anapaestic)   *Lancashire Sunday-School Songs* (1857)

This hymn may also be sung to the tune LLANGRISTIOLUS, No. 230

O the depth of the riches both of the wisdom and knowledge of God! (Romans xi. 33)

HOW good is the God we adore,
Our faithful, unchangeable Friend!
His love is as great as His power,
And knows neither measure nor end!

2 'Tis Jesus, the first and the last,
Whose Spirit shall guide us safe home;
We'll praise Him for all that is past,
We'll trust Him for all that's to come.

JOSEPH HART (1712-68)

93

EVELYNS (6 5. 6 5. D.)   WILLIAM HENRY MONK (1823-89)

ALTERNATIVE TUNE

CUDDESDON (6 5. 6 5. D.)   WILLIAM HAROLD FERGUSON (1874-1950)

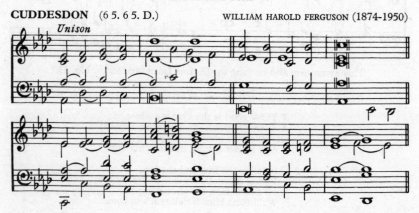

Based on Philippians ii. 9-11

A T the name of Jesus
  Every knee shall bow,
Every tongue confess Him
  King of glory now;
'Tis the Father's pleasure
  We should call Him Lord,
Who from the beginning
  Was the mighty Word.

2 Humbled for a season,
  To receive a name
From the lips of sinners
  Unto whom He came,
Faithfully He bore it
  Spotless to the last,
Brought it back victorious,
  When from death He passed.

* 3 Name Him, brothers, name Him
  With love strong as death,
But with awe and wonder,
  And with bated breath;
He is God the Saviour,
  He is Christ the Lord,
Ever to be worshipped,
  Trusted, and adored.

4 In your hearts enthrone Him;
  There let Him subdue
All that is not holy,
  All that is not true:
Crown Him as your Captain
  In temptation's hour;
Let His will enfold you
  In its light and power.

5 Brothers, this Lord Jesus
  Shall return again,
With His Father's glory,
  With His angel train;
For all wreaths of empire
  Meet upon His brow,
And our hearts confess Him
  King of glory now.

CAROLINE MARIA NOEL (1817-77)

* If desired, this verse may be omitted

94

HARTS (7 7. 7 7.)   BENJAMIN MILGROVE (1731-1810)

This hymn may also be sung to the tune CULBACH, No. 23

Let us exalt his name together (Psalm xxxiv. 3)

BRETHREN, let us join to bless
　　Christ, the Lord our righteousness;
Let our praise to Him be given,
High at God's right hand in heaven.

2 Son of God, to Thee we bow,
　Thou art Lord, and only Thou;
　Thou the blessed virgin's Seed,
　Glory of Thy Church, and Head.

3 Thee the angels ceaseless sing,
　Thee we praise, our Priest and King;
　Worthy is Thy name of praise,
　Full of glory, full of grace.

4 Thou hast the glad tidings brought
　Of salvation by Thee wrought;
　Wrought to set Thy people free;
　Wrought to bring our souls to Thee.

5 May we follow and adore
　Thee, our Saviour, more and more;
　Guide and bless us with Thy love,
　Till we join Thy saints above.

JOHN CENNICK (1718-55)

95

VIENNA (7 7. 7 7.)   Melody from JUSTIN HEINRICH KNECHT (1752-1817)

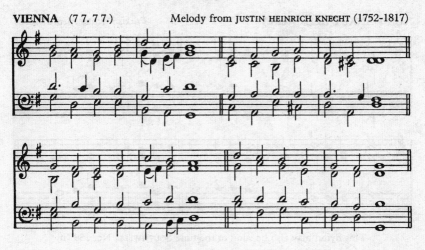

VICTIS SIBI COGNOMINA

Thou shalt call his name JESUS: for he shall save his people from their sins (Matthew i. 21)

CONQUERING kings their titles take
  From the foes they captive make:
Jesus, by a nobler deed,
From the thousands He hath freed.

2 Yes: none other name is given
  Unto mortals under heaven,
Which can make the dead arise,
And exalt them to the skies.

3 That which Christ so hardly wrought,
  That which He so dearly bought,
That salvation, brethren, say,
Shall we madly cast away?

4 Rather gladly for that name
  Bear the cross, endure the shame:
Joyfully for Him to die
Is not death but victory.

5 Jesu, who dost condescend
  To be called the sinner's Friend,
Hear us, as to Thee we pray,
Glorying in Thy name today.

                        Latin; tr. JOHN CHANDLER (1806-76)

E

96

NUN DANKET ALL (C.M.)   *Praxis Pietatis Melica* (1653)

This hymn may also be sung to the tune SOUTHWELL, No. 139 (ii)

Whom having not seen, ye love (1 Peter i. 8)

JESUS, these eyes have never seen
   That radiant form of Thine;
The veil of sense hangs dark between
   Thy blessèd face and mine.

2 I see Thee not, I hear Thee not,
   Yet art Thou oft with me;
And earth hath ne'er so dear a spot
   As where I meet with Thee.

3 Yet, though I have not seen, and still
   Must rest in faith alone,
I love Thee, dearest Lord, and will,
   Unseen but not unknown.

4 When death these mortal eyes shall seal,
   And still this throbbing heart,
The rending veil shall Thee reveal
   All glorious as Thou art.

RAY PALMER (1808-87)

97

ST. AGNES (C.M.)   JOHN BACCHUS DYKES (1823-76)

This hymn may also be sung to the tune NUN DANKET ALL, No. 96

JESU, DULCIS MEMORIA

How precious also are thy thoughts unto me, O God! (Psalm cxxxix. 17)

JESU, the very thought of Thee
  With sweetness fills the breast;
But sweeter far Thy face to see,
  And in Thy presence rest.

2 No voice can sing, no heart can frame,
    Nor can the memory find
  A sweeter sound than Jesus' name,
    The Saviour of mankind.

3 O hope of every contrite heart,
    O joy of all the meek,
  To those who ask how kind Thou art,
    How good to those who seek!

4 But what to those who find? Ah, this
    Nor tongue nor pen can show;
  The love of Jesus, what it is
    None but His loved ones know.

5 Jesu, our only joy be Thou,
    As Thou our prize wilt be;
  In Thee be all our glory now,
    And through eternity.

Latin (*c.* 11th century); tr. EDWARD CASWALL (1814-78)

98

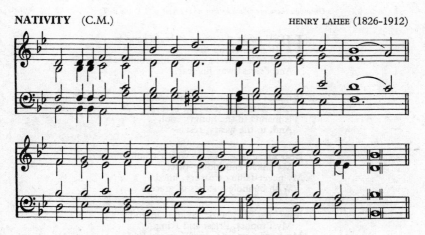

NATIVITY (C.M.)   HENRY LAHEE (1826-1912)

Based on Revelation v. 11-14

COME, let us join our cheerful songs
  With angels round the throne;
Ten thousand thousand are their
  But all their joys are one. [tongues,

2 'Worthy the Lamb that died,' they cry,
    'To be exalted thus';
  'Worthy the Lamb,' our lips reply,
    'For He was slain for us.'

3 Jesus is worthy to receive
    Honour and power divine;
  And blessings, more than we can give,
    Be, Lord, for ever Thine.

4 The whole creation join in one
    To bless the sacred name
  Of Him that sits upon the throne,
    And to adore the Lamb.

ISAAC WATTS (1674-1748)

99

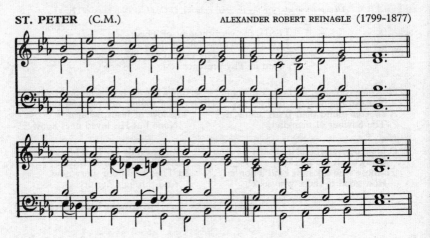

ST. PETER (C.M.)   ALEXANDER ROBERT REINAGLE (1799-1877)

Unto you therefore which believe he is precious (1 Peter ii. 7)

HOW sweet the name of Jesus sounds
    In a believer's ear!
It soothes his sorrows, heals his wounds,
    And drives away his fear.

2 It makes the wounded spirit whole,
    And calms the troubled breast;
'Tis manna to the hungry soul,
    And, to the weary, rest.

3 Dear name! the rock on which I build,
    My shield and hiding-place,
My never-failing treasury, filled
    With boundless stores of grace.

4 Jesus! my Shepherd, Saviour, Friend,
    My Prophet, Priest and King,
My Lord, my Life, my Way, my End,
    Accept the praise I bring.

5 Weak is the effort of my heart,
    And cold my warmest thought;
But when I see Thee as Thou art,
    I'll praise Thee as I ought.

6 Till then I would Thy love proclaim
    With every fleeting breath;
And may the music of Thy name
    Refresh my soul in death.

JOHN NEWTON (1725-1807)

100

PADERBORN (5 5. 5 5. 6 5. 6 5.)　　　　　　　　*Paderborn Gesangbuch (1765)*

This hymn may also be sung to the tune HANOVER, No. 25

God is my King of old, working salvation in the midst of the earth (Psalm lxxiv. 12)

YE servants of God,
　Your Master proclaim,
And publish abroad
　His wonderful name;
The name all-victorious
　Of Jesus extol;
His kingdom is glorious,
　And rules over all.

2 God ruleth on high,
　　Almighty to save;
And still He is nigh,
　　His presence we have;
The great congregation
　　His triumph shall sing,
Ascribing salvation
　　To Jesus our King.

3 Salvation to God,
　　Who sits on the throne!
Let all cry aloud,
　　And honour the Son:
The praises of Jesus
　　The angels proclaim,
Fall down on their faces,
　　And worship the Lamb.

4 Then let us adore,
　　And give Him His right,
All glory and power,
　　All wisdom and might,
All honour and blessing,
　　With angels above,
And thanks never-ceasing,
　　And infinite love.

CHARLES WESLEY (1707-88)

THE SON OF GOD

101

CHORUS ANGELORUM (C.M.) ARTHUR SOMERVELL (1863-1937)

This hymn may also be sung to the tunes RICHMOND, No. 371, and LYDIA, No. 102

I will be glad and rejoice in thee: I will sing praise to thy name, O thou most High (Psalm ix. 2)

O FOR a thousand tongues, to sing
    My dear Redeemer's praise,
The glories of my God and King,
    The triumphs of His grace!

2 Jesus! the name that charms our fears,
    That bids our sorrows cease;
'Tis music in the sinner's ears,
    'Tis life, and health, and peace.

3 He breaks the power of cancelled sin,
    He sets the prisoner free;
His blood can make the foulest clean,
    His blood availed for me.

4 See all your sins on Jesus laid;
    The Lamb of God was slain,
His soul was once an offering made
    For every soul of man.

*5 He speaks, and, listening to His voice,
    New life the dead receive,
The mournful, broken hearts rejoice,
    The humble poor believe.

*6 Hear Him, ye deaf; His praise, ye dumb,
    Your loosened tongues employ;
Ye blind, behold your Saviour come;
    And leap, ye lame, for joy!

7 My gracious Master and my God,
    Assist me to proclaim,
To spread through all the earth abroad
    The honours of Thy name.

CHARLES WESLEY (1707-88)

*If desired, verses 5 and 6 may be omitted

102

LYDIA (C.M.)   THOMAS PHILLIPS (1735-1807)

This hymn may also be sung to the tune RICHMOND, No. 371

God hath . . . given him a name which is above every name (Philippians ii. 9)

JESUS! the name high over all,
   In hell, or earth, or sky;
Angels and men before it fall,
   And devils fear and fly.

2 Jesus! the name to sinners dear,
   The name to sinners given;
It scatters all their guilty fear,
   It turns their hell to heaven.

3 Jesus! the prisoner's fetters breaks,
   And bruises Satan's head;
Power into strengthless souls it speaks,
   And life into the dead.

4 O that the world might taste and see
   The riches of His grace;
The arms of love that compass me
   Would all mankind embrace.

5 His only righteousness I show,
   His saving grace proclaim;
'Tis all my business here below
   To cry: Behold the Lamb!

6 Happy, if with my latest breath
   I might but gasp His name;
Preach Him to all, and cry in death:
   Behold, behold the Lamb!

CHARLES WESLEY (1707-88)

103

MARYTON (L.M.)   HENRY PERCY SMITH (1825-98)

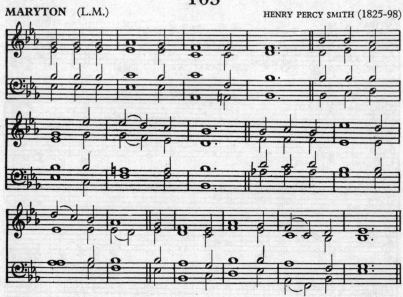

ALTERNATIVE TUNE

DULCIS MEMORIA (L.M.)   PERCY CARTER BUCK (1871-1947)

Unison

JESU, DULCEDO CORDIUM

He satisfieth the longing soul (Psalm cvii. 9)

JESU, Thou joy of loving hearts,
   Thou fount of life, Thou light of men,
From the best bliss that earth imparts
   We turn unfilled to Thee again.

2 Thy truth unchanged hath ever stood;
   Thou savest those that on Thee call:
To them that seek Thee, Thou art good.
   To them that find Thee, all in all.

3 We taste Thee, O Thou living bread,
   And long to feast upon Thee still;
We drink of Thee, the fountain-head,
   And thirst our souls from Thee to fill.

4 Our restless spirits yearn for Thee,
   Where'er our changeful lot is cast,
Glad when Thy gracious smile we see,
   Blest when our faith can hold
      Thee fast.

5 O Jesu, ever with us stay;
   Make all our moments calm and
      bright;
Chase the dark night of sin away;
   Shed o'er the world Thy holy light.

Latin (*c.* 11th century); tr. RAY PALMER (1808-87)

104

ST. MAGNUS   (C.M.)   Probably by JEREMIAH CLARK (*c.* 1670-1707)

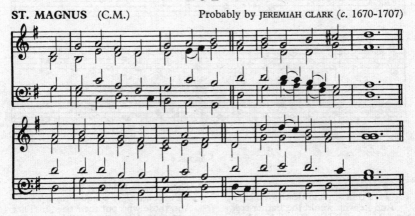

We see Jesus . . . crowned with glory and honour (Hebrews ii. 9)

THE head that once was crowned with thorns
   Is crowned with glory now;
A royal diadem adorns
   The mighty Victor's brow.

2 The highest place that heaven affords
   Is His, is His by right,
The King of kings, and Lord of lords,
   And heaven's eternal light;

3 The joy of all who dwell above,
   The joy of all below,
To whom He manifests His love,
   And grants His name to know.

4 To them the cross, with all its shame,
   With all its grace, is given;
Their name an everlasting name,
   Their joy the joy of heaven.

5 They suffer with their Lord below,
   They reign with Him above;
Their profit and their joy to know
   The mystery of His love.

6 The cross He bore is life and health,
   Though shame and death to Him;
His people's hope, His people's wealth,
   Their everlasting theme.

THOMAS KELLY (1769-1854)

105

ST. JAMES (C.M.)   RAPHAEL COURTEVILLE (d. *c.* 1772)

Based on John xiv. 6

THOU art the Way; to Thee alone
From sin and death we flee;
And he who would the Father seek
Must seek Him, Lord, by Thee.

2 Thou art the Truth; Thy Word alone
True wisdom can impart;
Thou only canst inform the mind
And purify the heart.

3 Thou art the Life; the rending tomb
Proclaims Thy conquering arm;
And those who put their trust in Thee
Nor death nor hell shall harm.

4 Thou art the Way, the Truth, the Life;
Grant us that way to know,
That truth to keep, that life to win,
Whose joys eternal flow.

GEORGE WASHINGTON DOANE (1799-1859)

106

ELLASGARTH (8 10. 10 4.)   PEGGY SPENCER PALMER

ALTERNATIVE VERSION FOR VERSE 3

Whom have I in heaven but thee? (Psalm lxxiii. 25)

NONE other Lamb, none other Name,
   None other Hope in heaven or earth or sea,
None other Hiding-place from guilt and shame,
   None beside Thee.

2 My faith burns low, my hope burns low;
   Only my heart's desire cries out in me,
By the deep thunder of its want and woe,
   Cries out to Thee.

3 Lord, Thou art life, though I be dead;
   Love's fire Thou art, however
      cold I be:
Nor heaven have I, nor place to lay my
   Nor home, but Thee.   [head,

CHRISTINA GEORGINA ROSSETTI (1830-94)

107

HAREWOOD (6 6. 6 6. 8 8.)   SAMUEL SEBASTIAN WESLEY (1810-76)

This hymn may also be sung to the tunes CHRISTCHURCH, No. 108, and DARWALL'S 148TH, No. 19

Far above . . . every name that is named (Ephesians i. 21)

JOIN all the glorious names
　　Of wisdom, love, and power,
That ever mortals knew,
　　That angels ever bore;
All are too mean to speak His worth,
Too mean to set my Saviour forth.

2 Great Prophet of my God,
　　My tongue would bless Thy name;
By Thee the joyful news
　　Of our salvation came;
The joyful news of sins forgiven,
Of hell subdued, and peace with heaven.

3 Jesus, my great High Priest,
　　Offered His blood and died;
My guilty conscience seeks
　　No sacrifice beside:
His powerful blood did once atone,
And now it pleads before the throne.

4 My dear almighty Lord,
　　My Conqueror and my King,
Thy sceptre and Thy sword,
　　Thy reigning grace, I sing:
Thine is the power; behold, I sit
In willing bonds before Thy feet.

5 Should all the hosts of death,
　　And powers of hell unknown,
Put their most dreadful forms
　　Of rage and mischief on,
I shall be safe, for Christ displays
Superior power, and guardian grace.

ISAAC WATTS (1674-1748)

108

CHRISTCHURCH (6 6. 6 6. 8 8.)   CHARLES STEGGALL (1826-1905)

I am the way, the truth, and the life (John xiv. 6)

WE come, O Christ, to Thee,
  True Son of God and man,
By whom all things consist,
  In whom all life began:
In Thee alone we live and move,
And have our being in Thy love.

2 Thou art the Way to God,
    Thy blood our ransom paid;
  In Thee we face our Judge
    And Maker unafraid.
  Before the throne absolved we stand:
  Thy love has met Thy law's demand.

3 Thou art the living Truth!
    All wisdom dwells in Thee,
  Thou source of every skill,
    Eternal verity!
  Thou great I AM! In Thee we rest,
  True answer to our every quest.

4 Thou only art true Life,
    To know Thee is to live
  The more abundant life
    That earth can never give:
  O risen Lord! We live in Thee
  And Thou in us eternally!

5 We worship Thee Lord Christ,
    Our Saviour and our King,
  To Thee our youth and strength
    Adoringly we bring:
  So fill our hearts that men may see
  Thy life in us and turn to Thee!

E. MARGARET CLARKSON (1915-)

129

109

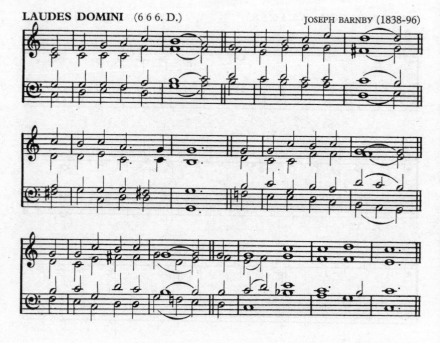

LAUDES DOMINI (6 6 6. D.)   JOSEPH BARNBY (1838-96)

BEIM FRÜHEN MORGENLICHT

Daily shall he be praised (Psalm lxxii. 15)

WHEN morning gilds the skies,
My heart awaking cries,
  'May Jesus Christ be praised!'
Alike at work and prayer
To Jesus I repair:
  'May Jesus Christ be praised!'

2 Be this, when day is past,
Of all my thoughts the last,
  'May Jesus Christ be praised!'
The night becomes as day,
When from the heart we say:
  'May Jesus Christ be praised!'

3 Does sadness fill my mind
A solace here I find,
  'May Jesus Christ be praised!'
When evil thoughts molest,
With this I shield my breast,
  'May Jesus Christ be praised!'

*4 To God, the Word, on high
The hosts of angels cry,
  'May Jesus Christ be praised!'
Let mortals, too, upraise
Their voice in hymns of praise:
  'May Jesus Christ be praised!'

*5 Let earth's wide circle round
In joyful notes resound,
  'May Jesus Christ be praised!'
Let air and sea and sky,
From depth to height, reply,
  'May Jesus Christ be praised!'

6 Be this while life is mine,
My canticle divine,
  'May Jesus Christ be praised!'
Be this the eternal song
Through all the ages long,
  ' May Jesus Christ be praised!'

19th century; tr. EDWARD CASWALL (1814-78)

If desired, verses 4 and 5 may be omitted

110

ALL SAINTS   (8 7. 8 7. 7 7.)   *Darmstadt Gesangbuch (1698)*

Unto him that loved us, and washed us from our sins in his own blood . . . be glory and dominion
(Revelation i. 5, 6)

LET us love, and sing, and wonder,
Let us praise the Saviour's name!
He has hushed the Law's loud thunder,
He has quenched Mount Sinai's flame;
He has washed us with His blood,
He has brought us nigh to God.

2 Let us love the Lord who bought us,
Pitied us when enemies,
Called us by His grace, and taught us,
Gave us ears, and gave us eyes:
He has washed us with His blood,
He presents our souls to God.

3 Let us sing, though fierce temptations
Threaten hard to bear us down!
For the Lord, our strong salvation,
Holds in view the conqueror's crown,
He who washed us with His blood,
Soon will bring us home to God.

4 Let us wonder; grace and justice
Join, and point to mercy's store;
When through grace in Christ our trust
Justice smiles, and asks no more: [is,
He who washed us with His blood,
Has secured our way to God.

5 Let us praise, and join the chorus
Of the saints enthroned on high;
Here they trusted Him before us,
Now their praises fill the sky:
'Thou hast washed us with Thy
blood;
Thou art worthy, Lamb of God.'

JOHN NEWTON (1725-1807)

111

ORIEL　(8 7. 8 7. 8 7.)　　　　　　　　CASPAR ETT, *Cantica Sacra* (1840)

ALTERNATIVE TUNE

MIDHURST　(8 7. 8 7. 8 7.)　　　　　　　CYRIL WINN (1884-　)

GLORIOSI SALVATORIS

There is none other name under heaven given among men, whereby we must be saved (Acts iv. 12)

TO the name of our salvation
    Laud and honour let us pay,
Which for many a generation
    Hid in God's foreknowledge lay,
But with holy exultation
    We may sing aloud today.

2 Jesus is the name we treasure,
    Name beyond what words can tell,
Name of gladness, name of pleasure,
    Ear and heart delighting well;
Name of sweetness passing measure,
    Saving us from sin and hell.

3 'Tis the name that whoso preacheth
    Speaks like music to the ear;
Who in prayer this name beseecheth
    Sweetest comfort findeth near;
Who its perfect wisdom reacheth
    Heavenly joy possesseth here.

4 Jesus is the name exalted
    Over every other name;
In this name, whene'er assaulted,
    We can put our foes to shame;
Strength to them who else had halted,
    Eyes to blind, and feet to lame.

5 Therefore we, in love adoring,
    This most blessèd name revere,
Holy Jesus, Thee imploring
    So to write it in us here
That hereafter, heavenward soaring,
    We may sing with angels there.

Latin (*c.* 15th century); tr. JOHN MASON NEALE (1818-66)
and Compilers of *Hymns A. and M.*

112

WOLVERCOTE (7 6. 7 6. D.)   WILLIAM HAROLD FERGUSON (1874-1950)

To . . . God our Saviour, be glory and majesty, dominion and power (Jude 25)

O SAVIOUR, precious Saviour,
  Whom yet unseen we love,
O name of might and favour,
  All other names above!
We worship Thee, we bless Thee,
  To Thee alone we sing;
We praise Thee, and confess Thee
  Our holy Lord and King.

2 O Bringer of salvation,
  Who wondrously hast wrought,
Thyself the revelation
  Of love beyond our thought;
We worship Thee, we bless Thee,
  To Thee alone we sing;
We praise Thee, and confess Thee
  Our gracious Lord and King.

3 In Thee all fullness dwelleth,
   All grace and power divine;
The glory that excelleth,
   O Son of God, is Thine;
We worship Thee, we bless Thee,
   To Thee alone we sing;
We praise Thee, and confess Thee
   Our glorious Lord and King.

4 O grant the consummation
   Of this our song above
In endless adoration.
   And everlasting love;
Then shall we praise and bless Thee
   Where perfect praises ring,
And evermore confess Thee
   Our Saviour and our King.

FRANCES RIDLEY HAVERGAL (1836-79)

113

METZLER'S REDHEAD   (C.M.)   RICHARD REDHEAD (1820-1901)

JESU, REX ADMIRABILIS

As I live, saith the Lord, every knee shall bow to me, and every tongue shall confess to God (Romans xiv. 11)

O JESUS, King most wonderful,
   Thou Conqueror renowned,
Thou sweetness most ineffable,
   In whom all joys are found!

2 When once Thou visitest the heart,
   Then truth begins to shine,
Then earthly vanities depart,
   Then kindles love divine.

3 O Jesus, light of all below,
   Thou Fount of life and fire,
Surpassing all the joys we know,
   And all we can desire,—

4 May every heart confess Thy name,
   And ever Thee adore,
And, seeking Thee, itself inflame
   To seek Thee more and more.

5 Thee may our tongues forever bless;
   Thee may we love alone,
And ever in our lives express
   The image of Thine own.

Latin (*c.* 11th century); tr. EDWARD CASWALL (1814-78)

114

VATER UNSER   (8 8. 8 8. 8 8.)

Later form of melody in
VALENTIN SCHUMANN'S *Gesangbuch* (1539).
Harmony from JOHANN SEBASTIAN BACH (1685-1750)

ALTERNATIVE TUNE

STELLA   (8 8. 8 8. 8 8.)

Melody from *Easy Tunes for Catholic Schools* (1852).
Harmonized by ERIC HARDING THIMAN (1900-)

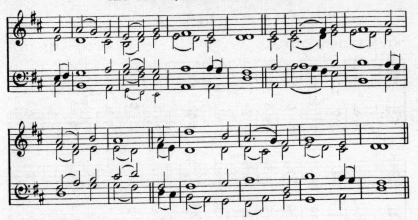

The peace of God . . . shall keep your hearts and minds through Christ Jesus (Philippians iv. 7)

THOU hidden source of calm repose,
  Thou all-sufficient love divine,
My help and refuge from my foes,
  Secure I am, if Thou art mine:
And lo! from sin, and grief, and shame
I hide me, Jesus, in Thy name.

2 Thy mighty name salvation is,
    And keeps my happy soul above;
  Comfort it brings, and power, and peace,
    And joy, and everlasting love:
  To me, with Thy dear name, are given
  Pardon, and holiness, and heaven.

3 Jesus, my all in all Thou art;
    My rest in toil, my ease in pain,
  The medicine of my broken heart,
    In war my peace, in loss my gain,
  My smile beneath the tyrant's frown,
  In shame my glory and my crown:

4 In want my plentiful supply,
    In weakness my almighty power,
  In bonds my perfect liberty,
    My light in Satan's darkest hour,
  My help and stay whene'er I call,
  My life in death, my heaven, my all.

CHARLES WESLEY (1707-88)

115

ST. MATTHEW (D.C.M.)   WILLIAM CROFT (1678-1727)

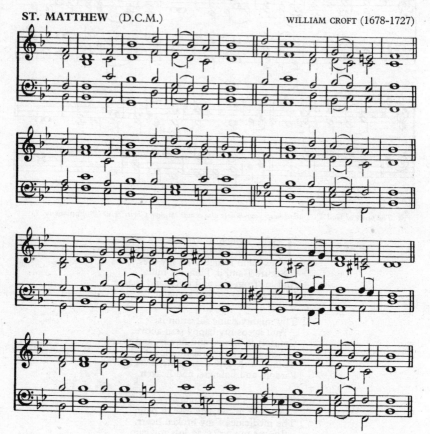

O sing unto the Lord a new song . . . his right hand, and his holy arm, hath gotten him the victory.
(Psalm xcviii. 1)

TO Thee, and to Thy Christ, O God,
    We sing, we ever sing;
For He the lonely wine-press trod
    Our cup of joy to bring.
His glorious arm the strife maintained,
    He marched in might from far;
His robes were with the vintage stained,
    Red with the wine of war.

2 To Thee, and to Thy Christ, O God,
    We sing, we ever sing;
For He invaded Death's abode
    And robbed him of his sting.
The house of dust enthralls no more,
    For He, the strong to save,
Himself doth guard that silent door,
    Great Keeper of the grave.

3 To Thee, and to Thy Christ, O God,
    We sing, we ever sing;
For He hath crushed beneath His rod
    The world's proud rebel king.
He plunged in His imperial strength
    To gulfs of darkness down,
He brought His trophy up at length,
    The foiled usurper's crown.

4 To Thee, and to Thy Christ, O God,
    We sing, we ever sing;
For He redeemed us with His blood
    From every evil thing.
Thy saving strength His arm upbore,
    The arm that set us free;
Glory, O God, for evermore
    Be to Thy Christ and Thee.

ANNE ROSS COUSIN (1824-1906)

116

EBENEZER (TON-Y-BOTEL) (8 7. 8 7. D.)   THOMAS JOHN WILLIAMS (1869-1944)

Unison

Having loved his own which were in the world, he loved them unto the end (John xiii. 1)

O THE deep, deep love of Jesus!
    Vast, unmeasured, boundless, free;
Rolling as a mighty ocean
    In its fullness over me.
Underneath me, all around me,
    Is the current of Thy love;
Leading onward, leading homeward,
    To Thy glorious rest above.

2 O the deep, deep love of Jesus!
    Spread His praise from shore to shore;
How He loveth, ever loveth,
    Changeth never, nevermore;
How He watches o'er His loved ones,
    Died to call them all His own;
How for them He intercedeth,
    Watcheth o'er them from the throne.

3 O the deep, deep love of Jesus!
    Love of every love the best:
'Tis an ocean vast of blessing,
    'Tis a haven sweet of rest.
O the deep, deep love of Jesus!
    'Tis a heaven of heavens to me;
And it lifts me up to glory,
    For it lifts me up to Thee.

SAMUEL TREVOR FRANCIS (1834-1925)·

117

CONSTANCE (8 7. 8 7. D.) (Iambic)   ARTHUR SEYMOUR SULLIVAN (1842-1900)

Ye are my friends, if ye do whatsoever I command you (John xv. 14)

I'VE found a Friend; O such a Friend!
He loved me ere I knew Him;
He drew me with the cords of love,
And thus He bound me to Him;
And round my heart still closely twine
Those ties which nought can sever,
For I am His, and He is mine,
For ever and for ever.

2 I've found a Friend; O such a Friend!
He bled, He died to save me;
And not alone the gift of life,
But His own self He gave me.
Nought that I have mine own I call,
I hold it for the Giver;
My heart, my strength, my life, my all,
Are His, and His for ever.

3 I've found a Friend; O such a Friend!
All power to Him is given
To guard me on my onward course,
And bring me safe to heaven.
The eternal glories gleam afar
To nerve my faint endeavour;
So now to watch, to work, to war,
And then to rest for ever.

4 I've found a Friend; O such a Friend,
So kind, and true, and tender!
So wise a Counsellor, and Guide,
So mighty a Defender!
From Him who loves me now so well
What power my soul shall sever?
Shall life or death, shall earth or hell?
No! I am His for ever.

JAMES GRINDLAY SMALL (1817-88)

See also the section THE GODHEAD: PRAISE AND ADORATION, Nos. 1-22. *The following hymns also refer to this theme:*

54 We sing the praise of Him who died
151 Hallelujah! sing to Jesus
253 I will sing the wondrous story

THE SPIRIT OF GOD
118

DOWN AMPNEY (6 6. 11. D.)　　　　　　RALPH VAUGHAN WILLIAMS (1872-　)

DISCENDI, AMOR SANTO

The love of God is shed abroad in our hearts by the Holy Ghost (Romans v. 5)

COME down, O Love divine,
Seek Thou this soul of mine,
And visit it with Thine own ardour glowing;
O Comforter, draw near,
Within my heart appear,
And kindle it, Thy holy flame bestowing.

2　O let it freely burn,
　　Till earthly passions turn
To dust and ashes, in its heat consuming;
　　And let Thy glorious light
　　Shine ever on my sight,
And clothe me round, the while my path illuming.

3　Let holy charity
　　Mine outward vesture be,
And lowliness become mine inner clothing;
　　True lowliness of heart,
　　Which takes the humbler part,
And o'er its own shortcomings weeps with loathing.

4　And so the yearning strong,
　　With which the soul will long,
Shall far outpass the power of human telling;
　　For none can guess its grace,
　　Till he become the place
Wherein the Holy Spirit makes His dwelling.

BIANCO DA SIENA (?-1434); tr. RICHARD FREDERICK LITTLEDALE (1833-90)

119

SHREWSBURY (8 6. 8 4.)   J. ERIC HUNT (1903-   )

ALTERNATIVE TUNE

ST. CUTHBERT (8 6. 8 4.)   JOHN BACCHUS DYKES (1823-76)

I will pray the Father, and he shall give you another Comforter (John xiv. 16)

OUR blest Redeemer, ere He breathed
　　His tender, last farewell,
A Guide, a Comforter bequeathed,
　　With us to dwell.

*2 He came in semblance of a dove,
　　With sheltering wings outspread,
The holy balm of peace and love
　　On earth to shed.

*3 He came in tongues of living flame
　　To teach, convince, subdue;
All-powerful as the wind He came,
　　As viewless too.

4 He came sweet influence to impart,
　　A gracious, willing Guest,
While He can find one humble heart
　　Wherein to rest.

5 And His that gentle voice we hear,
   Soft as the breath of even,
   That checks each fault, that calms each fear,
   And speaks of heaven.

6 And every virtue we possess,
   And every victory won,
   And every thought of holiness,
   Are His alone.

7 Spirit of purity and grace,
   Our weakness, pitying, see;
   O make our hearts Thy dwelling-place,
   And worthier Thee.

                        HARRIET AUBER (1773-1862)

If desired, verses 2 and 3 may be omitted

120

LÜBECK   (7 7. 7 7.)   FREYLINGHAUSEN's *Gesangbuch* (1704)

Strengthened with might by his Spirit in the inner man (Ephesians iii. 16)

HOLY Spirit, truth divine,
   Dawn upon this soul of mine;
Voice of God, and inward light,
Wake my spirit, clear my sight.

2 Holy Spirit, love divine,
   Glow within this heart of mine;
   Kindle every high desire;
   Perish self in Thy pure fire.

3 Holy Spirit, power divine,
   Fill and nerve this will of mine;
   By Thee may I strongly live,
   Bravely bear, and nobly strive.

4 Holy Spirit, law divine,
   Reign within this soul of mine;
   Be my law, and I shall be
   Firmly bound, for ever free.

5 Holy Spirit, peace divine,
   Still this restless heart of mine;
   Speak to calm this tossing sea,
   Stayed in Thy tranquillity.

6 Holy Spirit, joy divine,
   Gladden Thou this heart of mine;
   In the desert ways I sing,—
   'Spring, O Well, for ever spring.'

                        SAMUEL LONGFELLOW (1819-92)

121

DAY OF PRAISE (S.M.)   CHARLES STEGGALL (1826-1905)

This hymn may also be sung to the tune FRANCONIA, No. 318 (i)

He shall give you another Comforter (John xiv. 16)

COME, Holy Spirit, come;
  Let Thy bright beams arise;
Dispel the darkness from our minds,
  And open all our eyes.

2 Cheer our desponding hearts,
  Thou heavenly Paraclete;
Give us to lie with humble hope
  At our Redeemer's feet.

3 Revive our drooping faith;
  Our doubts and fears remove;
And kindle in our breasts the flame
  Of never-dying love.

4 Convince us of our sin;
  Then lead to Jesus' blood,
And to our wondering view reveal
  The secret love of God.

5 'Tis Thine to cleanse the heart,
  To sanctify the soul,
To pour fresh life on every part,
  And new create the whole.

6 Dwell, therefore, in our hearts;
  Our minds from bondage free;
Then shall we know and praise and love
  The Father, Son, and Thee.

JOSEPH HART (1712-68)

122

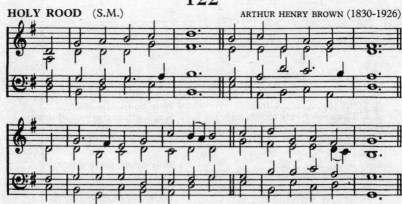

HOLY ROOD (S.M.)   ARTHUR HENRY BROWN (1830-1926)

This hymn may also be sung to the tune ST. BRIDE, No. 213

They were all filled with the Holy Ghost (Acts ii. 4)

LORD God the Holy Ghost,
  In this accepted hour,
As on the day of Pentecost,
  Descend in all Thy power.

2 We meet with one accord
  In our appointed place,
And wait the promise of our Lord,
  The Spirit of all grace.

3 Like mighty rushing wind
　Upon the waves beneath,
Move with one impulse every mind,
　One soul, one feeling breathe.

4 The young, the old, inspire
　With wisdom from above;
And give us hearts and tongues of fire,
　To pray and praise and love.

5 Spirit of light explore,
　And chase our gloom away—
With lustre shining more and more,
　Unto the perfect day.

6 Spirit of truth, be Thou
　In life and death our guide;
O Spirit of adoption, now
　May we be sanctified.

JAMES MONTGOMERY (1771-1854)

123

VENI SPIRITUS (S.M.)　　　　JOHN STAINER (1840-1901)

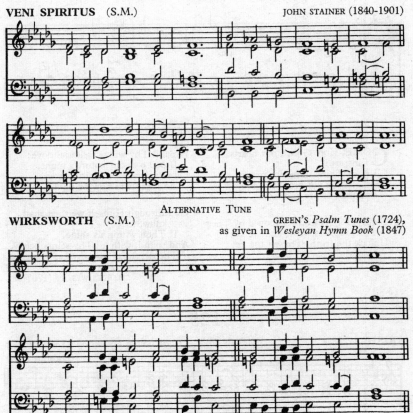

ALTERNATIVE TUNE

WIRKSWORTH (S.M.)　　GREEN'S *Psalm Tunes* (1724),
as given in *Wesleyan Hymn Book* (1847)

The Spirit of God hath made me, and the breath of the Almighty hath given me life (Job xxxiii. 4)

BREATHE on me, Breath of God;
　Fill me with life anew,
That I may love what Thou dost love,
And do what Thou wouldst do.

2 Breathe on me, Breath of God,
　Until my heart is pure,
Until with Thee I will one will,
　To do and to endure.

3 Breathe on me, Breath of God,
　Till I am wholly Thine,
Until this earthly part of me
　Glows with Thy fire divine.

4 Breathe on me, Breath of God;
　So shall I never die,
But live with Thee the perfect life
　Of Thine eternity.

EDWIN HATCH (1835-89)

124

STRACATHRO (C.M.)

Melody by CHARLES HUTCHESON (1792-1860)
from *Christian Vespers* (Glasgow, 1832)

Holy men of God spake as they were moved by the Holy Ghost (2 Peter i. 21)

COME, Holy Ghost, our hearts
    inspire;
  Let us Thine influence prove,
Source of the old prophetic fire,
  Fountain of life and love.

2 Come, Holy Ghost, for moved by Thee
  The prophets wrote and spoke;
Unlock the truth, Thyself the key;
  Unseal the sacred book.

3 Expand Thy wings, celestial dove;
  Brood o'er our nature's night;
On our disordered spirits move,
  And let there now be light.

4 God through Himself we then shall
    know,
  If Thou within us shine,
And sound, with all Thy saints below,
  The depths of love divine.

CHARLES WESLEY (1707-88)

125

IRISH (C.M.)

Melody from *A Collection of Hymns and Sacred Poems*
(Dublin, 1749)

As many as are led by the Spirit of God, they are the sons of God (Romans viii. 14)

O HOLY Ghost, Thy people bless,
　Who long to feel Thy might,
And fain would grow in holiness
　As children of the light.

2 To Thee we bring, who art the Lord,
　Ourselves to be Thy throne;
Let every thought, and deed, and word
　Thy pure dominion own.

3 Life-giving Spirit, o'er us move,
　As on the formless deep;
Give life and order, light and love,
　Where now is death or sleep.

4 Great Gift of our ascended King,
　His saving truth reveal;
Our tongues inspire His praise to sing,
　Our hearts His love to feel.

5 O Holy Ghost, of sevenfold might,
　All graces come from Thee;
Grant us to know and serve aright
　One God in Persons Three.

HENRY WILLIAMS BAKER (1821-77)

126

RATISBON (7 7. 7 7. 7 7.)　　　　　　WERNER'S *Choralbuch* (1815)

This hymn may also be sung to the tune WELLS, No. 198

He dwelleth with you, and shall be in you (John xiv. 17)

GRACIOUS Spirit, dwell with me!
　I myself would gracious be;
And with words that help and heal
Would Thy life in mine reveal;
And with actions bold and meek
Would for Christ, my Saviour, speak.

2 Truthful Spirit, dwell with me!
　I myself would truthful be;
And with wisdom kind and clear,
Let Thy life in mine appear;
And with actions brotherly,
Speak my Lord's sincerity.

3 Tender Spirit, dwell with me!
　I myself would tender be;
Shut my heart up like a flower
In temptation's darksome hour;
Open it when shines the sun,
And His love by fragrance own.

4 Holy Spirit, dwell with me!
　I myself would holy be;
Separate from sin, I would
Choose and cherish all things good,
And whatever I can be
Give to Him who gave me Thee.

THOMAS TOKE LYNCH (1818-71)

127

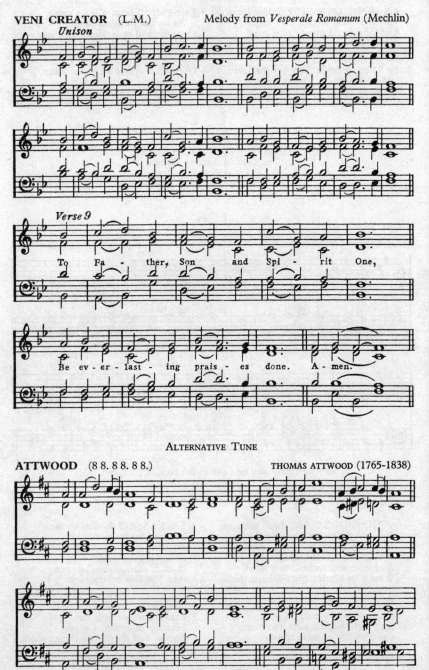

VENI CREATOR (L.M.)   Melody from *Vesperale Romanum* (Mechlin)

Unison

Verse 9

To Fa - ther, Son and Spi - rit One,

Be ev - er - last - ing prais - es done. A - men.

ALTERNATIVE TUNE

ATTWOOD (8 8. 8 8. 8 8.)   THOMAS ATTWOOD (1765-1838)

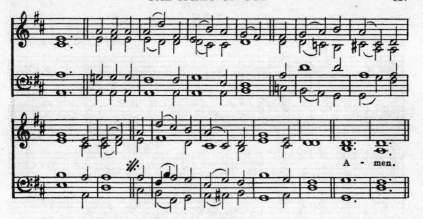

VENI CREATOR SPIRITUS

Ye have an unction from the Holy One (1 John ii. 20)

COME, Holy Ghost, our souls inspire
And lighten with celestial fire.

2 Thou the anointing Spirit art,
Who dost Thy sevenfold gifts impart.

3 Thy blessed unction from above
Is comfort, life, and fire of love.

4 Enable with perpetual light
The dullness of our blinded sight.

5 Anoint and cheer our soilèd face
With the abundance of Thy grace.

6 Keep far our foes; give peace at home,
Where Thou art Guide no ill can come.

7 Teach us to know the Father, Son,
And Thee, of Both, to be but One;

8 That through the ages all along
Thy praise may be our endless song.

9 To Father, Son and Spirit One,
Be everlasting praises done.

AMEN

Latin (9th century);
tr. JOHN COSIN (1594-1672)

If the tune ATTWOOD is used, sing three verses through and then repeat the last line

128

CHARITY (7 7 7. 5.)   JOHN STAINER (1840-1901)

Based on 1 Corinthians xiii

GRACIOUS Spirit, Holy Ghost,
Taught by Thee, we covet most,
Of Thy gifts at Pentecost,
   Holy, heavenly love.

2 Love is kind, and suffers long,
   Love is meek, and thinks no wrong,
   Love than death itself more strong;
      Therefore give us love.

3 Prophecy will fade away,
   Melting in the light of day;
   Love will ever with us stay;
      Therefore give us love.

4 Faith will vanish into sight;
   Hope be emptied in delight;
   Love in heaven will shine more bright;
      Therefore give us love.

5 Faith and hope and love we see,
   Joining hand in hand, agree;
   But the greatest of the three,
      And the best, is love.

CHRISTOPHER WORDSWORTH (1807-85)

129

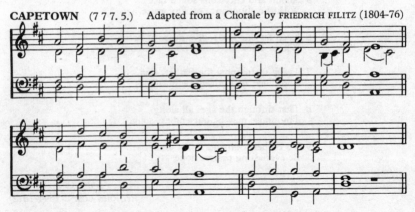

CAPETOWN (7 7 7. 5.)   Adapted from a Chorale by FRIEDRICH FILITZ (1804-76)

The Spirit itself maketh intercession for us (Romans viii. 26)

COME to our poor nature's night
With Thy blessèd inward light,
Holy Ghost the infinite,
   Comforter divine.

2 We are sinful—cleanse us, Lord;
   Sick and faint—Thy strength afford;
   Lost, until by Thee restored,
      Comforter divine.

3 Like the dew Thy peace distil;
   Guide, subdue our wayward will,
   Things of Christ unfolding still,
      Comforter divine.

4 With us, for us, intercede,
   And, with voiceless groanings, plead
   Our unutterable need,
      Comforter divine.

5 In us Abba, Father! cry,
   Earnest of the bliss on high,
   Seal of immortality,
      Comforter divine.

GEORGE RAWSON (1807-89)

130

STÖRL   (C.M.)   JOHANN GEORG CHRISTIAN STÖRL (1675-1719)

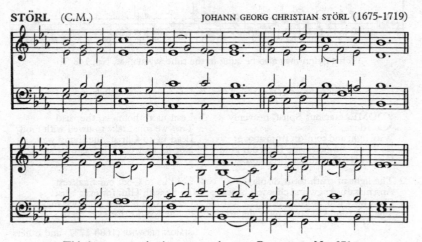

This hymn may also be sung to the tune RICHMOND, No. 371

The kingdom of God is . . . righteousness, and peace, and joy in the Holy Ghost (Romans xiv. 17)

SPIRIT divine, attend our prayers,
   And make this house Thy home;
Descend with all Thy gracious powers,
   O come, great Spirit, come!

2 Come as the light, to us reveal
   Our emptiness and woe;
And lead us in those paths of life
   Where all the righteous go.

3 Come as the fire, and purge our hearts
   Like sacrificial flame;
Let our whole soul an offering be
   To our Redeemer's name.

4 Come as the dew, and sweetly bless
   This consecrated hour;
May barrenness rejoice to own
   Thy fertilizing power.

5 Come as the dove, and spread Thy wings,
   The wings of peaceful love;
And let Thy Church on earth become
   Blest as the Church above.

6 Come as the wind, with rushing sound
   And Pentecostal grace
That all of woman born may see
   The glory of Thy face.

7 Spirit divine, attend our prayers,
   Make a lost world Thy home;
Descend with all Thy gracious powers,
   O come, great Spirit, come!

ANDREW REED (1787-1862)

131

EISENACH (L.M.)   JOHANN HERMANN SCHEIN (1586-1630)

This hymn may also be sung to the tune WAREHAM, No. 148 (ii)

As many as are led by the Spirit of God, they are the sons of God (Romans viii. 14)

COME, gracious Spirit, heavenly
　　dove,
With light and comfort from above;
Be Thou our guardian, Thou our guide,
O'er every thought and step preside.

2 The light of truth to us display,
And make us know and choose Thy way;
Plant holy fear in every heart,
That we from God may ne'er depart.

3 Lead us to holiness, the road
That we must take to dwell with God;
Lead us to Christ, the living way,
Nor let us from His pastures stray.

4 Lead us to God, our final rest,
To be with Him for ever blest:
Lead us to heaven, that we may share
Fullness of joy for ever there.

SIMON BROWNE (1680-1732) and others

132

ANGEL'S SONG (SONG 34) (L.M.)   Original version of melody by
ORLANDO GIBBONS (1583-1625)

This hymn may also be sung to the tune ANTWERP, No. 205

The Comforter, which is the Holy Ghost, . . . he shall teach you all things (John xiv. 26)

O BREATH of God, breathe on us
now,
And move within us while we pray;
The spring of our new life art Thou,
The very light of our new day.

2 O strangely art Thou with us, Lord,
Neither in height nor depth to seek:
In nearness shall Thy voice be heard;
. Spirit to spirit Thou dost speak.

3 Christ is our Advocate on high;
Thou art our Advocate within:
O plead the truth, and make reply
To every argument of sin.

4 But ah, this faithless heart of mine!
The way I know; I know my guide:
Forgive me, O my Friend divine,
That I so often turn aside.

5 Be with me when no other friend
The mystery of my heart can share;
And be Thou known, when fears transcend,
By Thy best name of Comforter.

ALFRED HENRY VINE (1845-1917)

133

SPIRITUS VITAE (9 8. 9 8.)   MARY J. HAMMOND

Wilt thou not revive us again? (Psalm lxxxv. 6)

O BREATH of Life, come sweeping through us,
Revive Thy Church with life and power;
O Breath of Life, come, cleanse, renew us,
And fit Thy Church to meet this hour.

2 O Wind of God, come bend us, break us,
Till humbly we confess our need;
Then in Thy tenderness remake us,
Revive, restore; for this we plead.

3 O Breath of Love, come breathe within us,
Renewing thought and will and heart:
Come, Love of Christ, afresh to win us,
Revive Thy Church in every part.

4 Revive us, Lord! Is zeal abating
While harvest fields are vast and white?
Revive us, Lord, the world is waiting,
Equip Thy Church to spread the light.

BESSIE PORTER HEAD (1850-1936)

134

VENI SANCTE SPIRITUS   (7 7 7. D.)   SAMUEL WEBBE (1740-1816)

VENI, SANCTE SPIRITUS

I will put a new spirit within you (Ezekiel xi. 19)

COME, Thou Holy Spirit, come;
   And from Thy celestial home
   Shed a ray of light divine;
Come, Thou Father of the poor,
Come, Thou source of all our store,
   Come, within our bosoms shine.

2 Thou of comforters the best,
   Thou the soul's most welcome guest,
      Sweet refreshment here below;
   In our labour rest most sweet,
   Grateful coolness in the heat,
      Solace in the midst of woe.

3 O most blessèd light divine,
   Shine within these hearts of Thine,
      And our inmost being fill;
   Where Thou art not, man hath nought,
   Nothing good in deed or thought,
      Nothing free from taint of ill.

4 Heal our wounds; our strength renew;
   On our dryness pour Thy dew;
      Wash the stains of guilt away;
   Bend the stubborn heart and will;
   Melt the frozen, warm the chill;
      Guide the steps that go astray.

5 On the faithful, who adore
   And confess Thee, evermore
      In Thy sevenfold gifts descend:
   Give them virtue's sure reward,
   Give them Thy salvation, Lord,
      Give them joys that never end.

Latin (13th century);
tr. EDWARD CASWALL (1814-78) and others

The following hymn also refers to this theme:

166   O Spirit of the living God

135

BREMEN (MUNICH) (76.76.D.) *Meiningen Gesangbuch (1693)*

The holy scriptures, which are able to make thee wise unto salvation (2 Timothy iii. 15)

O WORD of God incarnate,
O Wisdom from on high,
O Truth unchanged, unchanging,
O Light of our dark sky,
We praise Thee for the radiance
That from the hallowed page,
A lantern to our footsteps,
Shines on from age to age.

2 The Church from her dear Master
Received the gift divine,
And still that light she lifteth,
O'er all the earth to shine;
It is the golden casket
Where gems of truth are stored;
It is the heaven-drawn picture
Of Christ, the living Word;

3 It floateth like a banner
Before God's host unfurled;
It shineth like a beacon
Above the darkling world;
It is the chart and compass
That, o'er life's surging sea,
'Mid mists and rocks and quicksands,
Still guides, O Christ, to Thee.

O make Thy Church, dear Saviour,
A lamp of burnished gold,
To bear before the nations
Thy true light, as of old;
O teach Thy wandering pilgrims
By this their path to trace,
Till, clouds and darkness ended,
They see Thee face to face.

WILLIAM WALSHAM HOW (1823-97)

136

DUNDEE (FRENCH) (C.M.)

Scottish Psalter (1615) as given in
RAVENSCROFT'S *Psalter* (1621)

This hymn may also be sung to the tune DUNFERMLINE, No. 31

Let the word of Christ dwell in you richly in all wisdom (Colossians iii.16)

LAMP of our feet, whereby we trace
Our path when wont to stray;
Stream from the fount of heavenly grace,
Brook by the traveller's way;

2 Bread of our souls, whereon we feed,
   True manna from on high;
Our guide and chart, wherein we read
   Of realms beyond the sky;

3 Pillar of fire through watches dark,
   Or radiant cloud by day;
When waves would whelm our tossing
   Our anchor and our stay;   [bark,

4 Word of the ever-living God,
   Will of His glorious Son,—
Without thee how could earth be trod,
   Or heaven itself be won?

5 Lord, grant that we aright may learn
   The wisdom it imparts,
And to its heavenly teaching turn
   With simple, childlike hearts.

BERNARD BARTON (1784-1849)

137

STROUDWATER (C.M.)

WILLIAM ANCHORS
A Choice Collection of Psalm Tunes (c. 1721)

This hymn may also be sung to the tune ABRIDGE, No. 225

The entrance of thy words giveth light (Psalm cxix. 130)

THE Spirit breathes upon the
    Word,
    And brings the truth to sight;
Precepts and promises afford
    A sanctifying light.

2 A glory gilds the sacred page,
    Majestic, like the sun:
It gives a light to every age;
    It gives, but borrows none.

3 The hand that gave it still supplies
    The gracious light and heat;
His truths upon the nations rise;
    They rise, but never set.

4 Let everlasting thanks be Thine,
    For such a bright display
As makes a world of darkness shine
    With beams of heavenly day.

5 My soul rejoices to pursue
    The steps of Him I love,
Till glory breaks upon my view,
    In brighter worlds above.

WILLIAM COWPER (1731-1800)

138

RAVENSHAW (6 6. 6 6. Trochaic) Melody abridged by WILLIAM HENRY MONK
    (1823-89) from *Ave Hierarchia* (MICHAEL WEISSE, 1480-1534)

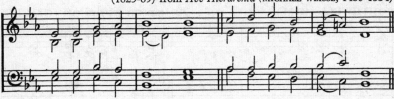

Thy word is a lamp unto my feet, and a light unto my path (Psalm cxix. 105)

LORD, Thy Word abideth,
    And our footsteps guideth;
Who its truth believeth
Light and joy receiveth.

2 When our foes are near us,
Then Thy Word doth cheer us,
Word of consolation,
Message of salvation.

3 When the storms are o'er us,
And dark clouds before us,
Then its light directeth,
And our way protecteth.

4 Who can tell the pleasure,
Who recount the treasure,
By Thy Word imparted
To the simple-hearted?

5 Word of mercy, giving
Succour to the living;
Word of life, supplying
Comfort to the dying!

6 O that we, discerning
Its most holy learning,
Lord, may love and fear Thee,
Evermore be near Thee.

HENRY WILLIAMS BAKER (1821-77)

139

FARRANT (C.M.)   Adapted from a melody attributed to RICHARD FARRANT
(c. 1530-80)

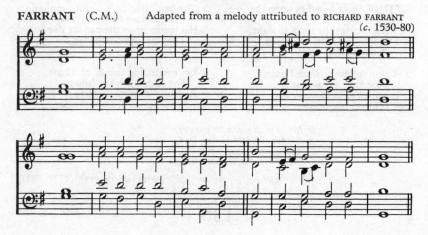

ALTERNATIVE TUNE

SOUTHWELL (C.M.)   HERBERT STEPHEN IRONS (1834-1905)

O how I love thy law! it is my meditation all the day (Psalm cxix. 97)

FATHER of mercies, in Thy Word
   What endless glory shines!
For ever be Thy name adored
   For these celestial lines.

2 Here may the blind and hungry come,
   And light and food receive;
Here shall the lowliest guest have room,
   And taste and see and live.

3 Here springs of consolation rise
   To cheer the fainting mind,
And thirsting souls receive supplies,
   And sweet refreshment find.

4 Here the Redeemer's welcome voice
   Spreads heavenly peace around,
And life and everlasting joys
   Attend the blissful sound.

5 O, may these heavenly pages be
   My ever dear delight;
And still new beauties may I see,
   And still increasing light.

6 Divine Instructor, gracious Lord,
   Be Thou for ever near;
Teach me to love Thy sacred Word,
   And view my Saviour there.

ANNE STEELE (1716-78)

140

CRIEFF (10. 10.)   KENNETH GEORGE FINLAY (1882-)

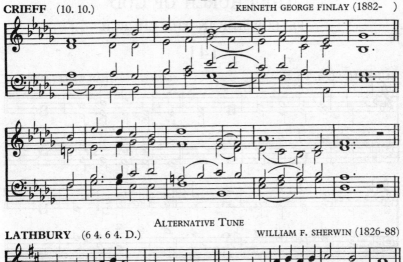

ALTERNATIVE TUNE

LATHBURY (6 4. 6 4. D.)   WILLIAM F. SHERWIN (1826-88)

I am the bread of life (John vi. 35)

BREAK Thou the bread of life,
  Dear Lord, to me,
As Thou didst break the loaves
  Beside the sea;

2 Beyond the sacred page
  I seek Thee, Lord;
My spirit pants for Thee,
  O living Word.

3 Thou art the bread of life,
  O Lord, to me,
Thy Holy Word the truth
  That saveth me;

4 Give me to eat and live
  With Thee above,
Teach me to love Thy truth,
  For Thou art love.

5 Oh, send Thy Spirit, Lord,
  Now unto me,
That He may touch my eyes
  And make me see;

6 Show me the truth concealed
  Within Thy Word,
And in Thy Book revealed,
  I see Thee, Lord.

MARY ARTEMISIA LATHBURY (1841-1913) (*verses 1 and 2*)
and ALEXANDER GROVES (1843-1909) (*verses 3 to 6*)

The following hymn also refers to this theme:
124 Come, Holy Ghost, our hearts inspire

THE CHURCH OF GOD
FELLOWSHIP IN THE CHURCH
141

AURELIA (7 6. 7 6. D.)　　　　　　　　　SAMUEL SEBASTIAN WESLEY (1810-76)

Christ also loved the church, and gave himself for it (Ephesians v. 25)

THE Church's one foundation
　Is Jesus Christ, her Lord;
She is His new creation
　By water and the Word:
From heaven He came and sought her
　To be His holy Bride,
With His own blood He bought her,
　And for her life He died.

2 Elect from every nation,
　　Yet one o'er all the earth,
　Her charter of salvation
　　One Lord, one faith, one birth;
　One holy name she blesses,
　　Partakes one holy food,
　And to one hope she presses
　　With every grace endued.

3 Though with a scornful wonder
　　Men see her sore oppressed,
　By schisms rent asunder,
　　By heresies distressed,
　Yet saints their watch are keeping,
　　Their cry goes up, ' How long ?'
　And soon the night of weeping
　　Shall be the morn of song.

4 'Mid toil and tribulation,
   And tumult of her war,
She waits the consummation
   Of peace for evermore;
Till with the vision glorious
   Her longing eyes are blest,
And the great Church victorious
   Shall be the Church at rest.

5 Yet she on earth hath union
   With God the Three in One,
And mystic sweet communion
   With those whose rest is won!
O happy ones and holy!
   Lord, give us grace that we,
Like them, the meek and lowly,
   On high may dwell with Thee.

SAMUEL JOHN STONE (1839-1900)

142

ST. SAVIOUR (C.M.)   FREDERICK GEORGE BAKER (1840-1908)

They overcame him by the blood of the Lamb, and by the word of their testimony (Revelation xii. 11)

GIVE me the wings of faith to rise
   Within the veil, and see
The saints above, how great their joys,
   How bright their glories be.

2 I ask them whence their victory came;
   They, with united breath,
Ascribe their conquest to the Lamb,
   Their triumph to His death.

3 They marked the footsteps that He trod,
   His zeal inspired their breast;
And, following their incarnate God,
   Possess the promised rest.

4 Our glorious Leader claims our praise
   For His own pattern given;
While the long cloud of witnesses
   Show the same path to heaven.

ISAAC WATTS (1674-1748)

143

ABBOT'S LEIGH (8 7. 8 7. D.)   CYRIL V. TAYLOR (1907-   )

This hymn may also be sung to the tune AUSTRIA, No. 20

Based on Isaiah xxxiii. 20, 21 and Psalm lxxxvii

GLORIOUS things of thee are
Zion, city of our God!   [spoken,
He whose word cannot be broken
Formed thee for His own abode.
On the Rock of Ages founded,
What can shake thy sure repose?
With salvation's walls surrounded,
Thou mayst smile at all thy foes.

2 See, the streams of living waters,
Springing from eternal love,
Well supply thy sons and daughters,
And all fear of want remove.
Who can faint while such a river
Ever flows their thirst to assuage—
Grace, which, like the Lord the Giver,
Never fails from age to age?

3 Saviour, if of Zion's city
I, through grace, a member am,
Let the world deride or pity,
I will glory in Thy name:
Fading is the wordling's pleasure,
All his boasted pomp and show,
Solid joys and lasting treasure
None but Zion's children know.

JOHN NEWTON (1725-1807)

144

WALTHAM (8 7. 8 7.)   Melody by HEINRICH ALBERT (1604-51)
Harmonized by JOHANN SEBASTIAN BACH (1685-1750)

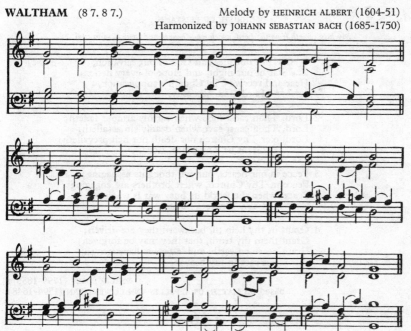

A longer form of this melody (8 7. 8 7. 7 7.) will be found under the title
GOTT DES HIMMELS, No. 344

Paraphrase of 2 Corinthians xiii. 14

MAY the grace of Christ our Saviour,
And the Father's boundless love,
With the Holy Spirit's favour,
Rest upon us from above.

2 Thus may we abide in union
With each other and the Lord;
And possess, in sweet communion,
Joys which earth cannot afford.

JOHN NEWTON (1725-1807)

145

CLOISTERS (11 11 11. 5.)   JOSEPH BARNBY (1838-96)

CHRISTE DU BEISTAND

My help cometh from the Lord, which made heaven and earth (Psalm cxxi. 2)

L ORD of our life, and God of our salvation,
  Star of our night, and Hope of every nation,
Hear and receive Thy Church's supplication,
    Lord God Almighty.

2 Lord, Thou canst help when earthly armour faileth;
Lord, Thou canst save when deadly sin assaileth;
Lord, o'er Thy Church nor death nor hell prevaileth;
    Grant us Thy peace, Lord.

3 Peace in our hearts, our evil thoughts assuaging;
Peace in Thy Church, where brothers are engaging;
Peace, when the world its busy war is waging;
    Calm Thy foes' raging.

4 Grant us thy help till backward they are driven;
Grant them thy truth, that they may be forgiven;
Grant peace on earth, and, after we have striven,
    Peace in thy heaven.

PHILIP PUSEY (1799-1855);
based on MATTHÄUS APPELLES VON LÖWENSTERN (1594-1648)

146

SONG 1 (10 10. 10 10. 10 10.)   ORLANDO GIBBONS (1583-1625)

That they all may be one (John xvii. 21)

ETERNAL Ruler of the ceaseless round
Of circling planets singing on their way;
Guide of the nations from the night profound
Into the glory of the perfect day;
Rule in our hearts, that we may ever be
Guided and strengthened and upheld by Thee.

2 We are of Thee, the children of Thy love,
The brothers of Thy well-belovèd Son;
Descend, O Holy Spirit, like a dove,
Into our hearts, that we may be as one;
As one with Thee, to whom we ever tend;
As one with Him, our Brother and our Friend.

3 We would be one in hatred of all wrong,
One in our love of all things sweet and fair,
One with the joy that breaketh into song,
One with the grief that trembleth into prayer,
One in the power that makes Thy children free
To follow truth, and thus to follow Thee.

4 O clothe us with Thy heavenly armour, Lord,
Thy trusty shield, Thy sword of love divine;
Our inspiration be Thy constant word;
We ask no victories that are not Thine;
Give or withhold, let pain or pleasure be;
Enough to know that we are serving Thee.

JOHN WHITE CHADWICK (1840-1904)

147

SINE NOMINE (10 10 10. 4.)   RALPH VAUGHAN WILLIAMS (1872-)
Unison. Verses 1, 2, 3, and 7, 8.

(small notes verses 2, 8)

Compassed about with so great a cloud of witnesses (Hebrews xii. 1)

FOR all the saints who from their labours rest,
Who Thee by faith before the world confessed,
Thy name, O Jesus, be for ever blest.
          Hallelujah!

2 Thou wast their rock, their fortress, and their might;
Thou, Lord, their captain in the well-fought fight;
Thou, in the darkness drear, their one true light.
          Hallelujah!

3 O may Thy soldiers, faithful, true and bold,
Fight as the saints who nobly fought of old,
And win, with them, the victor's crown of gold.
          Hallelujah!

4 O blest communion, fellowship divine!
We feebly struggle, they in glory shine;
Yet all are one in Thee, for all are Thine,
          Hallelujah!

Harmony. Verses 4, 5 and 6.

(small notes verse 6)

5 And when the strife is fierce, the warfare long,
   Steals on the ear the distant triumph song,
   And hearts are brave again, and arms are strong.
                                 Hallelujah!

*6 The golden evening brightens in the west;
   Soon, soon to faithful warriors cometh rest,
   Sweet is the calm of Paradise the blest.
                                 Hallelujah!

*7 But, lo! there breaks a yet more glorious day;
   The saints triumphant rise in bright array;
   The King of glory passes on His way.
                                 Hallelujah!

*8 From earth's wide bounds, from ocean's farthest coast,
   Through gates of pearl streams in the countless host,
   Singing to Father, Son, and Holy Ghost.
                                 Hallelujah!

                          WILLIAM WALSHAM HOW (1823-97)

*If desired, verses 6-8 may be omitted

148

GONFALON ROYAL (L.M.) PERCY CARTER BUCK (1871-1947)

ALTERNATIVE TUNE

WAREHAM (L.M.) WILLIAM KNAPP (1698-1768)

There is a friend that sticketh closer than a brother (Proverbs xviii. 24)

HE wants not friends that hath
    Thy love,
And may converse and walk with Thee,
And with Thy saints here and above,
    With whom for ever I must be.

2 In the communion of the saints
    Is wisdom, safety and delight;
And, when my heart declines and faints,
    It's raisèd by their heat and light.

3 As for my friends, they are not lost;
    The several vessels of Thy fleet,
Though parted now, by tempests tost,
    Shall safely in the haven meet.

4 Still we are centred all in Thee,
    Members, though distant, of one
        Head;
In the same family we be,
    By the same faith and Spirit led.

5 Before Thy throne we daily meet
    As joint-petitioners to Thee;
In spirit we each other greet,
    And shall again each other see.

6 The heavenly hosts, world without end,
    Shall be my company above;
And Thou, my best and surest Friend,
    Who shall divide me from Thy love?

RICHARD BAXTER (1615-91)

149

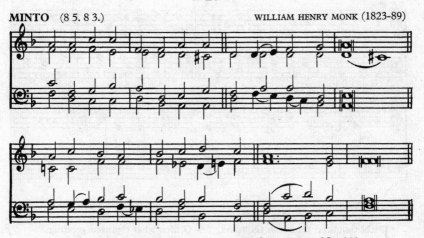

MINTO   (8 5. 8 3.)   WILLIAM HENRY MONK (1823-89)

This hymn may also be sung to the tune CAIRNBROOK, No. 222

The Lord watch between me and thee, when we are absent one from another (Genesis xxxi. 49)

HOLY Father, in Thy mercy,
    Hear our anxious prayer;
Keep our loved ones, now far distant,
    'Neath Thy care.

2 Jesus, Saviour, let Thy presence
    Be their light and guide;
Keep, O, keep them, in their weakness,
    At Thy side.

3 When in sorrow, when in danger,
    When in loneliness,
In Thy love look down and comfort
    Their distress.

4 May the joy of Thy salvation
    Be their strength and stay;
May they love and may they praise Thee
    Day by day.

5 Holy Spirit, let Thy teaching
    Sanctify their life;
Send Thy grace, that they may conquer
    In the strife.

6 Father, Son, and Holy Spirit,
    God the One in Three,
Bless them, guide them, save them,
    Near to Thee.   [keep them

ISABEL STEPHANA STEVENSON (1843-90)

150

ALFORD (7 6. 8 6. D.)   JOHN BACCHUS DYKES (1823-76)

A great multitude . . . of all nations, and kindreds, and people, and tongues, stood before the throne, and before the Lamb (Revelation vii. 9)

TEN thousand times ten thousand,
  In sparkling raiment bright,
The armies of the ransomed saints
  Throng up the steeps of light;
'Tis finished, all is finished,
  Their fight with death and sin;
Fling open wide the golden gates,
  And let the victors in.

2 What rush of hallelujahs
  Fills all the earth and sky!
What ringing of a thousand harps
  Bespeaks the triumph nigh!
O day for which creation
  And all its tribes were made!
O joy, for all its former woes
  A thousandfold repaid!

3 O then what raptured greetings
  On Canaan's happy shore,
What knitting severed friendships up,
  Where partings are no more!
Then eyes with joy shall sparkle
  That brimmed with tears of late;
Orphans no longer fatherless,
  Nor widows desolate.

4 Bring near Thy great salvation,
  Thou Lamb for sinners slain;
Fill up the roll of Thine elect,
  Then take Thy power and reign;
Appear, Desire of nations,
  Thine exiles long for home;
Show in the heavens Thy promised sign;
  Thou Prince and Saviour, come.

HENRY ALFORD (1810-71)

The following hymn also refers to this theme:
262   Great Shepherd of Thy people, hear

151

ALLELUIA (8 7. 8 7. D.) SAMUEL SEBASTIAN WESLEY (1810-76)

This hymn may also be sung to the tune HYFRYDOL, No. 171

Thou wast slain, and hast redeemed us to God by thy blood (Revelation v. 9)

*HALLELUJAH! sing to Jesus!
   His the sceptre, His the throne,
Hallelujah! His the triumph,
   His the victory alone.
Hark! The songs of peaceful Zion
   Thunder like a mighty flood:
'Jesus, out of every nation,
   Hath redeemed us by His blood.'

2 Hallelujah! not as orphans
   Are we left in sorrow now;
Hallelujah! He is near us,
   Faith believes, nor questions how.
Though the cloud from sight received
   When the forty days were o'er, [Him,
Shall our hearts forget His promise,
   'I am with you evermore'?

3 Hallelujah! Bread of Heaven,
   Thou on earth our food, our stay;
Hallelujah! here the sinful
   Flee to Thee from day to day.
Intercessor, Friend of sinners,
   Earth's Redeemer, plead for me,
Where the songs of all the sinless
   Sweep across the crystal sea.

WILLIAM CHATTERTON DIX (1837-98)

If desired, this verse may be repeated after verse 3

171

152

SONG 22 (10 10. 10 10.) ORLANDO GIBBONS (1583-1625)

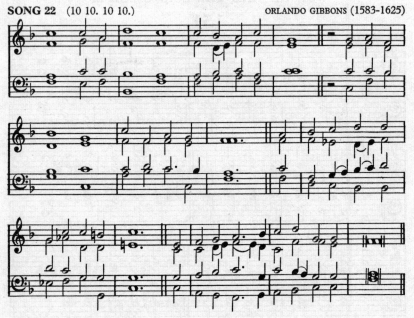

ALTERNATIVE TUNE

ST. AGNES (10 10. 10 10.) Melody by JAMES LANGRAN (1835-1909)

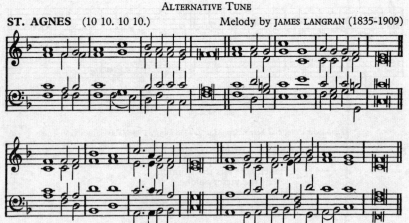

There were many coming and going, and they had no leisure (Mark vi. 31)

COME ye yourselves apart and rest awhile,
Weary, I know it, of the press and throng,
Wipe from your brow the sweat and dust of toil,
And in My quiet strength again be strong.

2 Come ye aside from all the world holds dear,
For converse which the world has never known,
Alone with Me and with My Father here,
With Me and with My Father not alone.

3 Come, tell Me all that ye have said and done,
   Your victories and failures, hopes and fears,
I know how hardly souls are wooed and won;
   My choicest wreaths are always wet with tears.

4 Come ye and rest: the journey is too great,
   And ye will faint beside the way and sink:
The bread of life is here for you to eat,
   And here for you the wine of love to drink.

5 Then, fresh from converse with your Lord, return
   And work till daylight softens into even:
The brief hours are not lost in which ye learn
   More of your Master and His rest in heaven.

EDWARD HENRY BICKERSTETH (1825-1906)

153

ADORO TE (10 10. 10 10.)   Plainsong Melody (from the Solesmes Version)

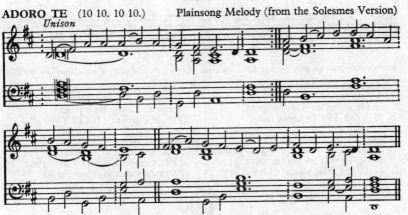

This hymn may also be sung to the tune ST. AGNES, No. 152 (ii)

Let us draw near with a true heart in full assurance of faith (Hebrews x. 22)

HERE, O my Lord, I see Thee face to face;
   Here would I touch and handle things unseen,
Here grasp with firmer hand the eternal grace,
   And all my weariness upon Thee lean.

2 Here would I feed upon the bread of God,
   Here drink with Thee the royal wine of heaven;
Here would I lay aside each earthly load,
   Here taste afresh the calm of sin forgiven.

＊   ＊   ＊

3 I have no help but Thine; nor do I need
   Another arm save Thine to lean upon:
It is enough, my Lord, enough indeed;
   My strength is in Thy might, Thy might alone.

4 Mine is the sin, but Thine the righteousness;
   Mine is the guilt, but Thine the cleansing blood;
Here is my robe, my refuge, and my peace—
   Thy blood, Thy righteousness, O Lord my God.

5 Feast after feast thus comes and passes by,
   Yet, passing, points to the glad feast above,
Giving sweet foretaste of the festal joy,
   The Lamb's great bridal feast of bliss and love.

HORATIUS BONAR (1808-89)

154

SONG 13 (7 7. 7 7.)   ORLANDO GIBBONS (1583-1625)

Where two or three are gathered together in my name, there am I in the midst of them (Matthew xviii. 20)

JESUS, we Thy promise claim,
  We are gathered in Thy name,
In the midst do Thou appear,
Manifest Thy presence here.

2 Sanctify us, Lord, and bless,
  Breathe Thy Spirit, give Thy peace;
Thou Thyself within us move,
Make our feast a feast of love.

3 Plant in us Thy humble mind;
  Patient, pitiful and kind,
Meek and lowly let us be,
Full of goodness, full of Thee.

4 Make us all in Thee complete,
  Make us all for glory meet,
Meet to appear before Thy sight,
Partners with the saints in light.

CHARLES WESLEY (1707-88)

155

LÜBECK (7 7. 7 7.)   FREYLINGHAUSEN'S *Gesangbuch* (1704)

This hymn may also be sung to the tunes HEINLEIN, No. 210, and SONG 13, No. 154

His own self bare our sins in his own body on the tree, that we, being dead to sins, should live unto righteousness
(1 Peter ii. 24)

NEVER further than Thy cross,
  Never higher than Thy feet;
Here earth's precious things seem dross,
  Here earth's bitter things grow sweet.

2 Gazing thus our sin we see,
  Learn Thy love while gazing thus;
Sin which laid the cross on Thee,
  Love which bore the cross for us.

3 Here we learn to serve and give,
　　And, rejoicing, self deny;
　Here we gather love to live,
　　Here we gather faith to die.

4 Symbols of our liberty
　　And our service here unite;
　Captives, by Thy cross set free,
　　Soldiers of Thy cross, we fight.

5 Till amid the hosts of light
　　We, in Thee redeemed, complete,
　Through Thy cross made pure and white,
　　Cast our crowns before Thy feet.

ELIZABETH RUNDLE CHARLES (1828-96)

156

BANGOR (C.M.)　　　　　　　　　　WILLIAM TANS'UR (1706-83)

This hymn may also be sung to the tune NUN DANKET ALL, No. 96

Based on Matthew viii. 8

I AM not worthy, holy Lord,
　That Thou shouldst come to me;
Speak but the word; one gracious word
　Can set the sinner free.

2 I am not worthy; cold and bare
　　The lodging of my soul;
　How canst Thou deign to enter there?
　　Lord, speak, and make me whole.

3 I am not worthy; yet, my God,
　　How can I say Thee nay,—
　Thee, who didst give Thy flesh and blood
　　My ransom-price to pay?

4 O come, in this sweet morning[1] hour,
　　Feed me with food divine;
　And fill with all Thy love and power
　　This worthless heart of mine.

HENRY WILLIAMS BAKER (1821-77)

[1] *or* 'evening'

157

QUAM DILECTA　(6 6. 6 6.)　　　　　　　HENRY LASCELLES JENNER (1820-98)

ALTERNATIVE TUNE

DOLOMITE CHANT　(6 6. 6 6.)　　Austrian melody harmonized by J. T. COOPER

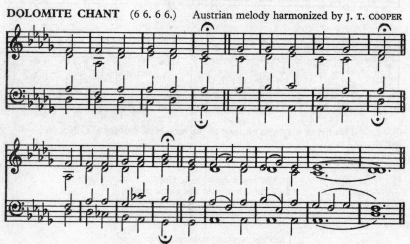

My soul thirsteth for God, for the living God (Psalm xlii. 2)

I HUNGER and I thirst;
　Jesus, my manna be;
Ye living waters, burst
　Out of the rock for me.

2 Thou bruised and broken Bread,
　　My life-long wants supply;
　As living souls are fed,
　　O feed me, or I die.

3 Thou true life-giving Vine,
　　Let me Thy sweetness prove;
　Renew my life with Thine,
　　Refresh my soul with love.

4 Rough paths my feet have trod,
　　Since first their course began;
　Feed me, Thou Bread of God;
　　Help me, Thou Son of Man.

5 For still the desert lies
　　My thirsting soul before;
　O living waters rise
　　Within me evermore.

JOHN SAMUEL BEWLEY MONSELL (1811-75)

158

RENDEZ À DIEU (9 8. 9 8. D.)   Melody composed or adapted by
LOUIS BOURGEOIS (1510-61) for Psalm 118 in the *Genevan Psalter* (1543)

Bread of the world in mer - cy bro - ken, Wine of the

soul in mer - cy shed, By whom the words of life were spo - ken,

And in whose death our sins are dead: Look on the heart by sor - row

bro - ken, Look on the tears by sin - ners shed; And be Thy

feast to us the to - ken— That by Thy grace our souls are fed.

(John vi. 35)   REGINALD HEBER (1783-1826)

159

ST. LAWRENCE (L.M.)   LEIGHTON GEORGE HAYNE (1836-83)

This hymn may also be sung to the tune ANTWERP, No. 205

Let us draw near with a true heart (Hebrews x. 22)

LORD Jesus Christ, we seek Thy
    face,
  Within the veil we bow the knee;
Oh, let Thy glory fill the place,
  And bless us while we wait on Thee.

2 We thank Thee for the precious blood
  That purged our sins and brought
    us nigh,
All cleansed and sanctified, to God,
  Thy holy Name to magnify.

3 Shut in with Thee, far, far above
  The restless world that wars below,
We seek to learn and prove Thy love,
  Thy wisdom and Thy grace to know.

4 The brow that once with thorns was
    bound,
  Thy hands, Thy side, we fain
    would see;
Draw near, Lord Jesus, glory-crowned,
  And bless us while we wait on Thee.

ALEXANDER STEWART (1843-1923)

160

ST. GILES (S.M.)   JOHN MONTGOMERIE BELL (1837-1910)

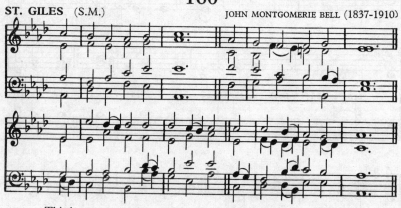

This hymn may also be sung to the tune ST. MICHAEL, No. 219 (i)

This do in remembrance of me (1 Corinthians xi. 24)

JESUS, we thus obey
  Thy last and kindest word,
Here in Thine own appointed way
  We come to meet Thee, Lord.

2 Our hearts we open wide,
  To make the Saviour room;
And lo! the Lamb, the Crucified,
  The sinner's Friend, is come.

3 Thy presence makes the feast;
   Now let our spirits feel
The glory not to be expressed,
   The joy unspeakable.

4 With high and heavenly bliss
   Thou dost our spirits cheer;
Thy house of banqueting is this,
   And Thou hast brought us here.

5 Now let our souls be fed
   With manna from above,
And over us Thy banner spread
   Of everlasting love.

CHARLES WESLEY (1707-88)

161

CASSEL   (7 7. 7 7. 7 7.)   THOMMEN'S *Gesangbuch* (Basle, 1745)

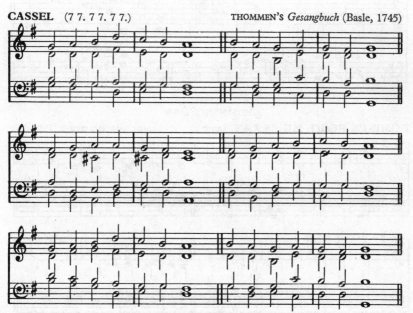

This is my body which is given for you (Luke xxii. 19)

BREAD of heaven, on Thee I feed,
   For Thy flesh is meat indeed:
Ever may my soul be fed
With this true and living bread;
Day by day with strength supplied
Through the life of Him who died.

2 Vine of heaven, Thy blood supplies
   This blest cup of sacrifice:
'Tis Thy wounds my healing give;
To Thy cross I look and live:
Thou my life, O let me be
Rooted, grafted, built in Thee!

JOSIAH CONDER (1789-1855)

179

162

ACH GOTT UND HERR (8 7. 8 7. Iambic)   Melody in *As Hymnodus Sacer*
(Leipzig, 1625). Adapted and harmonized by JOHANN SEBASTIAN BACH (1685-1750)

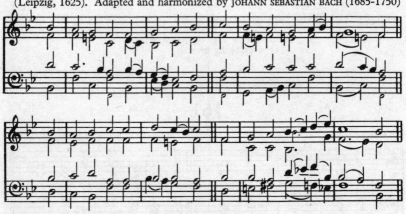

ALTERNATIVE TUNE

DOMINUS REGIT ME   (8 7. 8 7. Iambic)   JOHN BACCHUS DYKES (1823-76)

HAYYĒL MĀRAN' IDHĒ DAPHSHAT

The very God of peace sanctify you wholly (1 Thessalonians v. 23)

STRENGTHEN for service, Lord, the hands
   That holy things have taken;
Let ears that now have heard Thy songs
   To clamour never waken.

2 Lord, may the tongues which 'Holy' sang
   Keep free from all deceiving;
The eyes which saw Thy love be bright,
   Thy blessèd hope perceiving.

3 The feet that tread Thy hallowed courts
   From light do Thou not banish;
The bodies by Thy Spirit fed
   With Thy new life replenish.

Liturgy of Malabar; tr. C. W. HUMPHREYS, PERCY DEARMER (1867-1936), and others

163

BEVERLEY (8 7. 8 8 7. 7 7. 7 7.)   WILLIAM HENRY MONK (1823–89)

Surely I come quickly (Revelation xxii. 20)

THOU art coming, O my Saviour,
  Thou art coming, O my King,
In Thy beauty all-resplendent,
In Thy glory all-transcendent;
  Well may we rejoice and sing.
Coming! In the opening East
  Herald brightness slowly swells;
Coming! O my glorious Priest,
  Hear we not Thy golden bells?

2 Thou art coming; at Thy table
  We are witnesses for this;
While remembering hearts Thou
    meetest
In communion clearest, sweetest,
  Earnest of our coming bliss;
Showing not Thy death alone,
  And Thy love exceeding great,
But Thy coming and Thy throne,
  All for which we long and wait.

3 O, the joy to see Thee reigning,
  Thee, my own belovèd Lord!
Every tongue Thy name confessing,
Worship, honour, glory, blessing,
  Brought to Thee with one accord;
Thee, my Master and my Friend,
  Vindicated and enthroned,
Unto earth's remotest end
  Glorified, adored, and owned.

FRANCES RIDLEY HAVERGAL (1836–79)

See also the sections THE SON OF GOD: HIS GLORY, NAME AND PRAISE, Nos. 89-117,
and THE MAN OF GOD: PENITENCE AND FAITH, Nos. 201-230

G

164

MOSCOW (6 6 4. 6 6 6 4.)   FELICE DE GIARDINI (1716-96)

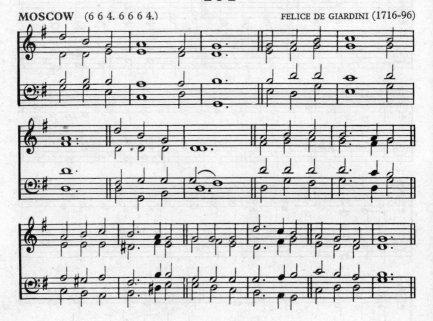

And God said, Let there be light: and there was light (Genesis i. 3)

THOU whose almighty word
Chaos and darkness heard,
And took their flight,
Hear us, we humbly pray,
And where the gospel day
Sheds not its glorious ray,
Let there be light.

2 Thou who didst come to bring,
On Thy redeeming wing,
Healing and sight,
Health to the sick in mind,
Sight to the inly blind,
O now to all mankind
Let there be light.

3 Spirit of truth and love,
Life-giving, holy Dove,
Speed forth Thy flight;
Move on the waters' face,
Bearing the lamp of grace,
And in earth's darkest place
Let there be light.

4 Blessèd and holy Three,
Glorious Trinity,
Wisdom, Love, Might,
Boundless as ocean's tide
Rolling in fullest pride,
Through the world, far and wide,
Let there be light.

JOHN MARRIOTT (1780-1825)

165

PICARDY (8 7. 8 7. 8 7.)   French Carol Melody

This hymn may also be sung to the tune RHUDDLAN, No. 229

The Lord is our judge, the Lord is our lawgiver, the Lord is our king; he will save us (Isaiah xxxiii. 22)

JUDGE eternal, throned in splendour,
Lord of lords and King of kings,
With Thy living fire of judgment
Purge this land of bitter things;
Solace all its wide dominion
With the healing of Thy wings.

2 Still the weary folk are pining
For the hour that brings release;
And the city's crowded clangour
Cries aloud for sin to cease;
And the homesteads and the woodlands
Plead in silence for their peace.

3 Crown, O God, Thine own endeavour;
Cleave our darkness with Thy sword;
Feed the faint and hungry heathen
With the richness of Thy Word;
Cleanse the body of this Empire
Through the glory of the Lord.

HENRY SCOTT HOLLAND (1847-1918)

166

MAINZER (L.M.)   JOSEPH MAINZER (1801-51)

This hymn may also be sung to the tune CHURCH TRIUMPHANT, No. 74 (ii)

When the Comforter is come . . . he shall testify of me (John xv. 26)

O SPIRIT of the living God,
In all the fullness of Thy grace,
Where'er the foot of man hath trod,
Descend on our apostate race.

2 Give tongues of fire and hearts of love,
To preach the reconciling word;
Give power and unction from above,
Whene'er the joyful sound is heard.

3 Be darkness, at Thy coming, light;
Confusion order, in Thy path;
Souls without strength inspire with might;
Bid mercy triumph over wrath.

4 O Spirit of the Lord, prepare
All the round earth her God to meet;
Breathe Thou abroad like morning air,
Till hearts of stone begin to beat.

5 Baptize the nations; far and nigh
The triumphs of the cross record;
The name of Jesus glorify,
Till every kindred call Him Lord.

JAMES MONTGOMERY (1771-1854)

167

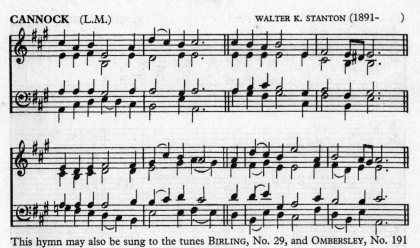

CANNOCK (L.M.)

WALTER K. STANTON (1891-)

This hymn may also be sung to the tunes BIRLING, No. 29, and OMBERSLEY, No. 191

Go ye into all the world, and preach the gospel to every creature (Mark xvi. 15)

SEND forth the gospel! Let it run
Southward and northward, east and west;
Tell all the earth Christ died and lives,
Who giveth pardon, life, and rest.

2 Send forth Thy gospel, mighty Lord!
Out of this chaos bring to birth
Thine own creation's promised hope;
The better days of heaven on earth.

3 Send forth Thy gospel, gracious Lord!
Thine was the blood for sinners shed;
Thy voice still pleads in human hearts;
To Thee Thine other sheep be led.

4 Send forth Thy gospel, holy Lord!
Kindle in us love's sacred flame;
Love giving all, and grudging naught
For Jesus' sake, in Jesus' name.

5 Send forth the gospel! Tell it out!
Go, brothers, at the Master's call;
Prepare His way, who comes to reign,
The King of kings, and Lord of all.

HENRY ELLIOTT FOX (1841-1926)

168

OAK HILL   (8 6. 8 6. 8 8. 8 8 6.)   F. DEREK KIDNER (1913-   )

rise through pain,   Je - sus, our ris - en

*VERSE 2 SHOULD BE SUNG THUS

DIE SACH' IST DEIN, HERR JESU CHRIST

Christ also suffered for us, leaving us an example (1 Peter ii. 21)

L ORD Jesus Christ, the work is Thine;
  Not ours, but Thine alone;
And prospered by Thy power divine
  Can ne'er be overthrown.
Before it pushes to the light
The corn of wheat is hid from sight.
Deep in the silent earth it lies,
Its very self decays and dies,
  Losing itself it dies.

2 To glory Thou didst rise through
   Jesus, our risen Head,   [pain,
And all who follow in Thy train
   The selfsame path must tread.
So in Thy fellowship we go,
Refusing not to share Thy woe,
   If only Thou dost lead us through·
   The gate of death to Life anew,
      Through death to Life anew.

3 Thou as a corn of wheat didst die
   And sink into the grave.
Now quicken, Fount of Life, we cry,
   The dead Thou cam'st to save!
O send Thy heralds everywhere
The tidings of Thy name to bear
   And, till its fame is fully shown,
   We pledge ourselves to make it
      We live to make it known! [known,

German; tr. FRANK HOUGHTON (1894-   )

169

HEATHLANDS (7 7. 7 7. 7 7.)   HENRY SMART (1813-79)

Based on Psalm lxvii

GOD of mercy, God of grace,
   Show the brightness of Thy face;
Shine upon us, Saviour, shine,
Fill Thy Church with light divine;
And Thy saving health extend
Unto earth's remotest end.

2 Let the people praise Thee, Lord;
Be by all that live adored;
Let the nations shout and sing
Glory to their Saviour King;
At Thy feet their tribute pay,
And Thy holy will obey.

3 Let the people praise Thee, Lord;
Earth shall then her fruits afford;
God to man His blessing give,
Man to God devoted live;
All below and all above,
One in joy and light and love.

HENRY FRANCIS LYTE (1793-1847)

170

EVERTON (8 7. 8 7. D.)   HENRY SMART (1813-79)

Pray ye therefore the Lord of the harvest, that he would send forth labourers (Luke x. 2)

L ORD, her watch Thy Church is keeping;
    When shall earth Thy rule obey?
When shall end the night of weeping?
    When shall break the promised day?
See the whitening harvest languish,
    Waiting still the labourers' toil;
Was it vain, Thy Son's deep anguish?
    Shall the strong retain the spoil?

2 Tidings, sent to every creature,
    Millions yet have never heard;
Can they hear without a preacher?
    Lord Almighty, give the word:
Give the word; in every nation
    Let the gospel trumpet sound,
Witnessing a world's salvation
    To the earth's remotest bound.

3 Then the end; Thy Church completed,
    All Thy chosen gathered in,
With their King in glory seated,
    Satan bound, and banished sin;
Gone for ever parting, weeping,
    Hunger, sorrow, death, and pain:
Lo! her watch Thy Church is keeping;
    Come, Lord Jesus, come to reign.

HENRY DOWNTON (1818-85)

171

HYFRYDOL (8 7. 8 7. D.)   Melody by ROWLAND HUGH PRICHARD (1811-87)

This hymn may also be sung to the tune EBENEZER, No. 116

Here am I; send me (Isaiah vi. 8)

FROM the depths of sin and failure,
    From despair as black as night,
Lord, we hear our brothers calling
For deliverance and for light.

Use us, Lord, to speed Thy kingdom;
    Through us may Thy will be done;
Give us eyes to see the vision
    Of a world redeemed and won.

2 By the love that bore in silence
    Man's contempt and Satan's dart;
By the longing for the lost ones
    That consumes the Saviour's heart;

3 By the Saviour's blood that bought us,
    By the peace His merits bring,
By the Spirit that constrains us
    Now on earth to crown Him King;

TIMOTHY REES (1874-1939)

172

BISHOPGARTH (8 7. 8 7. D. Iambic)   ARTHUR SEYMOUR SULLIVAN (1842-1900)

They went forth, and preached every where, the Lord working with them (Mark xvi. 20)

'FOR My sake and the gospel's, go
    And tell redemption's story';
His heralds answer, 'Be it so,
    And Thine, Lord, all the glory!'
They preach His birth, His life, His cross,
    The love of His atonement,
For whom they count the world but loss,
    His Easter, His enthronement.

2 Hark, hark, the trump of Jubilee
    Proclaims to every nation,
From pole to pole, by land and sea,
    Glad tidings of salvation:
As nearer draws the day of doom,
    While still the battle rages,
The heavenly dayspring through the gloom
    Breaks on the night of ages.

3 Still on and on the anthems spread
    Of hallelujah voices,
    In concert with the holy dead,
        The warrior Church rejoices;
    Their snow-white robes are washed in blood,
        Their golden harps are ringing;
    Earth and the Paradise of God
        One triumph-song are singing.

4 He comes, whose advent-trumpet drowns
    The last of time's evangels,
    Immanuel crowned with many crowns,
        The Lord of saints and angels:
    O Life, Light, Love, the great I AM,
        Triune, who changest never;
    The throne of God and of the Lamb
        Is Thine, and Thine for ever.

EDWARD HENRY BICKERSTETH (1825-1906)

173

ST. CECILIA (6 6. 6 6.)   LEIGHTON GEORGE HAYNE (1836-83)

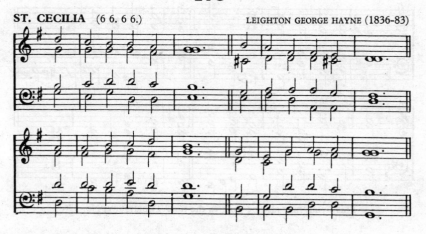

*The kingdoms of this world are become the kingaoms of our Lord, and of his Christ; and he shall reign
for ever and ever (Revelation xi. 15)*

THY kingdom come, O God;
    Thy rule, O Christ, begin;
Break with Thine iron rod
    The tyrannies of sin.

2 Where is Thy reign of peace
    And purity and love?
When shall all hatred cease,
    As in the realms above?

3 When comes the promised time
    That war shall be no more,
And lust, oppression, crime,
    Shall flee Thy face before?

4 We pray Thee, Lord, arise,
    And come in Thy great might;
Revive our longing eyes,
    Which languish for Thy sight.

5 Men scorn Thy sacred name,
    And wolves devour Thy fold;
By many deeds of shame
    We learn that love grows cold.

6 O'er heathen lands afar
    Thick darkness broodeth yet;
Arise, O Morning Star,
    Arise, and never set.

LEWIS HENSLEY (1824-1905)

174

KING'S LYNN   (7 6. 7 6. D.)   English Traditional Melody
Unison

This hymn may also be sung to the tune THORNBURY, No. 336

He saith unto them, Follow me, and I will make you fishers of men (Matthew iv. 19)

O MASTER! when Thou callest,
  No voice may say Thee nay,
For blest are they that follow
  Where Thou dost lead the way;
In freshest prime of morning,
  Or fullest glow of noon,
The note of heavenly warning
  Can never come too soon.

2 O Master! where Thou callest,
  No foot may shrink in fear,
For they who trust Thee wholly
  Shall find Thee ever near;
And quiet room and lonely,
  Or busy harvest field,
Where Thou, Lord, rulest only,
  Shall precious produce yield.

3 O Master! whom Thou callest,
  No heart may dare refuse;
'Tis honour, highest honour,
  When Thou dost deign to use
Our brightest and our fairest,
  Our dearest—all are Thine;
Thou who for each one carest,
  We hail Thy love's design.

4 They who go forth to serve Thee,
  We, too, who serve at home,
May watch and pray together
  Until Thy kingdom come;
In Thee for aye united,
  Our song of hope we raise,
Till that blest shore is sighted,
  Where all shall turn to praise!

SARAH GERALDINA STOCK (1838-98)

175

MISSIONARY (7 6. 7 6. D.)   LOWELL MASON (1792-1872)

This hymn may also be sung to the tune AURELIA, No. 182

Ye shall be witnesses unto me . . . unto the uttermost part of the earth (Acts i. 8)

FROM Greenland's icy mountains,
    From India's coral strand,
Where Afric's sunny fountains
    Roll down their golden sand,
From many an ancient river,
    From many a palmy plain,
They call us to deliver
    Their land from error's chain.

2 Can we, whose souls are lighted
    With wisdom from on high,
Can we to men benighted
    The lamp of life deny?
Salvation! O salvation!
    The joyful sound proclaim,
Till each remotest nation
    Has learnt Messiah's name.

3 Waft, waft, ye winds, His story,
    And you, ye waters, roll,
Till, like a sea of glory,
    It spreads from pole to pole;
Till o'er our ransomed nature
    The Lamb for sinners slain,
Redeemer, King, Creator,
    In bliss returns to reign.

REGINALD HEBER (1783-1826)

176

HARTS (7 7. 7 7.)   BENJAMIN MILGROVE (1731-1810)

This hymn may also be sung to the tune VIENNA, No. 95

WALTE, FÜRDER, NAH UND FERN

Go ye . . . and teach all nations (Matthew xxviii. 19)

SPREAD, O spread, thou mighty word,
Spread the kingdom of the Lord,
Whereso'er His breath has given
Life to beings meant for heaven.

2 Tell them how the Father's will
Made the world, and keeps it still,
How He sent His Son to save
All who help and comfort crave.

3 Tell of our Redeemer's love,
Who for ever doth remove
By His holy sacrifice
All the guilt that on us lies.

4 Tell them of the Spirit given
Now to guide us up to heaven,
Strong and holy, just and true,
Working both to will and do.

5 Word of life, most pure and strong,
Lo! for thee the nations long;
Spread, till from its dreary night
All the world awakes to light.

6 Up! the ripening fields ye see,
Mighty shall the harvest be;
But the reapers still are few,
Great the work they have to do.

7 Lord of harvest, let there be
Joy and strength to work for Thee,
Till the nations, far and near,
See Thy light, and learn Thy fear.

JONATHAN FRIEDRICH BAHNMAIER (1774-1841);
tr. CATHERINE WINKWORTH (1829-78)

177

ORIENTIS PARTIBUS (7 7. 7 7.)　　　　　　　Medieval French Melody

The sword of the Spirit, which is the word of God (Ephesians vi. 17)

SOLDIERS of the cross, arise!
　Gird you with your armour bright;
Mighty are your enemies,
　Hard the battle you must fight.

2 O'er a faithless fallen world
　Raise your banner in the sky;
Let it float there wide unfurled;
　Bear it onward; lift it high.

*3 'Mid the homes of want and woe,
　Strangers to the living Word,
Let the Saviour's heralds go,
　Let the voice of hope be heard.

*4 Where the shadows deepest lie,
　Carry truth's unsullied ray;
Where are crimes of blackest dye,
　There the saving sign display.

5 To the weary and the worn
　Tell of realms where sorrows cease;
To the outcast and forlorn
　Speak of mercy and of peace.

6 Guard the helpless; seek the strayed;
　Comfort troubles; banish grief;
In the might of God arrayed,
　Scatter sin and unbelief.

7 Be the banner still unfurled,
　Still unsheathed the Spirit's sword,
Till the kingdoms of the world
　Are the Kingdom of the Lord.

WILLIAM WALSHAM HOW (1823-97)

*If desired, verses 3 and 4 may be omitted

178

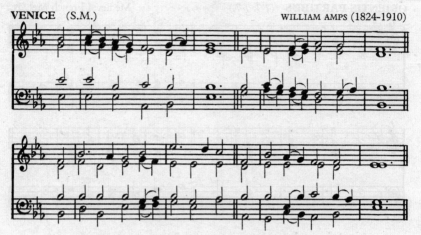

VENICE (S.M.)   WILLIAM AMPS (1824-1910)

This hymn may also be sung to the tune CARLISLE, No. 1

O Lord, revive thy work in the midst of the years (Habakkuk iii. 2)

REVIVE Thy work, O Lord,
  Thy mighty arm make bare;
Speak with the voice that wakes the dead,
  And make Thy people hear.

2 Revive Thy work, O Lord,
    Disturb this sleep of death;
  Quicken the smouldering embers now
    By Thine almighty breath.

3 Revive Thy work, O Lord,
    Create soul-thirst for Thee;
  And hungering for the Bread of Life,
    O may our spirits be.

4 Revive Thy work, O Lord,
    Exalt Thy precious name;
  And, by the Holy Ghost, our love
    For Thee and Thine inflame.

5 Revive Thy work, O Lord:
    Give Pentecostal showers;
  The glory shall be all Thine own,
    The blessing, Lord, be ours!

ALBERT MIDLANE (1825-1909)

179

QUINTA (S.M.) From the University of Wales *Students' Hymnal* (1923)

A lower setting of this tune is given at No. 370 (ii)

ALTERNATIVE TUNE

FAREHAM (S.M.) JOHN GOSS (1800-80)

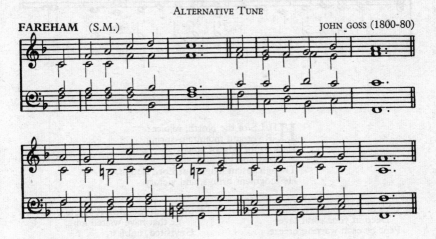

They that sow in tears shall reap in joy (Psalm cxxvi. 5)

SOW in the morn thy seed,
At eve hold not thine hand;
To doubt and fear give thou no heed,
Broadcast it o'er the land.

2 Beside all waters sow,
The highway furrows stock,
Drop it where thorns and thistles grow,
Scatter it on the rock.

3 The good, the fruitful ground,
Expect not here nor there,
O'er hill and dale, by plots 'tis found;
Go forth, then, everywhere.

4 And duly shall appear,
In verdure, beauty, strength,
The tender blade, the stalk, the ear,
And the full corn at length.

5 Thou canst not toil in vain;
Cold, heat, and moist, and dry,
Shall foster and mature the grain
For garners in the sky.

6 Thence, when the glorious end,
The day of God is come,
The angel-reapers shall descend,
And heaven cry: ' Harvest Home! '

JAMES MONTGOMERY (1771-1854)

180

LITTLE CORNARD   (6 6. 6 6. 8 8.)   MARTIN SHAW (1875-   )

He hath redeemed . . . and gathered them out of the lands (Psalm cvii. 2, 3)

Hills of the North, rejoice:
   River and mountain-spring,
Hark to the advent voice!
   Valley and lowland, sing!
Though absent long, your Lord is nigh,
He judgment brings, and victory.

2 Isles of the Southern seas,
   Deep in your coral caves
Pent be each warring breeze,
   Lulled be your restless waves:
He comes to reign with boundless sway,
And make your wastes His great
     highway.

3 Lands of the East, awake!
   Soon shall your sons be free,
The sleep of ages break,
   And rise to liberty:
On your far hills, long cold and grey,
Has dawned the everlasting day.

4 Shores of the utmost West,
   Ye that have waited long,
Unvisited, unblest,
   Break forth to swelling song;
High raise the note, that Jesus died,
Yet lives and reigns—the Crucified!

5 Shout while ye journey home!
   Songs be in every mouth!—
Lo, from the North we come,
   From East, and West, and South:
City of God, the bond are free;
We come to live and reign in thee.

CHARLES EDWARD OAKLEY (1832-65)

181

LIMPSFIELD (7 3. 7 3. 7 7. 7 3.)   JOSIAH BOOTH (1852-1930)

All the ends of the earth shall see the salvation of our God (Isaiah lii. 10)

WE have heard the joyful sound;
   Jesus saves!
Spread the gladness all around;
   Jesus saves!
Bear the news to every land,
Climb the steeps and cross the waves;
Onward! 'tis our Lord's command:
   Jesus saves!

2 Sing above the battle's strife;
   Jesus saves!
By His death and endless life,
   Jesus saves!
Sing it softly through the gloom,
When the heart for mercy craves;
Sing in triumph o'er the tomb:
   Jesus saves!

3 Give the winds a mighty voice:
   Jesus saves!
Let the nations now rejoice:
   Jesus saves!
Sing ye islands of the sea;
Echo back, ye ocean caves;
Shout salvation full and free:
   Jesus saves!

PRISCILLA JANE OWENS (1829-99)†

182

AURELIA (7 6. 7 6. D.)   SAMUEL SEBASTIAN WESLEY (1810-76)

This gospel of the kingdom shall be preached in all the world (Matthew xxiv. 14)

FACING a task unfinished,
    That drives us to our knees,
A need that, undiminished,
    Rebukes our slothful ease,
We, who rejoice to know Thee,
    Renew before Thy Throne
The solemn pledge we owe Thee
    To go and make Thee known.

2 Where other lords beside Thee
      Hold their unhindered sway,
  Where forces that defied Thee
      Defy Thee still today,
  With none to heed their crying
      For life, and love, and light,
  Unnumbered souls are dying,
      And pass into the night.

3 We bear the torch that flaming
      Fell from the hands of those
  Who gave their lives proclaiming
      That Jesus died and rose.
  Ours is the same commission,
      The same glad message ours,
  Fired by the same ambition,
      To Thee we yield our powers.

4 O Father who sustained them,
      O Spirit who inspired,
  Saviour, whose love constrained them
      To toil with zeal untired,
  From cowardice defend us,
      From lethargy awake!
  Forth on Thine errands send us
      To labour for Thy sake.

FRANK HOUGHTON (1894-   )

183

BREMEN (MUNICH) (7 6. 7 6. D.)   *Meiningen Gesangbuch* (1693)

Lift up your eyes, and look on the fields; for they are white already to harvest (John iv. 35)

L ORD of the living harvest
 That whitens o'er the plain,
Where angels soon shall gather
 Their sheaves of golden grain,
Accept these hands to labour,
 These hearts to trust and love,
And deign with them to hasten
 Thy kingdom from above.

2 As labourers in Thy vineyard,
 Lord, send them out to be,
Content to bear the burden
 Of weary days for Thee,
Content to ask no wages
 When Thou shalt call them home,
But to have shared the travail
 That makes Thy kingdom come.

3 Be with them, God the Father,
 Be with them, God the Son,
Be with them, God the Spirit,
 Eternal Three in One!
Make them a royal priesthood,
 Thee rightly to adore,
And fill them with Thy fullness
 Now and for evermore.

JOHN SAMUEL BEWLEY MONSELL (1811-75)

184

WOKING   (8 8. 8 8. 8 8.)   PEGGY SPENCER PALMER

This hymn may also be sung to the tune WYCH CROSS, No. 243

Whom shall I send, and who will go for us ? (Isaiah vi. 8)

THE Master comes! He calls for thee;
　　Go forth at His almighty word,
Obedient to His last command,
　　And tell to those who never heard,
Who sit in deepest shades of night,
That Christ has come to give them light!

2 The Master calls! Arise and go;
　　How blest His messenger to be!
He who has given thee liberty
　　Now bids thee set the captives free;
Proclaim His mighty power to save,
Who for the world His life-blood gave.

3 The Master calls! Shall not thy heart
　　In warm responsive love reply,
' Lord, here am I, send me, send me,
　　Thy willing slave, to live or die;
An instrument unfit indeed,
Yet Thou wilt give me what I need.'

4 And if thou canst not go, yet bring
　　An offering of a willing heart;
Then, though thou tarriest at home,
　　Thy God shall give thee, too, thy part.
The messengers of peace upbear
In ceaseless and prevailing prayer.

5 Short is the time for service true,
　　For soon shall dawn that glorious day
When, all the harvest gathered in,
　　Each faithful heart shall hear Him say,
' My child, well done! your toil is o'er,
Enter My joy for evermore.'

E. MAY GRIMES (1868-1927)

185

ST. HELEN'S (8 5. 8 3.)   ROBERT PRESCOTT STEWART (1825-94)

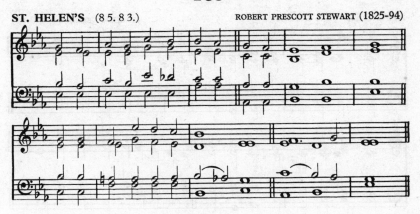

From henceforth expecting till his enemies be made his footstool (Hebrews x. 13)

HE expecteth, He expecteth!
  Down the stream of time,
Still the words come softly ringing
    Like a chime.

2 Oft-times faint, now waxing louder
  As the hour draws near,
When the King, in all His glory,
    Shall appear.

3 He is waiting with long patience
  For His crowning day,
For that kingdom which shall never
    Pass away.

4 And till every tribe and nation
  Bow before His throne,
He expecteth loyal service
    From His own.

5 He expecteth; but He heareth
  Still the bitter cry
From earth's millions, ' Come and help us,
    For we die.'

6 He expecteth; doth He see us
  Busy here and there,
Heedless of those pleading accents
    Of despair?

7 Shall we, dare we, disappoint Him?
  Brethren, let us rise!
He who died for us is watching
    From the skies;

8 Watching till His royal banner
  Floateth far and wide,
Till he seeth of His travail—
    Satisfied!

ALICE J. JANVRIN

186

NEANDER (8 7. 8 7. 8 7.)   JOACHIM NEANDER (1650-80)

They commended them to the Lord, on whom they believed (Acts xiv. 23)

Speed Thy servants, Saviour, speed them,
  Thou art Lord of winds and waves;
They were bound, but Thou hast freed them,
  Now they go to free the slaves.
    Be Thou with them;
  'Tis Thine arm alone that saves.

2 Friends, and home, and all forsaking,
  Lord, they go at Thy command;
As their stay Thy promise taking,
  While they traverse sea and land.
    O be with them!
  Lead them safely by the hand.

3 Where no fruit appears to cheer them,
  And they seem to toil in vain,
Then in mercy, Lord, draw near them,
  Then their sinking hopes sustain.
    Thus supported,
  Let their zeal revive again.

4 In the midst of opposition,
  Let them trust, O Lord, in Thee;
When success attends their mission,
  Let Thy servants humble be.
    Never leave them,
  Till Thy face in heaven they see:

5 There to reap in joy for ever
  Fruit that grows from seed here sown,
There to be with Him who never
  Ceases to preserve His own,
    And with gladness
  Give the praise to Him alone.

THOMAS KELLY (1769-1854)

See also the section THE MAN OF GOD: SERVICE, *Nos. 302-313. The following hymns also refer to this theme:*

100 Ye servants of God, your Master proclaim
133 O Breath of Life, come sweeping through us
294 Arm of the Lord, awake, awake!
301 ' We rest on Thee,' our shield and our defender

THE CALL OF GOD
187

CROSS OF JESUS (8 7. 8 7.)   JOHN STAINER (1840-1901)

I am the good shepherd: the good shepherd giveth his life for the sheep (John x. 11)

SOULS of men! why will ye scatter
Like a crowd of frightened sheep?
Foolish hearts! why will ye wander
From a love so true and deep?

2 There's a wideness in God's mercy,
Like the wideness of the sea;
There's a kindness in His justice,
Which is more than liberty.

3 There is plentiful redemption
In the blood that has been shed;
There is joy for all the members
In the sorrows of the Head.

4 For the love of God is broader
Than the measures of man's mind;
And the heart of the Eternal
Is most wonderfully kind.

5 If our love were but more simple,
We should take Him at His word;
And our lives would be all sunshine,
In the sweetness of our Lord.

FREDERICK WILLIAM FABER (1814-63)

205

188

PETERSHAM (D.C.M.)   CLEMENT WILLIAM POOLE (1828-1924)

This hymn may also be sung to the tune FOREST GREEN, No. 202 (i)

Take my yoke upon you, and learn of me (Matthew xi. 29)

THE Lord is rich and merciful,
    The Lord is very kind;
O come to Him, come now to Him
    With a believing mind;
His comforts, they shall strengthen thee,
    Like flowing waters cool;
And He shall for thy spirit be
    A fountain ever full.

2 The Lord is glorious and strong,
    Our God is very high;
O trust in Him, trust now in Him,
    And have security;
He shall be to thee like the sea,
    And thou shalt surely feel
His wind, that bloweth healthily,
    Thy sicknesses to heal.

3 The Lord is wonderful and wise,
    As all the ages tell;
O learn of Him, learn now of Him,
    Then with thee it is well;
And with His light thou shalt be blest,
    Therein to work and live;
And He shall be to thee a rest
    When evening hours arrive.

THOMAS TOKE LYNCH (1818-71)

189

SURREY (8 8. 8 8. 8 8.)   HENRY CAREY (c. 1692-1743)

John seeth Jesus . . . and saith, Behold the Lamb of God, which taketh away the sin of the world
(John i. 29)

BEHOLD, the Lamb of God, who bears
  The sins of all the world away!
A servant's form He meekly wears,
  He sojourns in a house of clay;
His glory is no longer seen,
But God with God is man with men.

2 See where the God incarnate stands,
  And calls His wandering creatures home!
He all day long spreads out His hands,
  Come, weary souls, to Jesus come!
Ye all may hide you in My breast;
Believe, and I will give you rest.

3 Sinners, believe the gospel word,
  Jesus is come your souls to save!
Jesus is come, your common Lord;
  Pardon ye all through Him may have,
May now be saved, whoever will;
This Man receiveth sinners still.

CHARLES WESLEY (1707-88)

190

WINCHESTER NEW (L.M.)   Adapted from a Chorale in the
Musikalisches Handbuch (Hamburg, 1690)

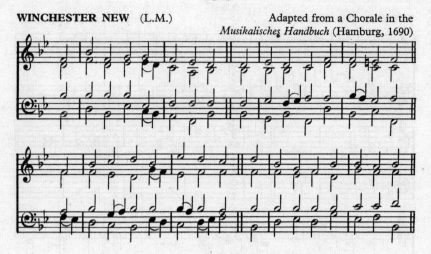

If any man hear my voice, and open the door, I will come in (Revelation iii. 20)

BEHOLD a Stranger at the door!
He gently knocks, has knocked before,
Has waited long, is waiting still:
You treat no other friend so ill.

2 Admit Him, for the human breast
Ne'er entertained so kind a guest;
No mortal tongue their joys can tell,
With whom He condescends to dwell.

3 Yet know, nor of the terms complain,
When Jesus comes He comes to reign,
To reign, and with no partial sway;
Thoughts must be slain that disobey.

4 Sovereign of souls, Thou Prince of Peace,
O may Thy gentle reign increase:
Throw wide the door, each willing mind;
And be His empire all mankind.

JOSEPH GRIGG (1728-68)

191

OMBERSLEY (L.M.)   WILLIAM HENRY GLADSTONE (1840-91)

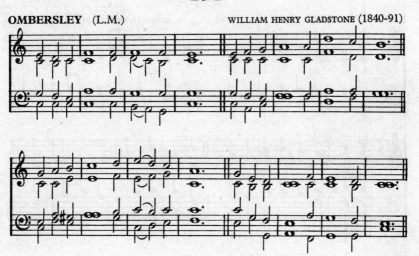

My sheep hear my voice, and I know them, and they follow me (John x. 27)

G OD calling yet! Shall I not hear?
Earth's pleasures shall I still hold dear?
Shall life's swift passing years all fly,
And still my soul in slumber lie?

2 God calling yet! Shall I not rise?
Can I His loving voice despise,
And basely His kind care repay?
He calls me still; can I delay?

3 God calling yet! And shall He knock,
And I my heart the closer lock?
He still is waiting to receive,
And shall I dare His Spirit grieve?

4 God calling yet! And shall I give
No heed, but still in bondage live?
I wait, but He does not forsake;
He calls me still; my heart, awake!

5 God calling yet! I cannot stay;
My heart I yield without delay:
Vain world, farewell, from thee I part;
The voice of God hath reached my heart.

GERHARD TERSTEEGEN (1697-1769);
tr. SARAH FINDLATER (1823-86) and others.

192

RENFREWSHIRE   (7 7. 7 7.)   KENNETH GEORGE FINLAY (1882-)

ALTERNATIVE TUNE

ST. BEES   (7 7. 7 7.)   JOHN BACCHUS DYKES (1823-76)

This hymn may also be sung to the tune SONG 13, No. 154

Lovest thou me? (John xxi. 15)

HARK, my soul! it is the Lord;
'Tis Thy Saviour, hear His word;
Jesus speaks, and speaks to thee:
' Say, poor sinner, lov'st thou Me?

2 'I delivered thee when bound,
And, when bleeding, healed thy wound;
Sought thee, wandering, set thee right;
Turned thy darkness into light.

3 'Can a woman's tender care
Cease towards the child she bare?
Yes, she may forgetful be,
Yet will I remember thee.

4 'Mine is an unchanging love,
   Higher than the heights above,
   Deeper than the depths beneath,
   Free and faithful, strong as death.

5 'Thou shalt see My glory soon,
   When the work of grace is done;
   Partner of My throne shalt be;
   Say, poor sinner, lov'st thou Me?'

6 Lord, it is my chief complaint
   That my love is weak and faint;
   Yet I love Thee, and adore;
   O for grace to love Thee more!

WILLIAM COWPER (1731-1800)

193

ST. BOTOLPH (C.M.)   GORDON SLATER (1896-   )

That Christ may dwell in your hearts by faith (Ephesians iii. 17)

ENTHRONE thy God within thy heart,
   Thy being's inmost shrine;
He doth to thee the power impart
   To live the life divine.

2 Seek truth in Him with Christlike mind;
   With faith His will discern;
Walk on life's way with Him, and find
   Thy heart within thee burn.

3 With love that overflows thy soul
   Love Him who first loved thee;
Is not His love thy life, thy goal,
   Thy soul's eternity?

4 Serve Him in His sufficing strength:
   Heart, mind, and soul employ;
And He shall crown thy days at length
   With everlasting joy.

WILLIAM JOSEPH PENN (1875-1956)

194

EWING (7 6. 7 6. D.)   ALEXANDER EWING (1830–95)

Him that cometh to me I will in no wise cast out (John vi. 37)

'COME unto me, ye weary,
    And I will give you rest.'
O blessèd voice of Jesus,
    Which comes to hearts oppressed!
It tells of benediction,
    Of pardon, grace and peace,
Of joy that hath no ending,
    Of love which cannot cease.

2 ' Come unto me, ye wanderers,
    And I will give you light.'
O loving voice of Jesus,
    Which comes to cheer the night!
Our hearts were filled with sadness,
    And we had lost our way;
But morning brings us gladness,
    And songs the break of day.

3 ' Come unto me, ye fainting,
    And I will give you life.'
O peaceful voice of Jesus,
    Which comes to end our strife!
The foe is stern and eager,
    The fight is fierce and long;
But Thou hast made us mighty,
    And stronger than the strong.

4 'And whosoever cometh,
    I will not cast him out.'
O patient voice of Jesus,
    Which drives away our doubt,
Which calls us—very sinners,
    Unworthy though we be
Of love so free and boundless—
    To come, dear Lord, to Thee!

WILLIAM CHATTERTON DIX (1837-98)

195

ST. CATHERINE (7 6. 7 6. D.)   REGINALD FRANCIS DALE (1845-1919)

Based on Revelation iii. 20

O JESUS, Thou art standing
Outside the fast-closed door,
In lowly patience waiting
To pass the threshold o'er.
Shame on us, Christian brothers,
His name and sign who bear,
O shame, thrice shame upon us,
To keep Him standing there!

2 O Jesus, Thou art knocking;
And, lo! that hand is scarred,
And thorns Thy brow encircle,
And tears Thy face have marred.
O love that passeth knowledge,
So patiently to wait!
O sin that hath no equal,
So fast to bar the gate!

3 O Jesus, Thou art pleading
In accents meek and low,
' I died for you, my children,
And will ye treat me so? '
O Lord, with shame and sorrow
We open now the door;
Dear Saviour, enter, enter,
And leave us nevermore.

WILLIAM WALSHAM HOW (1823-97)

196

BRYN CALFARIA (8 7. 8 7. 8 7.)   Melody by WILLIAM OWEN (1814-93)

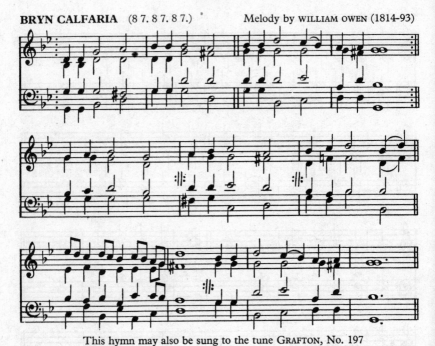

This hymn may also be sung to the tune GRAFTON, No. 197

I came not to call the righteous, but sinners to repentance (Luke v. 32)

COME, ye sinners, poor and needy,
  Weak and wounded, sick and sore;
Jesus ready stands to save you,
  Full of pity, joined with power:
    He is able,
    He is willing; doubt no more.

2 Come, ye needy, come, and welcome;
    God's free bounty glorify;
  True belief and true repentance,
    Every grace that brings us nigh,
      Without money
    Come to Jesus Christ and buy.

3 Come, ye weary, heavy-laden,
    Bruised and broken by the fall;
  If you tarry till you're better,
    You will never come at all:
      Not the righteous—
    Sinners Jesus came to call.

4 Let not conscience make you linger,
    Nor of fitness fondly dream;
  All the fitness He requireth
    Is to feel your need of Him:
      This He gives you;
    'Tis the Spirit's rising beam.

5 Lo! the incarnate God, ascended,
    Pleads the merit of His blood;
  Venture on Him, venture wholly;
    Let no other trust intrude:
      None but Jesus
    Can do helpless sinners good.

JOSEPH HART (1712-68)

197

GRAFTON (TANTUM ERGO SACRAMENTUM)   (8 7. 8 7. 8 7.)   French
Church Melody (19th century)

Based on Matthew xi. 28-30

COME, ye souls by sin afflicted,
  Bowed with fruitless sorrow down,
By the broken law convicted,
  Through the cross behold the crown;
    Look to Jesus;
  Mercy flows through Him alone.

2 Blessèd are the eyes that see Him,
   Blest the ears that hear His voice;
 Blessèd are the souls that trust Him
   And in Him alone rejoice;
     His commandments
   Then become their happy choice.

3 Take His easy yoke and wear it;
   Love will make obedience sweet;
 Christ will give you strength to bear it,
   While His wisdom guides your feet
     Safe to glory,
   Where His ransomed captives meet.

4 Sweet as home to pilgrims weary,
   Light to newly opened eyes,
 Or full springs in deserts dreary,
   Is the rest the cross supplies;
     All who taste it
   Shall to rest immortal rise.

JOSEPH SWAIN (1761-96)

WELLS   (7 7. 7 7. 7 7.)   Melody by DMITRI STEPANOVITCH BORTNIANSKI (1752-1825)
harmonized by ERIK ROUTLEY (1917-   )

JESUS NIMMT DIE SÜNDER AN

This man receiveth sinners (Luke xv. 2)

SINNERS Jesus will receive:
   Tell this word of grace to all
Who the heavenly pathway leave,
   All who linger, all who fall;
This can bring them back again:
' Christ receiveth sinful men.'

2 Shepherds seek their wandering sheep
   O'er the mountains bleak and cold;
Jesus such a watch doth keep
   O'er the lost ones of His fold,
Seeking them o'er moor and fen:
Christ receiveth sinful men.

3 Sick and sorrowful and blind,
   I with all my sins draw nigh;
O my Saviour, Thou canst find
   Help for sinners such as I;
Speak that word of love again;
' Christ receiveth sinful men.'

4 Christ receiveth sinful men,
   Even me with all my sin;
Openeth to me heaven again;
   With Him I may enter in.
Death hath no more sting nor pain:
Christ receiveth sinful men.

ERDMANN NEUMEISTER (1671-1756);
tr. EMMA FRANCES BEVAN (1827-1909)

199

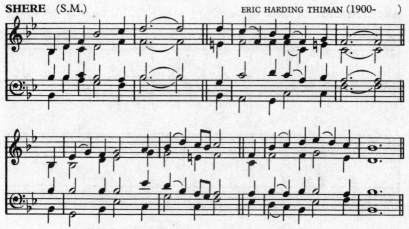

SHERE (S.M.)   ERIC HARDING THIMAN (1900-   )

This hymn may also be sung to the tune CARLISLE, No. 1

From BEFIEHL DU DEINE WEGE

Commit thy way unto the Lord; trust also in him; and he shall bring it to pass (Psalm xxxvii. 5)

PUT thou thy trust in God,
    In duty's path go on;
Walk in His strength with faith and hope,
    So shall thy work be done.

2 Commit thy ways to Him,
    Thy works into His hands,
And rest on His unchanging word,
    Who heaven and earth commands.

3 Though years on years roll on,
    His covenant shall endure;
Though clouds and darkness hide His path,
    The promised grace is sure.

4 Give to the winds thy fears;
    Hope, and be undismayed;
God hears thy sighs and counts thy tears;
    God shall lift up thy head.

5 Through waves, and clouds, and storms
    His power will clear thy way;
Wait thou His time; the darkest night
    Shall end in brightest day.

6 Leave to His sovereign sway
    To choose and to command;
So shalt thou, wondering, own His way
    How wise, how strong His hand.

PAUL GERHARDT (1607-76);
tr. JOHN WESLEY (1703-91) and others.

200

Seek ye first the kingdom of God, and his righteousness (Matthew vi. 33)

SEEK ye first, not earthly pleasure,
Fading joy and failing treasure;
But the love that knows no measure
  Seek ye first.

2 Seek ye first, not earth's aspirings,
Ceaseless longings, vain desirings;
But your precious soul's requirings
  Seek ye first.

3 Seek ye first God's peace and blessing,
Ye have all if this possessing;
Come, your need and sin confessing,
  Seek Him first.

4 Seek Him first; then, when forgiven,
Pardoned, made an heir of heaven,
Let your life to Him be given;
  Seek this first.

5 Seek this first: be pure and holy;
Like the Master, meek and lowly:
Yielded to His service wholly;
  Seek this first.

6 Seek the coming of His kingdom;
Seek the souls around to win them;
Seek to Jesus Christ to bring them;
  Seek this first.

7 Seek this first, His promise trying;
It is sure, all need supplying;
Heavenly things, on Him relying,
  Seek ye first.

G. M. TAYLOR

THE MAN OF GOD
PENITENCE AND FAITH
201

OLD 124TH (10 10. 10 10.)

LOUIS BOURGEOIS (1510-61)

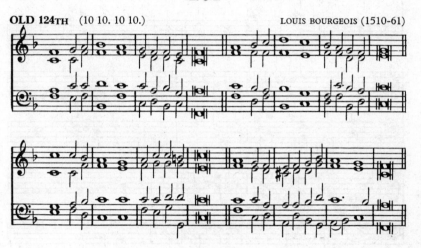

In Christ Jesus ye who sometimes were far off are made nigh by the blood of Christ (Ephesians ii. 13)

WEARY of self and laden with my sin,
I look at heaven and long to enter in;
But there no evil thing may find a home,
And yet I hear a voice that bids me, Come!

2 So vile I am, how dare I hope to stand
In the pure glory of that holy land,
Before the whiteness of that throne appear?
Yet there are hands stretched out to draw me near.

3 It is the voice of Jesus that I hear,
His are the hands stretched out to draw me near,
And His the blood that can for all atone,
And set me faultless there before the throne.

4 Yea, Thou wilt answer for me, righteous Lord;
Thine all the merits, mine the great reward;
Thine the sharp thorns, so mine the golden crown;
Mine the life won, through Thine the life laid down.

5 Nought can I bring Thee, Lord, for all I owe;
Yet let my full heart what it can bestow;
Myself my gift; let my devotion prove,
Forgiven greatly, how I greatly love.

SAMUEL JOHN STONE (1839-1900)†

202

FOREST GREEN   (D.C.M.)   English Traditional Melody

ALTERNATIVE TUNE

KINGSFOLD   (D.C.M.)   From an English Traditional Melody

He satisfieth the longing soul, and filleth the hungry soul with goodness (Psalm cvii. 9)

I HEARD the voice of Jesus say,
    ' Come unto Me and rest;
Lay down, thou weary one, lay down
    Thy head upon My breast ':
I came to Jesus as I was,
    Weary, and worn, and sad;
I found in Him a resting-place,
    And He has made me glad.

2 I heard the voice of Jesus say,
    ' Behold, I freely give
The living water; thirsty one,
    Stoop down and drink, and live ':
I came to Jesus, and I drank
    Of that life-giving stream;
My thirst was quenched, my soul revived,
    And now I live in Him.

3 I heard the voice of Jesus say,
    ' I am this dark world's Light;
Look unto Me, thy morn shall rise,
    And all thy day be bright ':
I looked to Jesus, and I found
    In Him my star, my sun;
And in that light of life I'll walk,
    Till travelling days are done.

HORATIUS BONAR (1808-89)

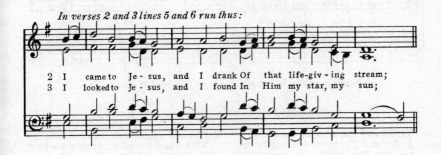

203

SAFFRON WALDEN (8 8 8. 6.) ARTHUR HENRY BROWN (1830-1926)

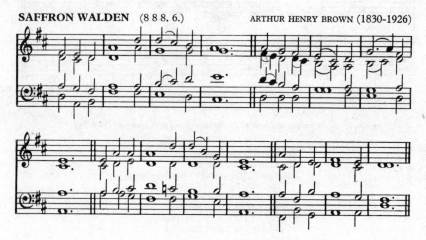

Christ also hath loved us, and hath given himself for us (Ephesians v. 2)

O SAVIOUR, I have nought to
plead,
In earth beneath or heaven above,
But just my own exceeding need,
And Thy exceeding love.

2 The need will soon be past and gone,
Exceeding great, but quickly o'er;
The love unbought is all Thine own,
And lasts for evermore.

JANE CREWDSON (1809-63)

204

MISERICORDIA (8 8 8. 6.) HENRY SMART (1813-79)

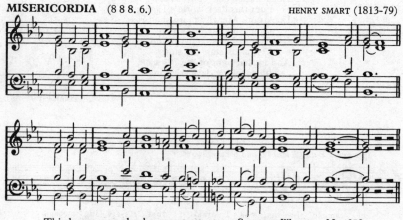

This hymn may also be sung to the tune SAFFRON WALDEN, No. 203

Him that cometh to me I will in no wise cast out (John vi. 37)

JUST as I am, without one plea
But that Thy blood was shed for me,
And that Thou bidd'st me come to
O Lamb of God, I come. [Thee,

2 Just as I am, though tossed about
With many a conflict, many a doubt,
Fightings and fears within, without,
O Lamb of God, I come.

3 Just as I am, poor, wretched, blind,—
   Sight, riches, healing of the mind,
   Yea, all I need, in Thee to find,
      O Lamb of God, I come.

4 Just as I am, Thou wilt receive,
   Wilt welcome, pardon, cleanse, relieve;
   Because Thy promise I believe,
      O Lamb of God, I come.

5 Just as I am—Thy love unknown
   Has broken every barrier down—
   Now to be Thine, yea, Thine alone,
      O Lamb of God, I come.

6 Just as I am, of that free love
   The breadth, length, depth and
      height to prove,
   Here for a season, then above,—
      O Lamb of God, I come.

                    CHARLOTTE ELLIOTT (1789-1871)

205

ANTWERP (L.M.)   WILLIAM SMALLWOOD (1831-97)

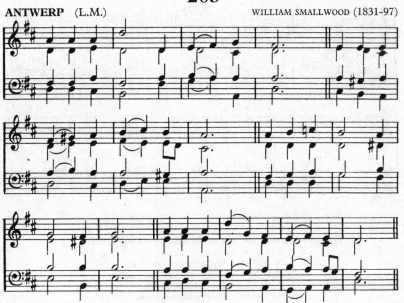

A higher setting of this tune is given at No. 28 (i)

This man receiveth sinners (Luke xv. 2)

JESUS, the sinner's Friend, to Thee,
   Lost and undone, for aid I flee,
Weary of earth, myself, and sin;
Open Thine arms, and take me in!

2 Pity, and heal my sin-sick soul;
   'Tis Thou alone canst make me whole;
   Fall'n, till in me Thine image shine,
   And cursed I am, till Thou art mine.

3 At last I own it cannot be
   That I should fit myself for Thee:
   Here then to Thee I all resign;
   Thine is the work, and only Thine.

4 The mansion for Thyself prepare,
   Dispose my heart by entering there;
   'Tis this alone can make me clean,
   'Tis this alone can cast out sin.

                    CHARLES WESLEY (1707-88)

206

BODMIN (L.M.)   ALFRED SCOTT-GATTY (1847-1918)

This hymn may also be sung to the tune OMBERSLEY, No. 191

You hath he quickened, who were dead in trespasses and sins (Ephesians ii. 1)

LORD, I was blind: I could not see
  In Thy marred visage any grace;
  But now the beauty of Thy face
  In radiant vision dawns on me.

2 Lord, I was deaf: I could not hear
  The thrilling music of Thy voice;
  But now I hear Thee and rejoice,
  And all Thine uttered words are dear.

3 Lord, I was dumb: I could not speak
  The grace and glory of Thy name;
  But now, as touched with living flame,
  My lips Thine eager praises wake.

4 Lord, I was dead: I could not stir
  My lifeless soul to come to Thee;
  But now, since Thou hast quickened me,
  I rise from sin's dark sepulchre.

5 Lord, Thou hast made the blind to see,
  The deaf to hear, the dumb to speak,
  The dead to live; and lo, I break
  The chains of my captivity!

WILLIAM TIDD MATSON (1833-99)

FULDA (L.M.)   GARDINER'S *Sacred Melodies* (1812)

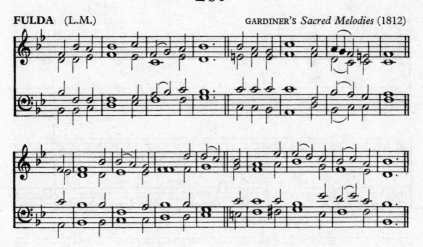

CHRISTI BLUT UND GERECHTIGKEIT

Christ Jesus, who of God is made unto us . . . righteousness (1 Corinthians i. 30)

JESU, Thy blood and righteousness
   My beauty are, my glorious dress;
Midst flaming worlds, in these arrayed,
With joy shall I lift up my head.

2 Bold shall I stand in Thy great day;
For who aught to my charge shall lay?
Fully absolved through these I am,
From sin and fear, from guilt and shame.

3 The holy, meek, unspotted Lamb,
Who from the Father's bosom came,
Who died for me, even me, to atone,
Now for my Lord and God I own.

4 Lord, I believe Thy precious blood,
Which at the mercy-seat of God
For ever doth for sinners plead,
For me, even for my soul, was shed.

5 When from the dust of death I rise
To claim my mansion in the skies,
Even then this shall be all my plea—
Jesus hath lived, hath died for me!

NICOLAUS LUDWIG VON ZINZENDORF (1700-60);
tr. JOHN WESLEY (1703-91)

208

HOLLINGSIDE (7 7. 7 7. D.)　　　　　　JOHN BACCHUS DYKES (1823–76)

ALTERNATIVE TUNE

ABERYSTWYTH (7 7. 7 7. D.)　　　Composed or adapted by
JOSEPH PARRY (1841-1903)

A man shall be as an hiding place (Isaiah xxxii. 2)

JESU, Lover of my soul,
  Let me to Thy bosom fly,
While the nearer waters roll,
  While the tempest still is high;
Hide me, O my Saviour, hide,
  Till the storm of life is past;
Safe into the haven guide;
  O receive my soul at last!

2 Other refuge have I none;
  Hangs my helpless soul on Thee;
Leave, ah! leave me not alone;
  Still support and comfort me.
All my trust on Thee is stayed;
  All my help from Thee I bring;
Cover my defenceless head
  With the shadow of Thy wing.

3 Thou, O Christ, art all I want;
  More than all in Thee I find;
Raise the fallen, cheer the faint,
  Heal the sick, and lead the blind.
Just and holy is Thy name,
  I am all unrighteousness;
False and full of sin I am,
  Thou art full of truth and grace.

4 Plenteous grace with Thee is found,
  Grace to cover all my sin;
Let the healing streams abound;
  Make and keep me pure within.
Thou of life the fountain art,
  Freely let me take of Thee;
Spring Thou up within my heart,
  Rise to all eternity.

CHARLES WESLEY (1707-88)

209

EUDOXIA (6 5. 6 5.)   SABINE BARING-GOULD (1834-1924)

ALTERNATIVE TUNE

PASTOR PASTORUM (6 5. 6 5.)   PHILIPP FRIEDRICH SILCHER (1789-1860)

And I, if I be lifted up from the earth, will draw all men unto me (John xii. 32)

O MY Saviour, lifted
   From the earth for me,
Draw me, in Thy mercy,
   Nearer unto Thee.

2 Lift my earth-bound longings,
   Fix them, Lord, above;
Draw me with the magnet
   Of Thy mighty love.

3 Lord, Thine arms are stretching
   Ever far and wide,
To enfold Thy children
   To Thy loving side.

4 And I come, O Jesus:—
   Dare I turn away?
No! Thy love hath conquered,
   And I come today;

5 Bringing all my burdens,
   Sorrow, sin, and care,
At Thy feet I lay them,
   And I leave them there.

WILLIAM WALSHAM HOW (1823-97)

210

HEINLEIN (7 7. 7 7.)

MARTIN HERBST (1654-81)

This hymn may also be sung to the tune SONG 13, No. 154

Whosoever shall call upon the name of the Lord shall be saved (Romans x. 13)

DEPTH of mercy! can there be
    Mercy still reserved for me?
Can my God His wrath forbear?
Me, the chief of sinners, spare?

2 I have long withstood His grace,
    Long provoked Him to His face,
    Would not hearken to His calls,
    Grieved Him by a thousand falls.

3 Whence to me this waste of love?
    Ask my Advocate above!
    See the cause in Jesu's face,
    Now before the throne of grace.

4 There for me the Saviour stands;
    Shows His wounds and spreads His hands,
    God is love; I know, I feel;
    Jesus lives, and loves me still.

5 Jesus, answer from above:
    Is not all Thy nature love?
    Wilt Thou not the wrong forget?
    Suffer me to kiss Thy feet?

6 If I rightly read Thy heart,
    If Thou all compassion art,
    Bow Thine ear, in mercy bow;
    Pardon and accept me now.

CHARLES WESLEY (1707-88)

211

PETRA (7 7. 7 7. 7 7.)   RICHARD REDHEAD (1820-1901)

This hymn may also be sung to the tune WELLS, No. 198

That Rock was Christ (1 Corinthians x. 4)

ROCK of ages, cleft for me,
 Let me hide myself in Thee;
Let the water and the blood,
From Thy riven side which flowed,
Be of sin the double cure,
Cleanse me from its guilt and power.

2 Not the labours of my hands
Can fulfil Thy law's demands;
Could my zeal no respite know,
Could my tears for ever flow,
All for sin could not atone:
Thou must save, and Thou alone.

3 Nothing in my hand I bring,
Simply to Thy cross I cling;
Naked, come to Thee for dress;
Helpless, look to Thee for grace;
Foul, I to the fountain fly;
Wash me, Saviour, or I die.

4 While I draw this fleeting breath,
When my eyes shall close in death,
When I soar to worlds unknown,
See Thee on Thy judgment throne;
Rock of ages, cleft for me,
Let me hide myself in Thee.

AUGUSTUS MONTAGUE TOPLADY (1740-78)

212

ELLERS (10 10. 10 10.)   EDWARD JOHN HOPKINS (1818-1901)

For ye are bought with a price: therefore glorify God in your body, and in your spirit, which are God's
(1 Corinthians vi. 20)

GOD made me for Himself, to serve Him here,
With love's pure service and in filial fear;
To show His praise, for Him to labour now;
Then see His glory where the angels bow.

2 All needful grace was mine through His dear Son,
Whose life and death my full salvation won;
The grace that would have strengthened me, and taught;
Grace that would crown me, when my work was wrought.

3 And I, poor sinner, cast it all away;
Lived for the toil or pleasure of each day;
As if no Christ had shed His precious blood,
As if I owed no homage to my God.

4 O Holy Spirit, with Thy fire divine,
Melt into tears this thankless heart of mine;
Teach me to love what once I seemed to hate,
And live to God before it be too late.

HENRY WILLIAMS BAKER (1821-77)

ST. BRIDE (S.M.)   SAMUEL HOWARD (1710-82)

By grace are ye saved through faith (Ephesians ii. 8)

NOT what these hands have done
    Can save this guilty soul;
Not what this toiling flesh has borne
    Can make my spirit whole.

2 Not what I feel or do
    Can give me peace with God;
Not all my prayers, and sighs, and tears
    Can bear my awful load.

3 Thy work alone, O Christ,
    Can ease this weight of sin;
Thy blood alone, O Lamb of God,
    Can give me peace within.

4 Thy love to me, O God,
    Not mine, O Lord, to Thee,
Can rid me of this dark unrest,
    And set my spirit free.

5 Thy grace alone, O God,
    To me can pardon speak;
Thy power alone, O Son of God,
    Can this sore bondage break.

6 I bless the Christ of God,
    I rest on love divine,
And with unfaltering lip and heart,
    I call this Saviour mine.

HORATIUS BONAR (1808-89)

BELMONT (C.M.)   GARDINER'S *Sacred Melodies* (1812)

This hymn may also be sung to the tune WILTSHIRE, No. 247 (i)

In that day there shall be a fountain opened . . . for sin and for uncleanness (Zechariah xiii. 1)

THERE is a fountain filled with blood
 Drawn from Immanuel's veins;
And sinners plunged beneath that flood,
 Lose all their guilty stains.

2 The dying thief rejoiced to see
 That fountain in his day;
And there may I, though vile as he,
 Wash all my sins away.

3 Dear dying Lamb, Thy precious blood
 Shall never lose its power
Till all the ransomed Church of God
 Be saved, to sin no more.

4 E'er since, by faith, I saw the stream
 Thy flowing wounds supply,
Redeeming love has been my theme,
 And shall be till I die.

5 Then, in a nobler, sweeter song,
 I'll sing Thy power to save,
When this poor lisping, stammering tongue
 Lies silent in the grave.

WILLIAM COWPER (1731-1800)

215

MALVERN (6 6 4. 6 6 6 4.)   Arranged by JOHN ROBERTS (IEUAN GWYLLT) (1822-77)

ALTERNATIVE TUNE

OLIVET (6 6 4. 6 6 6 4.)   LOWELL MASON (1792-1872)

Looking unto Jesus the author and finisher of our faith (Hebrews xii. 2)

MY faith looks up to Thee,
　　Thou Lamb of Calvary,
　　Saviour divine:
Now hear me while I pray;
Take all my guilt away;
O let me from this day
　　Be wholly Thine.

2 May Thy rich grace impart
　　Strength to my fainting heart,
　　My zeal inspire;
As Thou hast died for me,
O may my love to Thee
Pure, warm, and changeless be,
　　A living fire.

3 While life's dark maze I tread,
  And griefs around me spread,
    Be Thou my guide;
  Bid darkness turn to day,
  Wipe sorrow's tears away,
  Nor let me ever stray
    From Thee aside.

4 When ends life's transient dream,
  When death's cold, sullen stream
    Shall o'er me roll,
  Blest Saviour, then, in love,
  Fear and distrust remove;
  O bear me safe above,
    A ransomed soul.

RAY PALMER (1808-87)

216

RIVAULX (L.M.)   JOHN BACCHUS DYKES (1823-76)

Let us therefore come boldly unto the throne of grace (Hebrews iv. 16)

FATHER of heaven, whose love profound
  A ransom for our souls hath found,
Before Thy throne we sinners bend;
To us Thy pardoning love extend.

2 Almighty Son, incarnate Word,
  Our Prophet, Priest, Redeemer, Lord,
  Before Thy throne we sinners bend;
  To us Thy saving grace extend.

3 Eternal Spirit, by whose breath
  The soul is raised from sin and death,
  Before Thy throne we sinners bend;
  To us Thy quickening power extend.

4 Thrice Holy! Father, Spirit, Son,
  Mysterious Godhead, Three in One,
  Before Thy throne we sinners bend;
  Grace, pardon, life to us extend.

EDWARD COOPER (1770-1833)

217

GOSHEN (6 5. 6 5. D.)   *Bible Class Magazine* (1860)

In thee, O Lord, do I put my trust (Psalm lxxi. 1)

JESUS, I will trust Thee,
   Trust Thee with my soul;
Guilty, lost, and helpless,
   Thou canst make me whole.
There is none in heaven
   Or on earth like Thee;
Thou hast died for sinners—
   Therefore, Lord, for me.

2 Jesus, I must trust Thee,
   Pondering Thy ways,
Full of love and mercy
   All Thine earthly days;
Sinners gathered round Thee,
   Lepers sought Thy face;
None too vile or loathsome
   For a Saviour's grace.

3 Jesus, I can trust Thee,
   Trust Thy written Word,
Though Thy voice of pity
   I have never heard.
When Thy Spirit teacheth,
   To my taste how sweet!
Only may I hearken
   Sitting at Thy feet.

4 Jesus, I do trust Thee,
   Trust without a doubt;
Whosoever cometh
   Thou wilt not cast out.
Faithful is Thy promise,
   Precious is Thy blood;
These my soul's salvation,
   Thou my Saviour God.

MARY JANE WALKER (1816-78)

RUTHERFORD (7 6. 7 6. D.)   CHRÉTIEN URHAN (1790-1845)

This hymn may also be sung to the tune PASSION CHORALE, No. 52

While we were yet sinners, Christ died for us (Romans v. 8)

O TEACH me what it meaneth,
  That cross uplifted high,
With Thee, the Man of Sorrows,
  Condemned to bleed and die;
O teach me what it meaneth,
  That sacred crimson tide,
The blood and water flowing
  From Thine own wounded side.

2 O teach me what it meaneth,
  For I am full of sin;
And grace alone can reach me,
  And love alone can win.
Teach me that if none other
  Had sinned, but I alone,
Yet still Thy blood, Lord Jesus,
  Thine only, must atone.

3 O teach me what it meaneth,
  Thy love beyond compare,
The love that reacheth deeper
  Than depths of self-despair;
Yes, teach me, till there gloweth
  In this cold heart of mine,
Some feeble, pale reflection
  Of that pure love of Thine.

4 O infinite Redeemer!
  I bring no other plea;
Because Thou dost invite me
  I cast myself on Thee;
Because Thou dost accept me
  I love and I adore;
Because Thy love constraineth,
  I'll praise Thee evermore.

LUCY ANN BENNETT (1850-1927)†

237

219

ST. MICHAEL (S.M.)   Composed or adapted by LOUIS BOURGEOIS (1510-61)
in *Genevan Psalter* (1551)

ALTERNATIVE TUNE

SONG 20 (S.M.)   ORLANDO GIBBONS (1583-1625)

Being justified by faith, we have peace with God through our Lord Jesus Christ (Romans v. 1)

I HEAR the words of love,
I gaze upon the blood,
I see the mighty sacrifice,
And I have peace with God.

2 'Tis everlasting peace!
   Sure as Jehovah's name;
   'Tis stable as His steadfast throne,
   For evermore the same.

3 The clouds may go and come,
   And storms may sweep my sky—
   This blood-sealed friendship changes not:
   The cross is ever nigh. [

4 My love is oft-times low,
   My joy still ebbs and flows;
   But peace with Him remains the same—
   No change Jehovah knows.

5 I change, He changes not,
   The Christ can never die;
   His love, not mine, the resting-place,
   His truth, not mine, the tie.

HORATIUS BONAR (1808-89)

238

220

INNSBRUCK (7 7 6. 7 7 8.)

HEINRICH ISAAK (*c.*1455-*c.*1527). Adapted and
harmonized by JOHANN SEBASTIAN BACH (1685-1750)

Thou art a God ready to pardon (Nehemiah ix. 17)

O THOU who dost accord us
The highest prize and guerdon,
Thou hope of all our race,
Jesus, do thou afford us
The gift we ask of pardon
For all who humbly seek Thy face.

2 With whispered accusation
   Our conscience tells of sinning
   In thought, and word, and deed;
Thine is our restoration,
   The work of grace beginning
   For souls from every burthen freed.

3 O Trinity most glorious,
   Thy pardon free bestowing,
   Defend us evermore;
That in Thy courts victorious,
   Thy love more truly knowing,
   We may with all Thy saints adore.

JOHN WILLIAM HEWETT (1824-86) and others.
Based on *Summi largitor praemii* (*c.* 6th century)

221

JESU MEINE FREUDE (6 6 5. 6 6 5. 7 8 6.)
German Traditional Melody adapted by JOHANN CRÜGER (1598-1662)
Further adapted and harmonized by JOHANN SEBASTIAN BACH (1685-1750)

JESU, MEINE FREUDE

Peace I leave with you, my peace I give unto you (John xiv. 27)

JESU, priceless treasure,
  Source of purest pleasure,
    Truest friend to me;
Ah! how long I've panted,
And my heart hath fainted,
  Thirsting, Lord, for Thee!
Thine I am, O spotless Lamb,
I will suffer nought to hide Thee,
  Nought I ask beside Thee.

2 In Thine arm I rest me;
  Foes who would molest me
    Cannot reach me here;
Though the earth be shaking,
Every heart be quaking,
  Jesus calms my fear;
Sin and hell in conflict fell
With their bitter storms assail me:
  Jesus will not fail me.

3 Hence, all fears and sadness,
  For the Lord of gladness,
    Jesus, enters in;
Those who love the Father,
Though the storms may gather,
  Still have peace within;
Yes, whate'er I here must bear,
Still in Thee lies purest pleasure,
  Jesu, priceless treasure!

JOHANN FRANCK (1618-77);
tr. CATHERINE WINKWORTH (1829-78)

222

CAIRNBROOK   (8 5. 8 3.)   EBENEZER PROUT (1835-1909)

Trust in the Lord with all thine heart (Proverbs iii. 5)

I AM trusting Thee, Lord Jesus,
  Trusting only Thee,
Trusting Thee for full salvation,
  Great and free.

2 I am trusting Thee for pardon;
    At Thy feet I bow,
  For Thy grace and tender mercy
    Trusting now.

3 I am trusting Thee to guide me;
    Thou alone shalt lead,
  Every day and hour supplying
    All my need.

4 I am trusting Thee for power:
    Thine can never fail;
  Words which Thou Thyself shalt give
    me
    Must prevail.

5 I am trusting Thee, Lord Jesus;
    Never let me fall;
  I am trusting Thee for ever,
    And for all.

FRANCES RIDLEY HAVERGAL (1836-79)

223

CREDITON (C.M.)   THOMAS CLARK (1775-1859)

This hymn may also be sung to the tune MARTYRDOM, No. 282

Based on 2 Timothy i. 12

I'M not ashamed to own my Lord,
Or to defend His cause,
Maintain the honour of His word,
The glory of His cross.

2 Jesus, my God! I know His name,
His name is all my trust;
Nor will He put my soul to shame,
Nor let my hope be lost.

3 Firm as His throne His promise stands,
And He can well secure
What I've committed to His hands
Till the decisive hour.

4 Then will He own my worthless name
Before His Father's face,
And in the New Jerusalem
Appoint my soul a place.

ISAAC WATTS (1674-1748)

224

KILMARNOCK (C.M.)   NEIL DOUGALL (1776-1862)

Based on Hosea vi. 1-3

COME, let us to the Lord our God
With contrite hearts return;
Our God is gracious, nor will leave
The desolate to mourn.

2 His voice commands the tempest forth,
And stills the stormy wave;
And though His arm be strong to smite,
'Tis also strong to save.

3 Long hath the night of sorrow reigned,
   The dawn shall bring us light:
God shall appear, and we shall rise
   With gladness in His sight.

4 Our hearts, if God we seek to know,
   Shall know Him and rejoice;
His coming like the morn shall be,
   Like morning songs His voice.

5 As dew upon the tender herb,
   Diffusing fragrance round;
As showers that usher in the spring,
   And cheer the thirsty ground.

6 So shall His presence bless our souls,
   And shed a joyful light;
That hallowed morn shall chase away
   The sorrows of the night.

JOHN MORISON (1750-98),
as in *Scottish Paraphrases* (1781)

225

ABRIDGE (C.M.)   ISAAC SMITH (*c*.1725-*c*.1800)

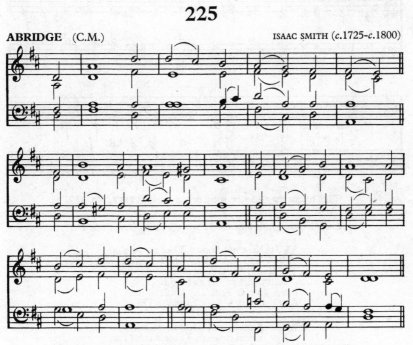

This hymn may also be sung to the tune MARTYRDOM, No. 282

Paraphrase of Psalm xlii

AS pants the hart for cooling streams,
   When heated in the chase,
So longs my soul, O God, for Thee,
   And Thy refreshing grace.

2 For Thee, my God, the living God,
   My thirsty soul doth pine;
O when shall I behold Thy face,
   Thou Majesty divine!

3 God of my strength, how long shall I,
   Like one forgotten, mourn?
Forlorn, forsaken, and exposed
   To my oppressor's scorn.

4 Why restless, why cast down, my soul?
   Hope still, and thou shalt sing
The praise of Him who is thy God,
   Thy health's eternal spring.

NAHUM TATE (1652-1715) and
NICHOLAS BRADY (1659-1726),
in *The New Version* (1696)

226

MELITA (8 8. 8 8. 8 8.)   JOHN BACCHUS DYKES (1823-76)

This hymn may also be sung to the tune SURREY, No. 189

I have gone astray like a lost sheep; seek thy servant (Psalm cxix. 176)

WE have not known Thee as we ought,
  Nor learned Thy wisdom, grace, and power;
The things of earth have filled our thought,
  And trifles of the passing hour.
Lord, give us light Thy truth to see,
And make us wise in knowing Thee.

2 We have not feared Thee as we ought,
  Nor bowed beneath Thine aweful eye,
Nor guarded deed, and word, and thought,
  Remembering that our God was nigh.
Lord, give us faith to know Thee near,
And grant the grace of holy fear.

3 We have not loved Thee as we ought,
  Nor cared that we are loved by Thee;
Thy presence we have coldly sought,
  And feebly longed Thy face, to see.
Lord, give a pure and loving heart
To feel and own the love Thou art.

4 We have not served Thee as we ought;
  Alas, the duties left undone,
The work with little fervour wrought,
  The battles lost or scarcely won!
Lord, give the zeal, and give the might,
For Thee to toil, for Thee to fight.

5 When shall we know Thee as we ought,
  And fear, and love, and serve aright?
  When shall we, out of trial brought,
  Be perfect in the land of light?
  Lord, may we day by day prepare
  To see Thy face, and serve Thee there.

                    THOMAS BENSON POLLOCK (1836-96)

227

FESTUS (L.M.)   Adapted from a melody in
                                     FREYLINGHAUSEN'S *Gesangbuch* (1704)

He left all, rose up, and followed him (Luke v. 28)

O HAPPY day that fixed my choice
   On Thee, my Saviour and my God:
Well may this glowing heart rejoice,
And tell its raptures all abroad.

2 'Tis done, the great transaction's done;
  I am my Lord's, and He is mine:
  He drew me, and I followed on,
  Charmed to confess the voice divine.

3 Now rest, my long-divided heart,
  Fixed on this blissful centre, rest:
  Nor ever from thy Lord depart,
  With Him of every good possessed.

4 High heaven, that heard the solemn vow,
  That vow renewed shall daily hear:
  Till in life's latest hour I bow,
  And bless in death a bond so dear.

                          PHILIP DODDRIDGE (1702-51)

228

Whom have I in heaven but thee ? (Psalm lxxiii. 25)

JESU, my Lord, my God, my All,
   Hear me, blest Saviour, when I call;
Hear me, and from Thy dwelling-place
Pour down the riches of Thy grace:

   Jesu, my Lord, I Thee adore;
   O make me love Thee more and more.

2 Jesu, too late I Thee have sought;
  How can I love Thee as I ought ?
And how extol Thy matchless fame,
The glorious beauty of Thy name ?

3 Jesu, what didst Thou find in me
  That Thou hast dealt so lovingly ?
How great the joy that Thou hast brought,
So far exceeding hope or thought!

4 Jesu, of Thee shall be my song;
  To Thee my heart and soul belong;
All that I have or am is Thine,
And Thou, blest Saviour, Thou art mine:

HENRY COLLINS (1827-1919)

229

RHUDDLAN   (8 7. 8 7. 8 7.)   Welsh Traditional Melody

The Lord shall deliver me from every evil work (2 Timothy iv. 18)

JESUS, Lord of life and glory,
  Bend from heaven Thy gracious ear;
While our waiting souls adore Thee,
  Friend of helpless sinners, hear:
    By Thy mercy,
    O deliver us, good Lord.

2 From the depths of nature's blindness,
    From the hardening power of sin,
  From all malice and unkindness,
    From the pride that lurks within:
      By Thy mercy,
      O deliver us, good Lord.

*3 When temptation sorely presses,
    In the day of Satan's power,
  In our times of deep distresses,
    In each dark and trying hour:
      By Thy mercy,
      O deliver us, good Lord.

*4 When the world around is smiling,
    In the time of wealth and ease,
  Earthly joys our hearts beguiling,
    In the day of health and peace:
      By Thy mercy,
      O deliver us, good Lord.

5 In the weary hours of sickness,
    In the times of grief and pain,
  When we feel our mortal weakness,
    When all human help is vain:
      By Thy mercy,
      O deliver us, good Lord.

6 In the solemn hour of dying,
    In the aweful judgment day,
  May our souls, on Thee relying,
    Find Thee still our Rock and Stay:
      By Thy mercy,
      O deliver us, good Lord.

JOHN JAMES CUMMINS (1795-1867)†

If desired, verses 3 and 4 may be omitted

230

LLANGRISTIOLUS (8 8. 8 8. D. Anapaestic)   JOSEPH PARRY (1841-1903)

This hymn may also be sung to the tunes TREWEN, No. 231 and CELESTE, No. 92

For I will be merciful to their unrighteousness (Hebrews viii. 12)

A DEBTOR to mercy alone,
Of covenant mercy I sing;
Nor fear, with Thy righteousness on,
My person and offering to bring,
The terrors of law and of God
With me can have nothing to do;
My Saviour's obedience and blood
Hide all my transgressions from view.

2 The work which His goodness began,
The arm of His strength will com-
His promise is Yea and Amen, [plete;
And never was forfeited yet.
Things future, nor things that are now,
Nor all things below or above,
Can make Him His purpose forgo,
Or sever my soul from His love.

3 My name from the palms of His hands
Eternity will not erase;
Impressed on His heart it remains,
In marks of indelible grace.
Yes, I to the end shall endure,
As sure as the earnest is given;
More happy, but not more secure,
The glorified spirits in heaven.

AUGUSTUS MONTAGUE TOPLADY (1740-78)

See also the section THE MAN OF GOD: CONSECRATION AND DISCIPLESHIP; Nos. 314–353
The following hymns also refer to this theme:

51. Ah, holy Jesu, how hast Thou offended   53. It is a thing most wonderful
266. Approach, my soul, the mercy-seat

231

TREWEN (8 8. 8 8. D. Anapaestic)   DAVID EMLYN EVANS (1843-1913)

He careth for you (1 Peter v. 7)

A SOVEREIGN Protector I have,
   Unseen, yet for ever at hand,
Unchangeably faithful to save,
   Almighty to rule and command.
He smiles, and my comforts abound;
   His grace as the dew shall descend,
And walls of salvation surround
   The soul He delights to defend.

2 Inspirer and Hearer of prayer,
   Thou Shepherd and Guardian of Thine,
My all to Thy covenant care
   I sleeping and waking resign.
If Thou art my Shield and my Sun,
   The night is no darkness to me;
And, fast as my moments roll on,
   They bring me but nearer to Thee.

AUGUSTUS MONTAGUE TOPLADY (1740-78)

232

EIN' FESTE BURG   (8 7. 8 7. 6 6. 6 6 7.)

Present form of melody by MARTIN LUTHER (1483-1546)

EIN' FESTE BURG

God is our refuge and strength, a very present help in trouble (Psalm xlvi. 1)

A SAFE stronghold our God is still,
    A trusty shield and weapon;
He'll help us clear from all the ill
    That hath us now o'ertaken.
        The ancient prince of hell
        Hath risen with purpose fell:
        Strong mail of craft and power
        He weareth in this hour,
    On earth is not his fellow.

2 With force of arms we nothing can,
        Full soon were we down-ridden;
But for us fights the proper Man,
        Whom God Himself hath bidden.
            Ask ye who is this same?
            Christ Jesus is His name,
            The Lord Sabaoth's Son;
            He, and no other one,
        Shall conquer in the battle.

3 And were this world all devils o'er,
    And watching to devour us,
We lay it not to heart so sore;
    Not they can overpower us.
        And let the prince of ill
        Look grim as e'er he will,
        He harms us not a whit;
        For why his doom is writ;
    A word shall quickly slay him.

4 God's word, for all their craft and force,
    One moment will not linger,
But, spite of hell, shall have its course;
    'Tis written by His finger.
        And, though they take our life,
        Goods, honour, children, wife,
        Yet is their profit small:
        These things shall vanish all:
    The city of God remaineth.

MARTIN LUTHER (1483-1546); tr. THOMAS CARLYLE (1795-1881)

233

EIN' FESTE BURG (8 7. 8 7. 6 6. 6 6 7.)

In my distress I cried unto the Lord, and he heard me (Psalm cxx. 1)

* REJOICE today with one accord,
Sing out with exultation;
Rejoice and praise our mighty Lord,
Whose arm hath brought salvation;
His works of love proclaim
The greatness of His name;
For He is God alone,
Who hath His mercy shown;
Let all His saints adore Him.

2 When in distress to Him we cried,
He heard our sad complaining;
O trust in Him, whate'er betide,
His love is all-sustaining;
Triumphant songs of praise
To Him our hearts shall raise;
Now every voice shall say,
'O praise our God alway';
Let all His saints adore Him!

HENRY WILLIAMS BAKER (1821-77)

**If desired, verse 1 may be repeated at the end*

234

SONG 46 (10 10.)   First strain of Song 46, ORLANDO GIBBONS (1583-1625)

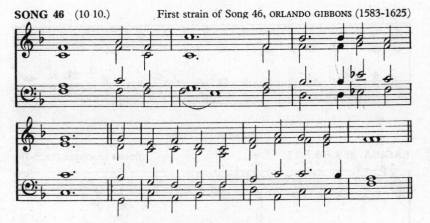

Thou wilt keep him in perfect peace, whose mind is stayed on thee (Isaiah xxvi. 3)

PEACE, perfect peace, in this dark world of sin?
The blood of Jesus whispers peace within.

2 Peace, perfect peace, by thronging duties pressed?
To do the will of Jesus, this is rest.

3 Peace, perfect peace, with sorrows surging round?
On Jesus' bosom nought but calm is found.

4 Peace, perfect peace, with loved ones far away?
In Jesus' keeping we are safe, and they.

5 Peace, perfect peace, our future all unknown?
Jesus we know, and He is on the throne.

6 Peace, perfect peace, death shadowing us and ours?
Jesus has vanquished death and all its powers.

7 It is enough: earth's struggles soon shall cease,
And Jesus call us to heaven's perfect peace.

EDWARD HENRY BICKERSTETH (1825-1906)

251

235

ABINGDON (8 8. 8 8. 8 8.)   ERIK ROUTLEY (1917-)

ALTERNATIVE TUNE

SAGINA (8 8. 8 8. 8 8.)   THOMAS CAMPBELL (1825-76)

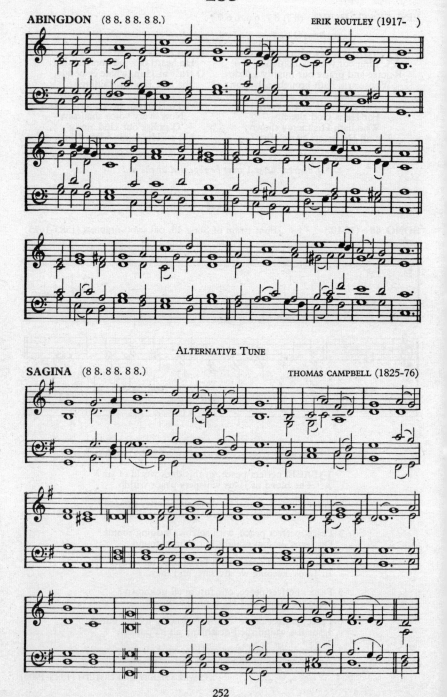

(Repeat lines 5 and 6)

This hymn may also be sung to the tune COTSWOLD, No. 236

While we were yet sinners, Christ died for us (Romans v. 8)

AND can it be, that I should gain
An interest in the Saviour's blood?
Died He for me, who caused His pain?
For me, who Him to death pursued?
Amazing love! how can it be
That Thou, my God, shouldst die for me?

2 'Tis mystery all! The Immortal dies:
Who can explore His strange design?
In vain the first-born seraph tries
To sound the depths of love divine.
'Tis mercy all! let earth adore,
Let angel minds inquire no more.

3 He left His Father's throne above,—
So free, so infinite His grace,—
Emptied Himself of all but love,
And bled for Adam's helpless race:
'Tis mercy all, immense and free;
For, O my God, it found out me!

4 Long my imprisoned spirit lay
Fast bound in sin and nature's night;
Thine eye diffused a quickening ray,—
I woke, the dungeon flamed with light;
My chains fell off, my heart was free,
I rose, went forth, and followed Thee.

5 No condemnation now I dread;
Jesus, and all in Him, is mine!
Alive in Him, my living Head,
And clothed in righteousness divine,
Bold I approach the eternal throne,
And claim the crown, through Christ my own.

CHARLES WESLEY (1707-88)

236

COTSWOLD   (8 8. 8 8. 8 8.)   ALEXANDER BRENT SMITH (1889-1950)

This hymn may also be sung to the tune SURREY, *No. 189*

He brought me up . . . out of the miry clay, and set my feet upon a rock (Psalm xl. 2)

M Y hope is built on nothing less
     Than Jesus' blood and righteousness;
No merit of my own I claim,
But wholly lean on Jesus' name.
     On Christ, the solid Rock, I stand;
     All other ground is sinking sand.

2 When darkness seems to veil His face,
     I rest on His unchanging grace;
     In every high and stormy gale
     My anchor holds within the veil.

3 His oath, His covenant, and blood,
     Support me in the whelming flood;
     When all around my soul gives way,
     He then is all my hope and stay.

4 When the last trumpet's voice shall sound·
     O may I then in Him be found,
     Clothed in His righteousness alone,
     Faultless to stand before His throne.

                       EDWARD MOTE (1797-1874) and others

237

FARMBOROUGH (8 8. 8 8. 8 8.)   ARTHUR S. WARRELL (1883-1939)

This hymn may also be sung to the tune MELITA, No. 226

ICH HABE NUN DEN GRUND GEFUNDEN

Which hope we have as an anchor of the soul, both sure and stedfast (Hebrews vi. 19)

NOW I have found the ground wherein
    Sure my soul's anchor may remain—
The wounds of Jesus, for my sin
    Before the world's foundation slain;
Whose mercy shall unshaken stay,
When heaven and earth are fled away.

2 Father, Thine everlasting grace
    Our scanty thought surpasses far,
Thy heart still melts with tenderness,
    Thy arms of love still open are
Returning sinners to receive,
That mercy they may taste and live.

3 O Love, Thou bottomless abyss,
    My sins are swallowed up in Thee!
Covered is my unrighteousness,
    Nor spot of guilt remains on me,
While Jesus' blood through earth and skies
'Mercy, free, boundless mercy!' cries.

4 Fixed on this ground will I remain,
    Though my heart fail and flesh decay;
This anchor shall my soul sustain,
    When earth's foundations melt away:
Mercy's full power I then shall prove,
Loved with an everlasting love.

JOHANN ANDREAS ROTHE (1688-1758);
tr. JOHN WESLEY (1703-91)

238

PENLAN (7 6. 7 6. D.)   DAVID JENKINS (1849-1915)

This hymn may also be sung to the tune CRÜGER, No. 82

If ye keep my commandments, ye shall abide in my love (John xv. 10)

IN heavenly love abiding,
  No change my heart shall fear;
And safe is such confiding,
  For nothing changes here:
The storm may roar without me,
  My heart may low be laid;
But God is round about me,
  And can I be dismayed?

2 Wherever He may guide me,
  No want shall turn me back;
My Shepherd is beside me,
  And nothing can I lack.
His wisdom ever waketh,
  His sight is never dim;
He knows the way He taketh,
  And I will walk with Him.

3 Green pastures are before me,
  Which yet I have not seen;
Bright skies will soon be o'er me,
  Where the dark clouds have been.
My hope I cannot measure:
  My path to life is free:
My Saviour has my treasure,
  And He will walk with me.

ANNA LAETITIA WARING (1820-1910)

239

UNDE ET MEMORES (10 10. 10 10. 10 10.)   WILLIAM HENRY MONK (1823-89)

This tune may also be sung to the tune Song 1, No. 146

STILLE, MEIN WILLE; DEIN JESUS HILFT SIEGEN

Be careful for nothing (Philippians iv. 6)

BE still, my soul: the Lord is on thy side;
　　Bear patiently the cross of grief or pain;
Leave to thy God to order and provide;
　　In every change He faithful will remain.
Be still, my soul: thy best, thy heavenly Friend
Through thorny ways leads to a joyful end.

2 Be still, my soul: thy God doth undertake
　　To guide the future as He has the past.
Thy hope, thy confidence let nothing shake;
　　All now mysterious shall be bright at last.
Be still, my soul: the waves and winds still know
His voice who ruled them while He dwelt below.

3 Be still, my soul: the hour is hastening on
　　When we shall be forever with the Lord,
When disappointment, grief, and fear are gone,
　　Sorrow forgot, love's purest joys restored.
Be still, my soul: when change and tears are past,
All safe and blessèd we shall meet at last.

KATHARINA VON SCHLEGEL (1697- ?); tr. JANE LAURIE BORTHWICK (1813-97)

240

HOUGHTON (5 5. 5 5. 6 5. 6 5.) HENRY JOHN GAUNTLETT (1805-76)

Rejoicing in hope; patient in tribulation (Romans xii. 12)

BEGONE, unbelief;
My Saviour is near,
And for my relief
Will surely appear:
By prayer let me wrestle,
And He will perform;
With Christ in the vessel,
I smile at the storm.

2 Why should I complain
Of want or distress,
Temptation or pain?
He told me no less;
The heirs of salvation,
I know from His word,
Through much tribulation
Must follow their Lord.

3 His love in time past
Forbids me to think
He'll leave me at last
In trouble to sink;
Though dark be my way,
Since He is my Guide,
'Tis mine to obey,
'Tis His to provide.

4 Since all that I meet
Shall work for my good,
The bitter is sweet,
The medicine food;
Though painful at present,
'Twill cease before long;
And then, O how pleasant
The conqueror's song!

JOHN NEWTON (1725-1807)†

241

ST. DENIO (11 11. 11 11.)   Welsh Hymn Melody

I will never leave thee, nor forsake thee (Hebrews xiii. 5)

HOW firm a foundation, ye saints of the Lord,
Is laid for your faith in His excellent word;
What more can He say than to you He hath said,
You who unto Jesus for refuge have fled?

2 Fear not, He is with thee, O be not dismayed;
For He is thy God, and will still give thee aid:
He'll strengthen thee, help thee, and cause thee to stand,
Upheld by His righteous, omnipotent hand.

3 When through the deep waters He calls thee to go,
The rivers of grief shall not thee overflow;
For He will be with thee in trouble to bless,
And sanctify to thee thy deepest distress.

4 When through fiery trials thy pathway shall lie,
His grace all-sufficient shall be thy supply;
The flame shall not hurt thee, His only design
Thy dross to consume and thy gold to refine.

5 The soul that on Jesus has leaned for repose
He will not, He cannot, desert to its foes:
That soul, though all hell should endeavour to shake,
He never will leave, He will never forsake.

RICHARD KEEN (*c.*1787)†

242

ALBERTA (10 4. 10 4. 10 10.)   WILLIAM H. HARRIS (1883-   )

Paraphrase of Psalm cxxi

UNTO the hills around do I lift up
　My longing eyes,
O! whence for me shall my salvation come,
　From whence arise?
From God the Lord doth come my certain aid,
From God the Lord, who heaven and earth hath made.

2 He will not suffer that thy foot be moved;
　Safe shalt thou be.
No careless slumber shall His eyelids close,
　Who keepeth thee.
Behold our God, the Lord, He slumbereth ne'er,
Who keepeth Israel in His holy care.

3 Jehovah is Himself thy keeper true,
　Thy changeless shade,
Jehovah thy defence on thy right hand
　Himself hath made.
And thee, no sun by day shall ever smite,
No moon shall harm thee in the silent night.

4 From every evil shall He keep thy soul,
　From every sin;
Jehovah shall preserve thy going out,
　Thy coming in.
Above thee watching, He, whom we adore,
Shall keep thee henceforth, yea, for evermore.

JOHN DOUGLAS SUTHERLAND CAMPBELL (1845-1914)

243

WYCH CROSS   (8 8. 8 8. 8 8.)   ERIK ROUTLEY (1917-)

This hymn may also be sung to the tune PATER OMNIUM, No. 275 (ii)

ICH WILL DICH LIEBEN, MEINE STÄRKE

Thou shalt love the Lord thy God with all thy heart, and with all thy soul, and with all thy strength, and with all thy mind (Luke x. 27)

THEE will I love, my strength, my tower,
    Thee will I love, my joy, my crown;
Thee will I love with all my power,
    In all Thy works, and Thee alone;
Thee will I love, till the pure fire
Fill my whole soul with chaste desire.

2 In darkness willingly I strayed,
    I sought Thee, yet from Thee I roved;
Far wide my wandering thoughts were spread,
    Thy creatures more than Thee I loved;
And now if more at length I see,
'Tis through Thy light, and comes from Thee.

3 I thank Thee, uncreated Sun,
    That Thy bright beams on me have shined;
I thank Thee, who hast overthrown
    My foes, and healed my wounded mind;
I thank Thee, whose enlivening voice
Bids my freed heart in Thee rejoice.

4 Thee will I love, my joy, my crown;
    Thee will I love, my Lord, my God;
Thee will I love, beneath Thy frown
    Or smile, Thy sceptre or Thy rod;
What though my flesh and heart decay,
Thee shall I love in endless day!

JOHANN SCHEFFLER (1624-77);
tr. JOHN WESLEY (1703-91)

244

ST. STEPHEN (C.M.)   WILLIAM JONES (1726-1800)

This hymn may also be sung to the tune BISHOPTHORPE, No. 48

Paraphrase of 1 Peter i. 3-5

BLEST be the everlasting God,
The Father of our Lord!
Be His abounding mercy praised,
His majesty adored!

2 When from the dead He raised His son,
And called Him to the sky,
He gave our souls a lively hope
That they should never die.

3 To an inheritance divine
He taught our hearts to rise;
'Tis uncorrupted, undefiled,
Unfading in the skies.

4 Saints by the power of God are kept,
Till the salvation come:
We walk by faith as strangers here,
But Christ shall call us home.

ISAAC WATTS (1674-1748) and WILLIAM CAMERON (1751-1811),
as in *Scottish Paraphrases* (1781)

245

BALLERMA (C.M.)   Adapted by ROBERT SIMPSON (1790-1832)

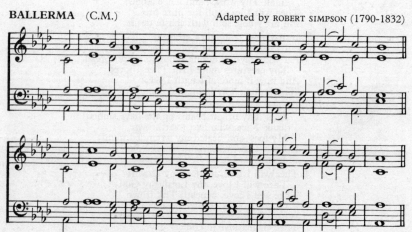

This hymn may also be sung to the tune ST. STEPHEN, No. 244

Based on 1 John iii. 1-4

BEHOLD the amazing gift of love
The Father hath bestowed
On us, the sinful sons of men,
To call us sons of God!

2 Concealed as yet this honour lies,
   By this dark world unknown,—
A world that knew not when He came,
   Even God's eternal Son.

3 High is the rank we now possess,
   But higher we shall rise,
Though what we shall hereafter be
   Is hid from mortal eyes.

4 Our souls, we know, when He appears,
   Shall bear His image bright;
For all His glory, full disclosed,
   Shall open to our sight.

5 A hope so great, and so divine,
   May trials well endure;
And purge the soul from sense and sin,
   As Christ Himself is pure.

Scottish Paraphrases (1781);
based on ISAAC WATTS (1674-1748)

246

CONTEMPLATION   (C.M.)   FREDERICK ARTHUR GORE OUSELEY (1825-89)

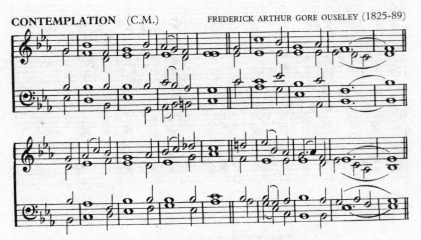

I will sing of the mercies of the Lord for ever (Psalm lxxxix. 1)

WHEN all Thy mercies, O my God,
   My rising soul surveys,
Transported with the view, I'm lost
   In wonder, love, and praise.

2 Unnumbered comforts to my soul
   Thy tender care bestowed,
Before my infant heart conceived
   From whom these comforts flowed.

3 Through every period of my life
   Thy goodness I'll pursue;
And after death, in distant worlds,
   The glorious theme renew.

4 Through all eternity to Thee
   A joyful song I'll raise;
But O! eternity's too short
   To utter all Thy praise.

JOSEPH ADDISON (1672-1719)

247

WILTSHIRE (C.M.)   GEORGE THOMAS SMART (1776-1867)

ALTERNATIVE TUNE

UNIVERSITY (C.M.)   ? JOHN RANDALL (1715-99)

Based on Psalm xxxiv

THROUGH all the changing scenes of life,
   In trouble and in joy,
The praises of my God shall still
   My heart and tongue employ.

2 O magnify the Lord with me,
   With me exalt His name;
When in distress to Him I called,
   He to my rescue came.

3 The hosts of God encamp around
   The dwellings of the just;
Deliverance He affords to all
   Who on His succour trust.

4 O make but trial of His love;
   Experience will decide
How blest are they, and only they,
   Who in His truth confide.

5 Fear Him, ye saints, and you will then
   Have nothing else to fear;
Make you His service your delight,
   Your wants shall be His care.

NAHUM TATE (1652-1715) and NICHOLAS BRADY (1659-1726)
in *The New Version* (1696)

248

RICHMOND (C.M.)   THOMAS HAWEIS (1734-1820)

ALTERNATIVE VERSION

Melody in the Tenor   Fa-burden **by** MARTIN SHAW (1875-)

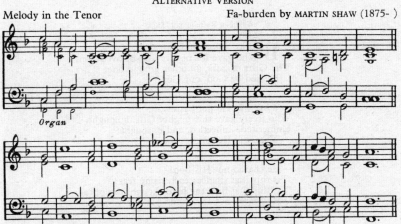

This hymn may also be sung to the tune WEST BURN, No. 34 (ii)

This people have I formed for myself; they shall shew forth my praise (Isaiah xliii. 21)

FILL Thou my life, O Lord my God,
    In every part with praise,
That my whole being may proclaim
    Thy being and Thy ways.

2 Not for the lip of praise alone,
    Nor e'en the praising heart,
I ask, but for a life made up
    Of praise in every part.

3 Praise in the common things of life,
    Its goings out and in;
Praise in each duty and each deed,
    However small and mean.

4 Fill every part of me with praise;
    Let all my being speak
Of Thee and of Thy love, O Lord,
    Poor though I be, and weak.

5 So shalt Thou, Lord, from me, e'en me,
    Receive the glory due;
And so shall I begin on earth
    The song for ever new.

6 So shall no part of day or night
    From sacredness be free;
But all my life, in every step,
    Be fellowship with Thee.

HORATIUS BONAR (1808-89)

249

HEREFORD NEW (6. 10 10. 6.)   Melody ANON

Based on Romans viii. 31-37

BLESSÈD be God, our God,
Who gave for us His well-belovèd Son,
The Gifts of gifts, all other gifts in one;
Blessèd be God, our God!

2   What will He not bestow,
Who freely gave this mighty Gift unbought,
Unmerited, unheeded, and unsought;
  What will He not bestow?

3   He sparèd not His Son!
'Tis this that silences each rising fear;
'Tis this that bids the hard thought disappear;
  He sparèd not His Son!

4   Who shall condemn us now!
Since Christ has died, and risen, and gone above,
For us to plead at the right hand of Love,
  Who shall condemn us now?

5   'Tis God that justifies!
Who shall recall the pardon or the grace,
Or who the broken chain of guilt replace?
  'Tis God that justifies!

6   The victory is ours!
For us in might came forth the mighty One;
For us He fought the fight, the triumph won;
  The victory is ours!

HORATIUS BONAR (1808-89)

250

PISGAH (6 6. 8 6. 8 8.) Melody ANON

Based on Ephesians i. 3-14

O GOD of matchless grace,
    We sing unto Thy name;
We stand accepted in the place
    That none but Christ could claim;
Our willing hearts have heard Thy voice,
And in Thy mercy we rejoice.

2 'Tis meet that Thy delight
    Should centre in Thy Son;
That Thou shouldst place us in Thy sight
    In Him, Thy Holy One:
Thy perfect love has cast out fear;
Thy favour shines upon us here.

3 Eternal is our rest,
    O Christ of God, in Thee!
Now of Thy peace, Thy joy possest,
    We wait Thy face to see:
Now to the Father's heart received,
We know in whom we have believed.

4 A sacrifice to God,
    In life or death to be—
Oh keep us ever, blessed Lord,
    Thus set apart to Thee:
Bought with a price, we're not our own:
We died, to live to God alone.

HANNAH KILHAM BURLINGHAM (1842-1901)

251

RIDGE (D.S.M.)   SAMUEL WESLEY (1766-1837)

ALTERNATIVE TUNE

ISHMAEL (D.S.M.)   CHARLES VINCENT (1852-1934)

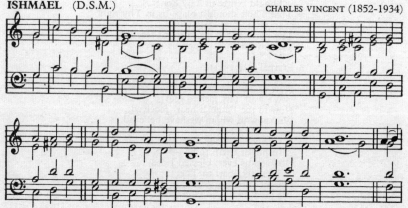

This hymn may also be sung to the tune of ICH HALTE TREULICH STILL, No. 332 (ii)

Singing with grace in your hearts to the Lord (Colossians iii. 16)

COME, ye that love the Lord,
   And let your joys be known;
Join in a song with sweet accord,
   And thus surround the throne.
Let those refuse to sing
   That never knew our God;
But children of the heavenly King
   Must speak their joys abroad.

2 The men of grace have found
   Glory begun below;
Celestial fruits on earthly ground
   From faith and hope may grow.
The hill of Zion yields
   A thousand sacred sweets,
Before we reach the heavenly fields
   Or walk the golden streets.

3 There shall we see His face,
   And never, never sin;
There from the rivers of His grace
   Drink endless pleasures in.
Then let our songs abound,
   And every tear be dry;
We're marching through Immanuel's
   To fairer worlds on high.   [ground

ISAAC WATTS (1674-1748)

252

SHIPSTON   (8 7. 8 7.)   English Traditional Melody

This hymn may also be sung to the tunes ALL FOR JESUS, No. 64, and LUX EOI, No. 66

Hitherto hath the Lord helped us (1 Samuel vii. 12)

COME, Thou fount of every blessing,
   Tune my heart to sing Thy grace;
Streams of mercy never ceasing
   Call for songs of loudest praise.

2 Jesus sought me when a stranger,
   Wandering from the fold of God;
He, to rescue me from danger,
   Interposed His precious blood.

3 O to grace how great a debtor
   Daily I'm constrained to be!
Let that grace now, like a fetter,
   Bind my wandering heart to Thee.

4 Prone to wander—Lord, I feel it—
   Prone to leave the God I love,
Take my heart, O take and seal it,
   Seal it from Thy courts above.

ROBERT ROBINSON (1735-90)

253

HYFRYDOL   (8 7. 8 7. D.)   Melody by ROWLAND HUGH PRICHARD (1811-87)

The Son of God, who loved me, and gave himself for me (Galatians ii. 20)

I WILL sing the wondrous story
Of the Christ who died for me,
How He left the realms of glory
For the cross on Calvary.

Yes, I'll sing the wondrous story
Of the Christ who died for me,
Sing it with His saints in glory,
Gathered by the crystal sea.

2 I was lost: but Jesus found me,
Found the sheep that went astray,
Raised me up and gently led me
Back into the narrow way.

3 Faint was I, and fears possessed me,
Bruised was I from many a fall;
Hope was gone, and shame distressed
But His love has pardoned all. [me:

4 Days of darkness still may meet me,
Sorrow's paths I oft may tread;
But His presence still is with me,
By His guiding hand I'm led.

5 He will keep me till the river
Rolls its waters at my feet:
Then He'll bear me safely over,
Made by grace for glory meet.

FRANCIS HAROLD RAWLEY (1854- ?)

254

DAVID'S HARP (L.M.)   JOHN DANIEL (1842)

The Lord is my helper (Hebrews xiii. 6)

HOW blest is life if lived for Thee,
   My loving Saviour and my Lord:
No pleasures that the world can give
   Such perfect gladness can afford.

2 To know I am Thy ransomed child,
   Bought by Thine own most precious blood,
And from Thy loving hand to take
   With grateful heart each gift of good;

3 All day to walk beneath Thy smile,
   Watching Thine eye to guide me still,
To rest at night beneath Thy care,
   Guarded by Thee from every ill;

4 To feel that though I journey on
   By stony paths and rugged ways,
Thy blessèd feet have gone before,
   And strength is given for weary days.

5 Such love shall ever make me glad,
   Strong in Thy strength to work or rest,
Until I see Thee face to face,
   And in Thy light am fully blest.

ANON.   PRUST'S *Supplementary Hymn Book* (1869)

255

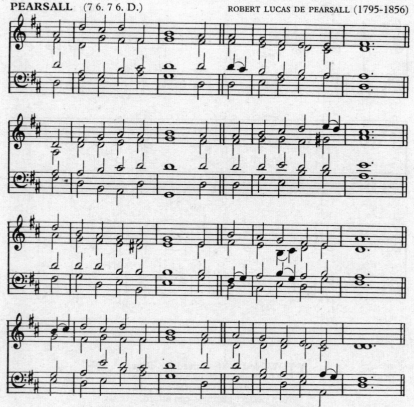

PEARSALL (7 6. 7 6. D.)   ROBERT LUCAS DE PEARSALL (1795-1856)

The hymn may also be sung to the tune CRÜGER, No. 82

I will joy in the God of my salvation (Habakkuk iii. 18)

SOMETIMES a light surprises
  The Christian while he sings;
It is the Lord who rises
  With healing in His wings:
When comforts are declining,
  He grants the soul again
A season of clear shining,
  To cheer it after rain.

2 In holy contemplation,
  We sweetly then pursue
The theme of God's salvation,
  And find it ever new.
Set free from present sorrow.
  We cheerfully can say,
'E'en let the unknown morrow
  Bring with it what it may:

3 'It can bring with it nothing
  But He will bear us through;
Who gives the lilies clothing
  Will clothe His people too.
Beneath the spreading heavens,
  No creature but is fed;
And He who feeds the ravens
  Will give His children bread.'

4 Though vine nor fig-tree neither
  Their wonted fruit should bear,
Though all the fields should wither,
  Nor flocks nor herds be there,
Yet, God the same abiding,
  His praise shall tune my voice;
For, while in Him confiding,
  I cannot but rejoice.

WILLIAM COWPER (1731-1800)

256

MELLING (7 7. 7 7.)   JOHN FAWCETT (1789-1867)

This hymn may also be sung to the tune MONKLAND, No. 12

God . . . hath prepared for them a city (Hebrews xi. 16)

CHILDREN of the heavenly King,
    As ye journey, sweetly sing;
Sing your Saviour's worthy praise,
Glorious in His works and ways.

2 We are travelling home to God,
    In the way the fathers trod;
    They are happy now, and we
    Soon their happiness shall see.

3 Lift your eyes, ye sons of light;
    Zion's city is in sight;
    There our endless home shall be,
    There our Lord we soon shall see.

4 Fear not, brethren; joyful stand
    On the borders of your land;
    Jesus Christ, your Father's Son,
    Bids you undismayed go on.

5 Lord, obediently we go,
    Gladly leaving all below;
    Only Thou our Leader be,
    And we still will follow Thee.

JOHN CENNICK (1718-55)

257

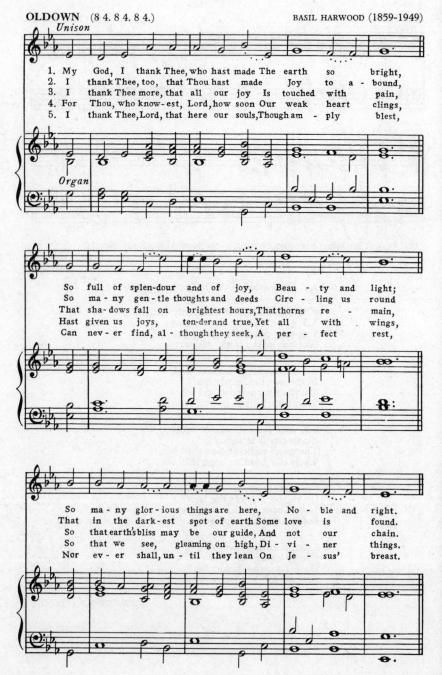

OLDOWN   (8 4. 8 4. 8 4.)   BASIL HARWOOD (1859-1949)

1. My God, I thank Thee, who hast made The earth so bright,
2. I thank Thee, too, that Thou hast made Joy to abound,
3. I thank Thee more, that all our joy Is touched with pain,
4. For Thou, who knowest, Lord, how soon Our weak heart clings,
5. I thank Thee, Lord, that here our souls, Though amply blest,

So full of splendour and of joy, Beauty and light;
So many gentle thoughts and deeds Circling us round
That shadows fall on brightest hours, That thorns remain,
Hast given us joys, tenderand true, Yet all with wings,
Can never find, although they seek, A perfect rest,

So many glorious things are here, Noble and right.
That in the darkest spot of earth Some love is found.
So that earth's bliss may be our guide, And not our chain.
So that we see, gleaming on high, Diviner things.
Nor ever shall, until they lean On Jesus' breast.

WENTWORTH   (8 4. 8 4. 8 4.)   FREDERICK CHARLES MAKER (1844-1927)

We also joy in God through our Lord Jesus Christ (Romans v. 11)

MY God, I thank Thee, who hast made
The earth so bright,
So full of splendour and of joy,
Beauty and light;
So many glorious things are here,
Noble and right.

2 I thank Thee, too, that Thou hast made
Joy to abound,
So many gentle thoughts and deeds
Circling us round
That in the darkest spot of earth
Some love is found.

3 I thank Thee more, that all our joy
Is touched with pain,
That shadows fall on brightest hours,
That thorns remain,
So that earth's bliss may be our guide,
And not our chain.

4 For Thou, who knowest, Lord, how
Our weak heart clings,   [soon
Hast given us joys, tender and true,
Yet all with wings,
So that we see, gleaming on high,
Diviner things.

5 I thank Thee, Lord, that here our
Though amply blest,   [souls,
Can never find, although they seek,
A perfect rest,
Nor ever shall, until they lean
On Jesus' breast.

ADELAIDE ANNE PROCTER (1825-64)

258

ALMSGIVING (8 8 8. 4) JOHN BACCHUS DYKES (1823-76)

ALTERNATIVE TUNE

ES IST KEIN TAG (8 8 8. 4.) Melody from JOHANN MEYER'S *Seelenfreud* (1692)

The living God, who giveth us richly all things to enjoy (1 Timothy vi. 17)

O LORD of heaven and earth and sea,
   To Thee all praise and glory be;
How shall we show our love to Thee,
   Who givest all?

2 The golden sunshine, vernal air,
   Sweet flowers and fruits Thy love
      declare;
   Where harvests ripen, Thou art there,
      Who givest all.

3 For peaceful homes and healthful days,
   For all the blessings earth displays,
   We owe Thee thankfulness and praise,
      Who givest all.

4 Thou didst not spare Thine only Son,
   But gav'st Him for a world undone,
   And freely with that blessed One
      Thou givest all.

5 Thou giv'st the Spirit's blessèd dower,
   Spirit of life and love and power,
   And dost His sevenfold graces shower
      Upon us all.

6 For souls redeemed, for sins forgiven,
   For means of grace and hopes of
      heaven,
   Father, all praise to Thee be given,
      Who givest all.

CHRISTOPHER WORDSWORTH (1807-85)

259

NEWINGTON (7 7. 7 7.)   WILLIAM DALRYMPLE MACLAGAN (1826-1910)

No man is able to pluck them out of my Father's hand (John x. 29)

THINE for ever! God of love,
   Hear us from Thy throne above;
Thine for ever may we be,
Here and in eternity.

2 Thine for ever! Lord of life,
   Shield us through our earthly strife;
   Thou the Life, the Truth, the Way,
   Guide us to the realms of day.

3 Thine for ever! O how blest
   They who find in Thee their rest!
   Saviour, Guardian, Heavenly Friend,
   O defend us to the end.

4 Thine for ever! Thou our guide,
   All our wants by Thee supplied,
   All our sins by Thee forgiven,
   Lead us, Lord, from earth to heaven.

MARY FAWLER MAUDE (1819-1913)

See also the sections THE GODHEAD: PRAISE AND ADORATION, Nos. 1-22, *and* THE SON
OF GOD: HIS GLORY, NAME AND PRAISE, Nos. 89-117.

WARRINGTON (L.M.)   RALPH HARRISON (1748-1810)

For this shall every one that is godly pray unto thee in a time when thou mayest be found (Psalm xxxii. 6)

JESUS, where'er Thy people meet,
  There they behold Thy mercy-seat;
Where'er they seek Thee, Thou art found,
And every place is hallowed ground.

2 For Thou, within no walls confined,
  Inhabitest the humble mind;
Such ever bring Thee where they come,
And going, take Thee to their home.

3 Dear Shepherd of Thy chosen few,
  Thy former mercies here renew;
Here to our waiting hearts proclaim
The sweetness of Thy saving name.

4 Here may we prove the power of prayer,
  To strengthen faith and sweeten care,
To teach our faint desires to rise,
And bring all heaven before our eyes.

5 Lord, we are few, but Thou art near,
  Nor short Thine arm, nor deaf Thine ear;
O rend the heavens, come quickly down,
And make a thousand hearts Thine own!

WILLIAM COWPER (1731-1800)

261

TYHOLLAND (7 7 7.)

German Carol Melody, adapted by
DAVID FREDERICK RUDDELL WILSON (1871-)

ALTERNATIVE TUNE

ST. PHILIP (7 7 7.)

WILLIAM HENRY MONK (1823-89)

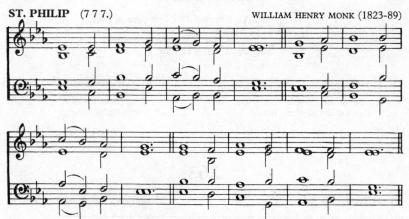

Where two or three are gathered together in my name, there am I in the midst of them (Matthew xviii. 20)

PRESENT with the two or three
Deign, most gracious God, to be,
While we lift our souls to Thee.

2 Jesus, by Thy blood alone
Who didst for our sins atone,
Dare we come before Thy throne.

3 Holy Spirit, from on high
Helping our infirmity,
Aid us in our feeble cry.

4 Flesh and heart would faint and fail,
But there stands within the veil
One who ever doth prevail.

5 Thou who knowest all our need,
Grant the prayer of faith to plead,
Teach us how to intercede.

FANNY FREER (1801-91)

262

STRACATHRO (C.M.)

Melody by CHARLES HUTCHESON (1792-1860)
from *Christian Vespers* (Glasgow, 1832)

Lord, teach us to pray (Luke xi. 1)

GREAT Shepherd of Thy people, hear;
Thy presence now display;
As Thou hast given a place for prayer,
So give us hearts to pray.

2 Within these walls let holy peace,
And love, and concord dwell;
Here give the troubled conscience ease,
The wounded spirit heal.

3 May we in faith receive Thy word,
In faith present our prayers;
And in the presence of our Lord
Unbosom all our cares.

JOHN NEWTON (1725-1807)

263

ST. HUGH (C.M.)

EDWARD JOHN HOPKINS (1818-1901)

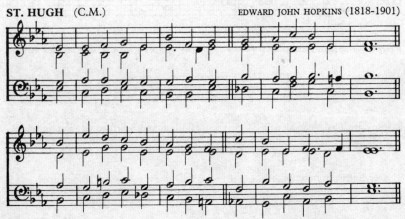

This hymn may also be sung to the tune STRACATHRO, No. 262

Let us draw near with a true heart in full assurance of faith (Hebrews x. 22)

LORD, teach us how to pray aright
 With reverence and with fear;
Though dust and ashes in Thy sight,
We may, we must draw near.

2 We perish if we cease from prayer;
 O grant us power to pray;
And, when to meet Thee we prepare,
 Lord, meet us by the way.

3 God of all grace, we bring to Thee
 A broken contrite heart;
Give, what Thine eye delights to see,
 Truth in the inward part;

4 Faith in the only Sacrifice
 That can for sin atone;
To cast our hopes, to fix our eyes,
 On Christ, on Christ alone;

5 Patience to watch, and wait, and weep,
 Though mercy long delay;
Courage, our fainting souls to keep,
 And trust Thee, though Thou slay;

6 Give these, and then Thy will be done;
 Thus, strengthened with all might,
We, through Thy Spirit and Thy Son,
 Shall pray, and pray aright.

JAMES MONTGOMERY (1771-1854)

264

TALLIS' ORDINAL   (C.M.)   THOMAS TALLIS (*c.* 1510-85)

Pray without ceasing. In every thing give thanks (1 Thessalonians v. 17, 18)

BEHOLD us, Lord, a little space
 From daily tasks set free,
And met within Thy holy place
 To rest awhile with Thee.

2 Around us rolls the ceaseless tide
 Of business, toil, and care,
And scarcely can we turn aside
 For one brief hour of prayer.

3 Yet these are not the only walls
 Wherein Thou mayst be sought;
On homeliest work Thy blessing falls,
 In truth and patience wrought.

4 Thine is the loom, the forge, the mart,
 The wealth of land and sea,
The worlds of science and of art,
 Revealed and ruled by Thee.

5 Then let us prove our heavenly birth
 In all we do and know,
And claim the kingdom of the earth
 For Thee, and not Thy foe.

JOHN ELLERTON (1826-93)

265

ST. FRANCIS XAVIER   (C.M.)   JOHN STAINER (1840-1901)

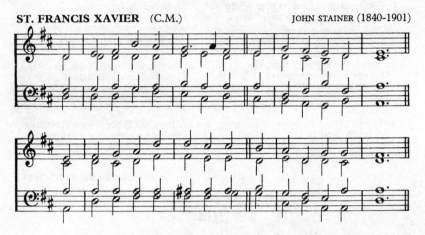

What shall I render unto the Lord for all his benefits toward me? (Psalm cxvi. 12)

FOR mercies, countless as the sands,
    Which daily I receive
From Jesus, my Redeemer's hands,
    My soul, what canst thou give?

2 Alas, from such a heart as mine,
    What can I bring Him forth?
My best is stained and dyed with sin,
    My all is nothing worth.

3 Yet this acknowledgment I'll make
    For all He has bestowed,
Salvation's sacred cup I'll take,
    And call upon my God.

WILLIAM COWPER (1731-1800)

266

THIS ENDRIS NYGHT   (C.M.)   English Carol (15th Century)

This hymn may also be sung to the tune STRACATHRO, No. 262

Let us therefore come boldly unto the throne of grace, that we may obtain mercy (Hebrews iv. 16)

APPROACH, my soul, the mercy-seat,
Where Jesus answers prayer;
There humbly fall before His feet,
For none can perish there.

2 Thy promise is my only plea;
With this I venture nigh:
Thou callest burdened souls to Thee,
And such, O Lord, am I.

3 Bowed down beneath a load of sin,
By Satan sorely pressed,
By war without and fears within,
I come to Thee for rest.

4 Be Thou my shield and hiding-place,
That, sheltered near Thy side,
I may my fierce accuser face,
And tell him Thou hast died.

5 O wondrous love! to bleed and die,
To bear the cross and shame,
That guilty sinners, such as I,
Might plead Thy gracious name!

JOHN NEWTON (1725-1807)

267

BEATITUDO (C.M.)   JOHN BACCHUS DYKES (1823-76)

Continue in prayer (Colossians iv. 2)

PRAYER is the soul's sincere desire,
Uttered or unexpressed,
The motion of a hidden fire
That trembles in the breast.

2 Prayer is the simplest form of speech
That infant lips can try;
Prayer the sublimest strains that reach
The majesty on high.

3 Prayer is the contrite sinner's voice
Returning from his ways,
While angels in their songs rejoice,
And cry: 'Behold he prays!'

4 Prayer is the Christian's vital breath,
The Christian's native air,
His watchword at the gates of death;
He enters heaven with prayer.

5 O Thou by whom we come to God,
The Life, the Truth, the Way!
The path of prayer Thyself hast trod:
Lord! teach us how to pray.

JAMES MONTGOMERY (1771-1854)

268

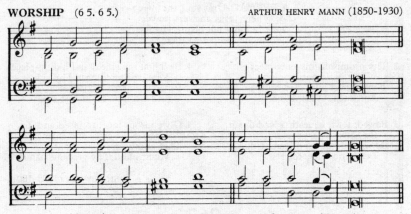

WORSHIP (6 5. 6 5.)   ARTHUR HENRY MANN (1850-1930)

This hymn may also be sung to the tune QUIETUDE, No. 269

Jesus himself stood in the midst of them (Luke xxiv. 36)

JESUS, stand among us
  In Thy risen power;
Let this time of worship
  Be a hallowed hour.

2 Breathe the Holy Spirit
  Into every heart;
Bid the fears and sorrows
  From each soul depart.

3 Thus with quickened footsteps
  We'll pursue our way,
Watching for the dawning
  Of eternal day.

WILLIAM PENNEFATHER (1816-73)

269

QUIETUDE (6 5. 6 5.)   HAROLD GREEN (1871-1931)

This hymn may also be sung to the tune EUDOXIA, No. 209 (i)

The words that I speak unto you, they are spirit, and they are life (John vi. 63)

SPEAK, Lord, in the stillness,
  While I wait on Thee;
Hushed my heart to listen
  In expectancy.

2 Speak, O blessèd Master,
  In this quiet hour;
Let me see Thy face, Lord,
  Feel Thy touch of power.

3 For the words Thou speakest,
   They are life indeed;
   Living Bread from heaven,
    Now my spirit feed!

4 Speak, Thy servant heareth!
   Be not silent, Lord;
   Waits my soul upon Thee
   For the quickening word.

5 Fill me with the knowledge
   Of Thy glorious will;
   All Thine own good pleasure
   In Thy child fulfil.

E. MAY GRIMES (1868-1927)

270

VIENNA (7 7. 7 7.)   Melody from JUSTIN HEINRICH KNECHT (1752-1817)

This hymn may also be sung to the tune SONG 13, No. 154

And God said, Ask what I shall give thee (1 Kings iii. 5)

COME, my soul, thy suit prepare;
   Jesus loves to answer prayer;
He Himself has bid thee pray,
   Therefore will not say thee nay.

2 Thou art coming to a King;
   Large petitions with thee bring;
For His grace and power are such,
   None can ever ask too much.

3 With my burden I begin:
   Lord, remove this load of sin;
Let Thy blood, for sinners spilt,
   Set my conscience free from guilt.

4 Lord, I come to Thee for rest;
   Take possession of my breast;
There Thy blood-bought right maintain,
   And without a rival reign.

5 While I am a pilgrim here,
   Let Thy love my spirit cheer;
Be my guide, my guard, my friend,
   Lead me to my journey's end.

JOHN NEWTON (1725-1807)

271

BLAENWERN   (8 7. 8 7. D.)   WILLIAM PENFRO ROWLANDS (1860-1937)

The eyes of the Lord are over the righteous, and his ears are open unto their prayers (1 Peter iii. 12)

WHAT a Friend we have in Jesus,
    All our sins and griefs to bear!
What a privilege to carry
    Everything to God in prayer!
O what peace we often forfeit,
    O what needless pain we bear,
All because we do not carry
    Everything to God in prayer!

2 Have we trials and temptations?
    Is there trouble anywhere?
We should never be discouraged:
    Take it to the Lord in prayer.
Can we find a friend so faithful,
    Who will all our sorrows share?
Jesus knows our every weakness:
    Take it to the Lord in prayer.

3 Are we weak and heavy-laden,
    Cumbered with a load of care?
Jesus only is our refuge:
    Take it to the Lord in prayer.
Do thy friends despise, forsake thee?
    Take it to the Lord in prayer;
In His arms He'll take and shield thee!
    Thou wilt find a solace there.

JOSEPH MEDLICOTT SCRIVEN (1820-86)

The following hymns also refer to this theme:

    122   Lord God the Holy Ghost   132   O Breath of God, breathe on us now
           152   Come ye yourselves apart and rest awhile

272

MARCHING   (8 7. 8 7.)   MARTIN SHAW (1875-   )

IGJENNEM NAT OG TRÆNGSEL

He brought forth his people with joy, and his chosen with gladness (Psalm cv. 43)

THROUGH the night of doubt
    and sorrow
Onward goes the pilgrim band,
Singing songs of expectation,
    Marching to the promised land.

2 Clear before us through the darkness,
    Gleams and burns the guiding light;
Brother clasps the hand of brother,
    Stepping fearless through the night.

3 One the light of God's own presence
    O'er His ransomed people shed,
Chasing far the gloom and terror,
    Brightening all the path we tread.

4 One the object of our journey,
    One the faith which never tires,
One the earnest looking forward,
    One the hope our God inspires.

*5 One the strain that lips of thousands
    Lift as from the heart of one;
One the conflict, one the peril,
    One the march in God begun.

*6 One the gladness of rejoicing
    On the far eternal shore,
Where the one almighty Father
    Reigns in love for evermore.

7 Onward, therefore, pilgrim brothers,
    Onward with the cross our aid;
Bear its shame, and fight its battle,
    Till we rest beneath its shade.

8 Soon shall come the great awaking,
    Soon the rending of the tomb;
Then the scattering of all shadows,
    And the end of toil and gloom.

BERNHARDT SEVERIN INGEMANN (1789-1862);
tr. SABINE BARING-GOULD (1834-1924)

If desired, verses 5 and 6 may be omitted

273

SUSSEX (8 7. 8 7.)   Adapted from an English Traditional Melody.

ALTERNATIVE TUNE

SHIPSTON (8 7. 8 7.)   English Traditional Melody

They that wait upon the Lord shall renew their strength (Isaiah xl. 31)

FATHER, hear the prayer we offer;
Not for ease that prayer shall be,
But for strength that we may ever
Live our lives courageously.

2 Not for ever in green pastures
Do we ask our way to be;
But the steep and rugged pathway
May we tread rejoicingly.

3 Not for ever by still waters
Would we idly rest and stay;
But would smite the living fountains
From the rocks along our way.

4 Be our strength in hours of weakness,
In our wanderings be our guide;
Through endeavour, failure, danger,
Father, be Thou at our side.

LOVE MARIA WILLIS (1824-1908) and others

274

IBSTONE   (6 6. 6 6.)   MARIA TIDDEMAN (1837-1911)

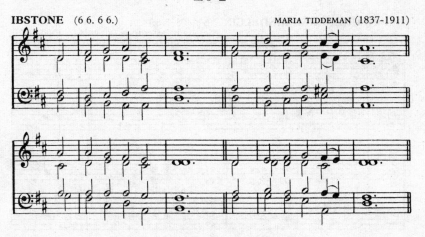

Pray for us . . . that the Lord thy God may shew us the way wherein we may walk, and the thing that we may do (Jeremiah xlii. 2, 3)

THY way, not mine, O Lord,
    However dark it be!
Lead me by Thine own hand,
    Choose out the path for me.

2 Smooth let it be or rough,
    It will be still the best;
Winding or straight, it leads
    Right onward to Thy rest.

3 I dare not choose my lot;
    I would not if I might;
Choose Thou for me, my God,
    So shall I walk aright.

4 Take Thou my cup, and it
    With joy or sorrow fill,
As best to Thee may seem;
    Choose Thou my good or ill:

5 Choose Thou for me my friends,
    My sickness or my health;
Choose Thou my cares for me,
    My poverty or wealth.

6 Not mine, not mine the choice,
    In things or great or small;
Be Thou my guide and strength,
    My wisdom and my all.

HORATIUS BONAR (1808-89)

275

DAS NEUGEBORNE KINDELEIN   (8 8. 8 8. 8 8.)
Melody by MELCHIOR VULPIUS (*c.* 1560-1616)
Harmony chiefly by JOHANN SEBASTIAN BACH (1685-1750)

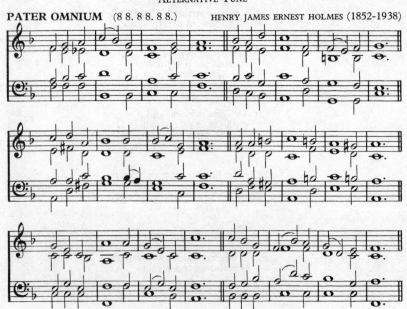

ALTERNATIVE TUNE

PATER OMNIUM   (8 8. 8 8. 8 8.)   HENRY JAMES ERNEST HOLMES (1852-1938)

He looked for a city which hath foundations, whose builder and maker is God (Hebrews xi. 10)

LEADER of faithful souls, and guide
　Of all that travel to the sky,
Come and with us, even us, abide,
Who would on Thee alone rely.
On Thee alone our spirits stay,
While held in life's uneven way.

2 We have no lasting city here,
　But seek a city out of sight;
Thither our steady course we steer,
Aspiring to the plains of light,
Jerusalem, the saints' abode,
Whose founder is the living God.

3 Through Thee, who all our sins hast
　　borne,
Freely and graciously forgiven,
With songs to Zion we return,
Contending for our native heaven;
That palace of our glorious King,
We find it nearer while we sing.

4 Raised by the breath of love divine,
　We urge our way with strength
　　renewed;
The Church of Thy first-born to join,
We travel to the mount of God.
With joy upon our heads arise,
And meet our Captain in the skies.

CHARLES WESLEY (1707-88)†

276

ST. AELRED　(8 8 8. 3. Iambic)　　　　　　JOHN BACCHUS DYKES (1823-76)

Based on Mark iv. 35-41

FIERCE raged the tempest o'er the deep,
　Watch did Thine anxious servants keep,
But Thou wast wrapt in guileless sleep,
　Calm and still.

2 ' Save, Lord, we perish,' was their cry,
　' O save us in our agony! '
Thy word above the storm rose high,
　' Peace, be still.'

3 The wild winds hushed, the angry deep
Sank like a little child to sleep,
The sullen billows ceased to leap,
　At Thy will.

4 So, when our life is clouded o'er,
And storm-winds drift us from the shore,
Say, lest we sink to rise no more,
　' Peace, be still.'

GODFREY THRING (1823-1903)

277

ST. COLUMBA   (8 7. 8 7. Iambic)   Ancient Irish Hymn Melody (Original form)
arranged by CHARLES VILLIERS STANFORD (1852-1924)

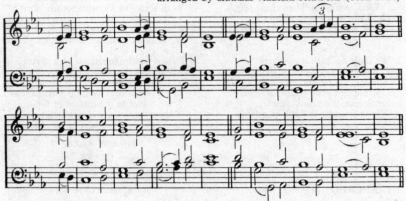

ALTERNATIVE TUNE

DOMINUS REGIT ME   (8 7. 8 7. Iambic)   JOHN BACCHUS DYKES (1823-76)

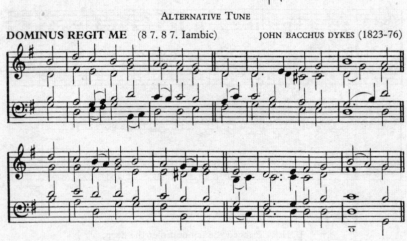

Paraphrase of Psalm xxiii

THE King of love my Shepherd is,
     Whose goodness faileth never;
I nothing lack if I am His
     And He is mine for ever.

2 Where streams of living water flow
     My ransomed soul He leadeth,
And where the verdant pastures grow
     With food celestial feedeth.

3 Perverse and foolish oft I strayed,
     But yet in love He sought me,
And on His shoulder gently laid,
     And home, rejoicing, brought me.

4 In death's dark vale I fear no ill
     With Thee, dear Lord, beside me;
Thy rod and staff my comfort still,
     Thy cross before to guide me.

5 Thou spread'st a table in my sight;
     Thy unction grace bestoweth;
And O, what transport of delight
     From Thy pure chalice floweth!

6 And so through all the length of days
     Thy goodness faileth never;
Good Shepherd, may I sing Thy praise
     Within Thy house for ever.

HENRY WILLIAMS BAKER (1821-77)

278

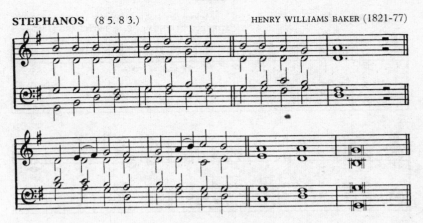

STEPHANOS (8 5. 8 3.) HENRY WILLIAMS BAKER (1821-77)

Come unto me, all ye that labour and are heavy laden, and I will give you rest (Matthew xi. 28)

★ ART thou weary, heavy laden,
Art thou sore distressed?
'Come to me,' saith One, 'and, coming,
Be at rest.'

2 Hath He marks to lead me to Him,
If He be my guide?
In His feet and hands are wound-prints,
And His side.

3 Hath He diadem as Monarch
That His brow adorns?
Yea, a crown in very surety,
But of thorns!

4 If I find Him, if I follow,
What His guerdon here?
Many a sorrow, many a labour,
Many a tear!

5 If I still hold closely to Him,
What hath He at last?
Sorrow vanquished, labour ended,
Jordan past.

6 If I ask Him to receive me,
Will He say me nay?
Not till earth and not till heaven
Pass away.

7 Finding, following, keeping, struggling,
Is He sure to bless?
Saints, apostles, prophets, martyrs,
Answer, Yes!

JOHN MASON NEALE (1818-66)†;
based on STEPHEN THE SABAITE (725-94)

★ *This hymn is suitable for antiphonal singing*

279

CRIMOND (C.M.)

Melody by JESSIE SEYMOUR IRVINE (1836-87)
arranged by THOMAS C. L. PRITCHARD (1885-)

This hymn may also be sung to the tune UNIVERSITY, No. 247 (ii)

Paraphrase of Psalm xxiii

THE Lord's my Shepherd, I'll not want:
  He makes me down to lie
In pastures green; He leadeth me
  The quiet waters by.

2 My soul He doth restore again,
    And me to walk doth make
Within the paths of righteousness,
    E'en for His own name's sake.

3 Yea, though I walk in death's dark vale,
    Yet will I fear none ill;
For Thou art with me, and Thy rod
    And staff me comfort still.

4 My table Thou hast furnished
    In presence of my foes;
My head Thou dost with oil anoint,
    And my cup overflows.

5 Goodness and mercy all my life
    Shall surely follow me;
And in God's house for evermore
    My dwelling-place shall be.

The Scottish Psalter (1650)

280

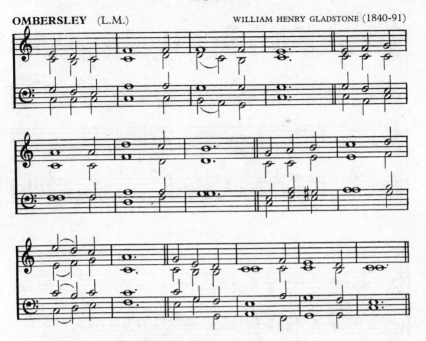

OMBERSLEY (L.M.)   WILLIAM HENRY GLADSTONE (1840-91)

Jesus himself drew near, and went with them (Luke xxiv. 15)

O WALK with Jesus, would'st thou know
  How deep, how wide His love can flow!
They only fail His love to prove
Who in the ways of sinners rove.

2 Walk thou with Him; that way is light,
  All other pathways end in night:
Walk thou with Him; that way is rest,
All other pathways are unblest.

3 O walk with Jesus! to thy view
  He will make all things sweet and new;
Will bring new fragrance from each flower,
And hallow every passing hour.

4 Jesus, a great desire have we
  To walk life's troubled path with Thee:
Come to us now, in converse stay;
And O! walk with us day by day.

EDWIN PAXTON HOOD (1820-85)

281

HORBURY (6 4. 6 4. 6 6 4.)   JOHN BACCHUS DYKES (1823-76)

ALTERNATIVE TUNE

GLENPARK (6 4. 6 4. 6 6 4.)   KENNETH GEORGE FINLAY (1882-)

Small note and dotted slur for verse 2

Based on Genesis xxviii. 10-22

NEARER, my God, to Thee
  Nearer to Thee!
E'en though it be a cross
  That raiseth me;
Still all my song shall be,
Nearer, my God, to Thee,
  Nearer to Thee!

2 Though, like the wanderer,
  The sun gone down,
Darkness be over me,
  My rest a stone;
Yet in my dreams I'd be
Nearer, my God, to Thee,
  Nearer to Thee!

3 There let the way appear,
   Steps unto heaven;
 All that Thou sendest me
   In mercy given:
 Angels to beckon me
 Nearer, my God, to Thee,
   Nearer to Thee!

4 Then, with my waking thoughts
   Bright with Thy praise,
 Out of my stony griefs
   Bethel I'll raise:
 So by my woes to be
 Nearer, my God, to Thee,
   Nearer to Thee!

5 Or if on joyful wing
   Cleaving the sky,
 Sun, moon, and stars forgot,
   Upwards I fly,
 Still all my song shall be,
 Nearer, my God, to Thee,
   Nearer to Thee!

SARAH FLOWER ADAMS (1805-48)

282

MARTYRDOM (C.M.)

HUGH WILSON (1766-1824)
adapted by ROBERT ARCHIBALD SMITH (1780-1829)

This hymn may also be sung to the tune BELMONT, No. 214

Based on Genesis xxviii. 20-22

O GOD of Bethel! by whose hand
   Thy people still are fed;
 Who through this weary pilgrimage
   Hast all our fathers led:

2 Our vows, our prayers we now present
   Before Thy throne of grace:
 God of our fathers! be the God
   Of their succeeding race.

3 Through each perplexing path of life
   Our wandering footsteps guide;
 Give us each day our daily bread,
   And raiment fit provide.

4 O spread Thy covering wings around,
   Till all our wanderings cease,
 And at our Father's loved abode
   Our souls arrive in peace.

*5 Such blessings from Thy gracious
   Our humble prayers implore; [hand
 And Thou shalt be our chosen God,
   And portion evermore.

PHILIP DODDRIDGE (1702-51) and JOHN LOGAN (1748-88),
as in *Scottish Paraphrases* (1781)

If desired, this verse may be omitted

283

ST. HELEN (8 7. 8 7. 8 7.)   GEORGE CLEMENT MARTIN (1844-1916)

ALTERNATIVE TUNE

CWM RHONDDA (8 7. 8 7. 8 7.)   JOHN HUGHES (1873-1932)

ARGLWYDD ARWAIN TRWY'R ANIALWCH

The Lord shall guide thee continually (Isaiah lviii. 11)

GUIDE me, O Thou great Jehovah,
   Pilgrim through this barren land;
I am weak, but Thou art mighty,
   Hold me with Thy powerful hand;
      Bread of heaven,
   Feed me till I want no more.

2 Open now the crystal fountain
   Whence the healing stream doth flow;
Let the fire and cloudy pillar
   Lead me all my journey through;
      Strong deliverer,
Be Thou still my strength and shield.

3 When I tread the verge of Jordan,
   Bid my anxious fears subside;
Death of death, and hell's Destruction,
   Land me safe on Canaan's side;
      Songs of praises
I will ever give to Thee.

WILLIAM WILLIAMS (1716-91);
tr. PETER WILLIAMS (1723-96) and others

284

CANNOCK (L.M.)   WALTER K. STANTON (1891-   )

That I may know him . . . and the fellowship of his sufferings (Philippians iii. 10)

O THOU who dost direct my feet
   To right or left where pathways
      part,
Wilt Thou not, faithful Paraclete,
   Direct the journeying of my heart?

2 Into the love of God, I pray,
   Deeper and deeper let me press,
Exploring all along the way
   Its secret strength and tenderness.

3 Into the stedfastness of One
   Who patiently endured the cross,
Of Him who, though He were a Son,
   Came to His crown through bitter
      loss.

4 This is the road of my desire—
   Learning to love as God loves me,
Ready to pass through flood or fire
   With Christ's unwearying constancy.

FRANK HOUGHTON (1894-

285

ALLELUIA, DULCE CARMEN (8 7. 8 7. 8 7.)   SAMUEL WEBBE (1740-1816)
from *Essay on the Church Plain Chant* (1782)

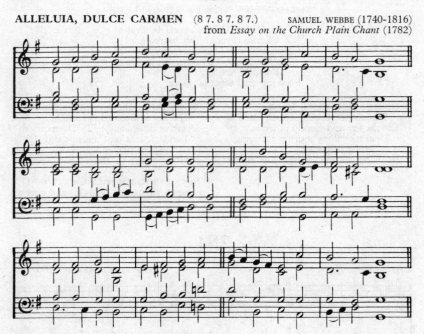

ALTERNATIVE TUNE

MANNHEIM (8 7. 8 7. 8 7.)   FRIEDRICH FILITZ (1804-76)

The God of hope fill you with all joy and peace in believing (Romans xv. 13)

LEAD us, heavenly Father, lead us
O'er the world's tempestuous sea;
Guard us, guide us, keep us, feed us,
For we have no help but Thee;
Yet possessing every blessing
If our God our Father be.

2 Saviour, breathe forgiveness o'er us;
All our weakness Thou dost know;
Thou didst tread this earth before us,
Thou didst feel its keenest woe;
Lone and dreary, faint and weary,
Through the desert Thou didst go.

3 Spirit of our God, descending,
Fill our hearts with heavenly joy,
Love with every passion blending,
Pleasure that can never cloy;
Thus provided, pardoned, guided,
Nothing can our peace destroy.

JAMES EDMESTON (1791-1867)

286

BINCHESTER (C.M.)   WILLIAM CROFT (1678-1727)

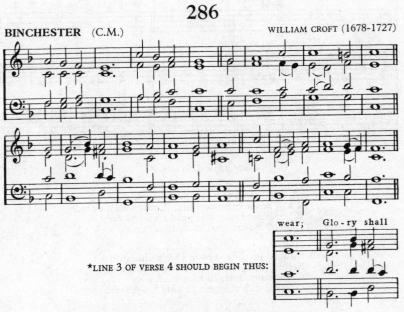

wear;   Glo-ry shall

*LINE 3 OF VERSE 4 SHOULD BEGIN THUS:

This hymn may also be sung to the tune ST. AGNES, No. 97

Based on 1 John i. 5-7

WALK in the light: so shalt thou know
That fellowship of love
His Spirit only can bestow
Who reigns in light above.

2 Walk in the light: and thou shalt find
Thy heart made truly His
Who dwells in cloudless light
In whom no darkness is. [enshrined,

3 Walk in the light: and thou shalt own
Thy darkness passed away,
Because that light hath on thee shone
In which is perfect day.

4 Walk in the light: and e'en the tomb
No fearful shade shall wear;
Glory shall chase away its gloom,
For Christ hath conquered there.

5 Walk in the light: and thine shall be
A path, though thorny, bright;
For God, by grace, shall dwell in thee,
And God Himself is light.

BERNARD BARTON (1784-1849)

301

287

EVENTIDE   (10 10. 10 10.)   WILLIAM HENRY MONK (1823-89)

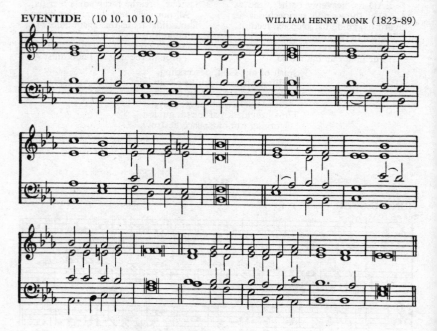

Abide with us (Luke xxiv. 29)

ABIDE with me: fast falls the eventide;
   The darkness deepens; Lord, with me abide:
When other helpers fail, and comforts flee,
Help of the helpless, O abide with me.

2 Swift to its close ebbs out life's little day;
  Earth's joys grow dim, its glories pass away;
  Change and decay in all around I see:
  O Thou who changest not, abide with me.

3 I need Thy presence every passing hour;
  What but Thy grace can foil the tempter's power?
  Who like Thyself my guide and stay can be?
  Through cloud and sunshine, O abide with me.

4 I fear no foe, with Thee at hand to bless;
  Ills have no weight, and tears no bitterness:
  Where is death's sting? where, grave, thy victory?
  I triumph still if Thou abide with me.

5 Hold Thou Thy cross before my closing eyes,
  Shine through the gloom, and point me to the skies;
  Heaven's morning breaks, and earth's vain shadows flee:
  In life, in death, O Lord, abide with me.

HENRY FRANCIS LYTE (1793-1847)

288

BRESLAU (L.M.)   Melody in *As Hymnodus Sacer* (Leipzig, 1625)

If any man will come after me, let him deny himself, and take up his cross (Matthew xvi. 24)

'TAKE up thy cross,' the Saviour said,
    'If thou wouldst My disciple be;
Take up thy cross, with willing heart,
    And humbly follow after Me.'

2 Take up thy cross; let not its weight
    Fill thy weak soul with vain alarm;
His strength shall bear thy spirit up,
    And brace thy heart, and nerve thine arm.

3 Take up thy cross, nor heed the shame,
    Not let thy foolish pride rebel;
The Lord for thee the cross endured
    To save thy soul from death and hell.

4 Take up thy cross, then, in His strength,
    And calmly every danger brave;
'Twill guide thee to a better home,
    And lead to victory o'er the grave.

5 Take up thy cross, and follow Christ,
    Nor think till death to lay it down;
For only he who bears the cross
    May hope to wear the glorious crown.

CHARLES WILLIAM EVEREST (1814-77)

289

FARLEY CASTLE   (10 10. 10 10.)   HENRY LAWES (1596-1662)

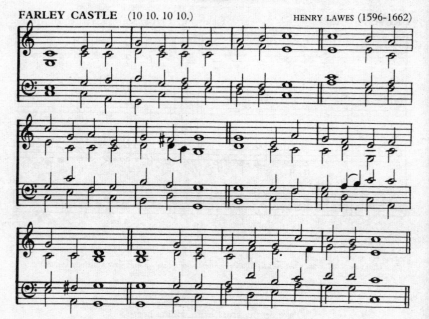

This hymn may also be sung to the tune WOODLANDS, No. 16

Lo, I am with you alway (Matthew xxviii. 20)

I TAKE Thy promise, Lord, in all its length,
   And breadth and fullness, as my daily strength,
Into life's future fearless I may gaze,
For, Jesus, Thou art with me all the days.

2 Days may be coming fraught with loss and change,
   New scenes surround my life and faces strange;
I thank Thee that no day can ever break,
Saviour, when Thou wilt leave me or forsake.

3 There may be days of darkness and distress,
   When sin has power to tempt, and care to press,
Yet in the darkest day I will not fear,
For, 'mid the shadows, Thou wilt still be near.

4 Days there may be of joy, and deep delight,
   When earth seems fairest, and her skies most bright;
Then draw me closer to Thee, lest I rest
Elsewhere, my Saviour, than upon Thy breast.

5 And all the other days that make my life,
   Marked by no special joy or grief or strife,
Days filled with quiet duties, trivial care,
Burdens too small for other hearts to share;

6 Spend Thou these days with me, all shall be Thine;
   So shall the darkest hour with glory shine.
Then when these earthly years have passed away,
Let me be with Thee in the perfect day.

                    HENRY LEGH RICHMOND DECK (1853-1910)

290

ARNSTADT (5 5. 8 8. 5 5.)   ADAM DRESE (1620-1791)

JESU, GEH' VORAN

In all thy ways acknowledge him, and he shall direct thy paths (Proverbs iii. 6)

JESUS, still lead on,
    Till our rest be won,
And, although the way be cheerless,
We will follow, calm and fearless;
    Guide us by Thy hand
    To our fatherland.

2   If the way be drear,
      If the foe be near,
    Let not faithless fears o'ertake us,
    Let not faith and hope forsake us;
      For, through many a foe,
      To our home we go.

3   When we seek relief
      From a long-felt grief,
    When oppressed by new temptations,
    Lord, increase and perfect patience;
      Show us that bright shore
      Where we weep no more.

4   Jesus, still lead on,
      Till our rest be won;
    Heavenly Leader, still direct us,
    Still support, console, protect us,
      Till we safely stand
      In our fatherland.

NICOLAUS LUDWIG VON ZINZENDORF (1700-60);
tr. JANE LAURIE BORTHWICK (1813-97)

291

DEUS TUORUM MILITUM (L.M.)   Grenoble Church Melody

Unison

ALTERNATIVE TUNE

SAMSON (L.M.)   Adapted from GEORGE FREDERICK HANDEL (1685-1759)

This hymn may also be sung to the tune ST. BARTHOLOMEW, No. 313

They that wait upon the Lord shall renew their strength (Isaiah xl. 31)

AWAKE, our souls! away our fears!
  Let every trembling thought be gone!
Awake, and run the heavenly race,
  And put a cheerful courage on.

2 True, 'tis a strait and thorny road,
  And mortal spirits tire and faint;
But they forget the mighty God
  That feeds the strength of every saint.

3 The mighty God, whose matchless
  Is ever new and ever young, [power
And firm endures, while endless years
  Their everlasting circles run.

4 From Thee, the ever-flowing spring,
  Our souls shall drink a fresh supply;
While such as trust their native strength
  Shall melt away, and droop, and die.

5 Swift as an eagle cuts the air,
  We'll mount aloft to Thine abode;
On wings of love our souls shall fly,
  Nor tire along the heavenly road.

ISAAC WATTS (1674-1748)

292

ELLACOMBE   (D.C.M.)   *Mainz Gesangbuch* (c. 1833)

This hymn may also be sung to the tune LADYWELL, No. 90 (ii)

If we suffer, we shall also reign with him (2 Timothy ii. 12)

THE Son of God goes forth to war,
    A kingly crown to gain;
His blood-red banner streams afar:
    Who follows in His train?
Who best can drink his cup of woe,
    Triumphant over pain,
Who patient bears his cross below,
    He follows in His train.

2 The martyr first, whose eagle eye
    Could pierce beyond the grave,
Who saw His Master in the sky,
    And called on Him to save:
Like Him, with pardon on his tongue
    In midst of mortal pain,
He prayed for them that did the wrong:
    Who follows in his train?

3 A glorious band, the chosen few
    On whom the Spirit came,
Twelve valiant saints, their hope they knew,
    And mocked the cross and flame;
They met the tyrant's brandished steel,
    The lion's gory mane,
They bowed their necks, the death to feel:
    Who follows in their train?

4 A noble army, men and boys,
    The matron and the maid,
Around the Saviour's throne rejoice,
    In robes of light arrayed;
They climbed the steep ascent of heaven,
    Through peril, toil, and pain:
O God, to us may grace be given
    To follow in their train.

REGINALD HEBER (1783-1826)

293

RUSHFORD (L.M.)   HENRY GEORGE LEY (1887-)

ALTERNATIVE TUNE

DUKE STREET (L.M.)   JOHN HATTON (d. 1793)

Fight the good fight of faith (1 Timothy vi. 12)

FIGHT the good fight with all thy might;
Christ is thy strength, and Christ thy right;
Lay hold on life, and it shall be
Thy joy and crown eternally.

2 Run the straight race through God's good grace,
Lift up thine eyes, and seek His face;
Life with its way before thee lies;
Christ is the path and Christ the prize.

3 Cast care aside, lean on thy Guide,
His boundless mercy will provide,—
Trust, and thy trusting soul shall prove
Christ is its life, and Christ its love.

4 Faint not, nor fear, His arm is near;
He changeth not, and thou art dear;
Only believe, and thou shalt see
That Christ is all in all to thee.

JOHN SAMUEL BEWLEY MONSELL (1811-75)

294

TRURO (L.M.)   *Psalmodia Evangelica* (1789)

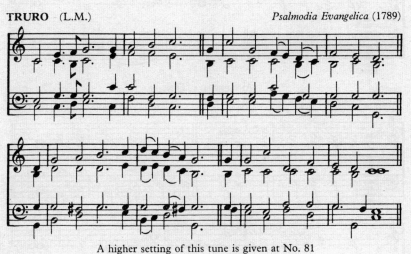

A higher setting of this tune is given at No. 81

Awake, awake, put on strength, O arm of the Lord (Isaiah li. 9)

ARM of the Lord, awake, awake!
   Thine own immortal strength put on;
With terror clothed, hell's kingdom shake,
And cast Thy foes with fury down.

2 As in the ancient days appear;
   The sacred annals speak Thy fame:
Be now omnipotently near,
   To endless ages still the same.

3 Thy arm, Lord, is not shortened now,
   It wants not now the power to save;
Still present with Thy people, Thou
   Bear'st them through life's disparted wave.

4 By death and hell pursued in vain,
   To Thee the ransomed seed shall come;
Shouting, their heavenly Zion gain,
   And pass through death triumphant home.

CHARLES WESLEY (1707-88)

295

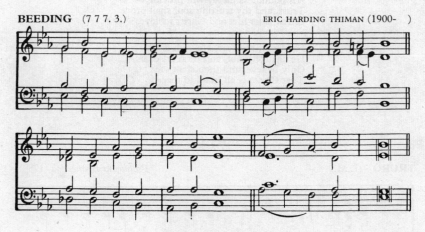

BEEDING (7 7 7. 3.)   ERIC HARDING THIMAN (1900-   )

ALTERNATIVE TUNE

VIGILATE (7 7 7. 3.)   WILLIAM HENRY MONK (1823-89)

Watch and pray (Matthew xxvi. 41)

CHRISTIAN, seek not yet repose;
  Hear thy guardian angel say,
'Thou art in the midst of foes:
    Watch and pray.'

2 Principalities and powers,
  Mustering their unseen array,
Wait for thy unguarded hours:
    Watch and pray.

3 Gird thy heavenly armour on;
  Wear it ever, night and day;
Ambushed lies the evil one:
    Watch and pray.

4 Hear the victors who o'ercame;
  Still they mark each warrior's way;
All with one sweet voice exclaim,
    'Watch and pray.'

5 Hear, above all, hear thy Lord,
  Him thou lovest to obey;
Hide within thy heart His word,
    'Watch and pray.'

6 Watch, as if on that alone
  Hung the issue of the day:
Pray, that help may be sent down:
    Watch and pray.

CHARLOTTE ELLIOTT (1789-1871)

296

MORNING LIGHT (7 6. 7 6. D.)   GEORGE JAMES WEBB (1803-87)

Watch ye, stand fast in the faith, quit you like men, be strong (1 Corinthians xvi. 13)

STAND up, stand up for Jesus,
  Ye soldiers of the cross!
Lift high His royal banner,
  It must not suffer loss.
From victory unto victory
  His army shall He lead,
Till every foe is vanquished,
  And Christ is Lord indeed.

2 Stand up, stand up for Jesus!
  The trumpet call obey;
Forth to the mighty conflict
  In this His glorious day.
Ye that are men, now serve Him
  Against unnumbered foes;
Let courage rise with danger,
  And strength to strength oppose.

3 Stand up, stand up for Jesus!
  Stand in His strength alone;
The arm of flesh will fail you,
  Ye dare not trust your own.
Put on the gospel armour,
  And, watching unto prayer,
Where duty calls, or danger,
  Be never wanting there.

4 Stand up, stand up for Jesus!
  The strife will not be long;
This day the noise of battle,
  The next the victor's song.
To him that overcometh
  A crown of life shall be;
He with the King of glory
  Shall reign eternally.

GEORGE DUFFIELD (1818-88)

297

UNIVERSITY COLLEGE (7 7. 7 7.) HENRY JOHN GAUNTLETT (1805-76)

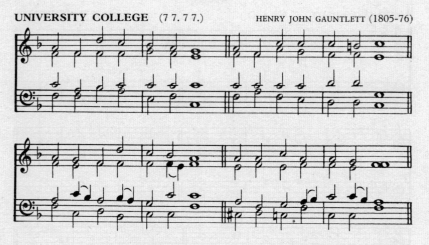

Be strong in the Lord, and in the power of his might (Ephesians vi. 10)

OFT in danger, oft in woe,
Onward, Christians, onward go;
Fight the fight, maintain the strife,
Strengthened with the Bread of life.

2 Shrink not, Christians; will ye yield?
Will ye quit the painful field?
Will ye flee in danger's hour?
Know ye not your Captain's power?

3 Let your drooping hearts be glad;
March, in heavenly armour clad;
Fight, nor think the battle long;
Victory soon shall tune your song.

4 Let not sorrow dim your eye,
Soon shall every tear be dry;
Let not fears your course impede,
Great your strength, if great your need.

5 Onward then in battle move,
More than conquerors ye shall prove;
Though opposed by many a foe,
Christian soldiers, onward go.

HENRY KIRKE WHITE (1785-1806),
FRANCES SARA FULLER-MAITLAND (1809-77) and others

IRISH (C.M.)   Melody from *A Collection of Hymns and Sacred Poems* (Dublin, 1749)

Thou desirest truth in the inward parts (Psalm li. 6)

O GOD of truth, whose living word
 Upholds whate'er hath breath,
Look down on Thy creation, Lord,
 Enslaved by sin and death.

2 Set up Thy standard, Lord, that we,
 Who claim a heavenly birth,
May march with Thee to smite the lies
 That vex Thy ransomed earth.

3 Ah! would we join that blest array,
 And follow in the might
Of Him, the Faithful and the True,
 In raiment clean and white?

4 We fight for truth? we fight for God?
 Poor slaves of lies and sin!
He who would fight for Thee on earth
 Must first be true within.

5 Then, God of truth, for whom we long,
 Thou who wilt hear our prayer,
Do Thine own battle in our hearts,
 And slay the falsehood there.

6 Yes, come! then, tried as in the fire,
 From every lie set free,
Thy perfect truth shall dwell in us,
 And we shall live in Thee.

THOMAS HUGHES (1823-96)

299

ST. ETHELWALD (S.M.)   WILLIAM HENRY MONK (1823-89)

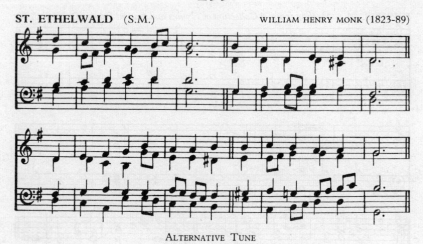

ALTERNATIVE TUNE

FROM STRENGTH TO STRENGTH (D.S.M.)

EDWARD WOODALL NAYLOR (1867-1934)

Take unto you the whole armour of God (Ephesians vi. 13)

SOLDIERS of Christ, arise,
　And put your armour on;
Strong in the strength which God
　Through His eternal Son; [supplies

2 Strong in the Lord of hosts,
　And in His mighty power;
Who in the strength of Jesus trusts
　Is more than conqueror.

3 Stand, then, in His great might,
　With all His strength endued;
And take, to arm you for the fight,
　The panoply of God.

4 To keep your armour bright
　Attend with constant care,
Still walking in your Captain's sight,
　And watching unto prayer.

5 From strength to strength go on;
　Wrestle, and fight, and pray;
Tread all the powers of darkness down,
　And win the well-fought day;

6 That, having all things done,
　And all your conflicts past,
Ye may o'ercome, through Christ alone,
　And stand complete at last.

CHARLES WESLEY (1707-88)

300

KEYNSHAM   (8 8 8.)   PEGGY SPENCER PALMER

I can do all things through Christ which strengtheneth me (Philippians iv. 13)

WHY should I fear the darkest hour,
　Or tremble at the tempter's power?
Jesus vouchsafes to be my tower.

2 Though hot the fight, why quit the field?
　Why must I either fly or yield,
　Since Jesus is my mighty shield?

3 I know not what may soon betide,
　Or how my wants shall be supplied;
　But Jesus knows, and will provide.

4 Though sin would fill me with distress,
　The throne of grace I dare address,
　For Jesus is my righteousness.

5 Though faint my prayers and cold my love,
　My steadfast hope shall not remove,
　While Jesus intercedes above.

6 Against me earth and hell combine;
　But on my side is power divine;
　Jesus is all, and He is mine!

JOHN NEWTON (1725-1807)

301

O PERFECT LOVE (11 10. 11 10.)   JOSEPH BARNBY (1838-96)

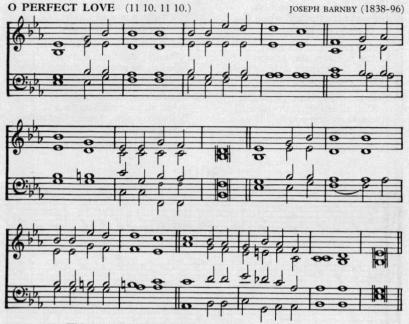

This hymn may also be sung to the tune ST. OSYTH, No. 302

We rest on thee, and in thy name we go against this multitude (2 Chronicles xiv. 11)

'WE rest on Thee,' our shield and our defender;
    We go not forth alone against the foe;
Strong in Thy strength, safe in Thy keeping tender,
    'We rest on Thee, and in Thy name we go.'

2 Yea, 'in Thy name', O Captain of salvation!
    In Thy dear name, all other names above;
Jesus our righteousness, our sure foundation,
    Our Prince of glory and our King of love.

3 'We go' in faith, our own great weakness feeling,
    And needing more each day Thy grace to know:
Yet from our hearts a song of triumph pealing;
    'We rest on Thee, and in Thy name we go.'

4 'We rest on Thee,' our shield and our defender;
    Thine is the battle; Thine shall be the praise
When passing through the gates of pearly splendour,
    Victors, we rest, *with* Thee, through endless days.

EDITH GILLING CHERRY (d. 1897)

The following hymns also refer to this theme:

177 Soldiers of the cross, arise
251 Come, ye that love the Lord
254 How blest is life if lived for Thee
256 Children of the heavenly King
303 He who would valiant be
305 Who is on the Lord's side?

SERVICE

302

ST. OSYTH (11 10. 11 10.) THOMAS WOOD (1892-)

Unison

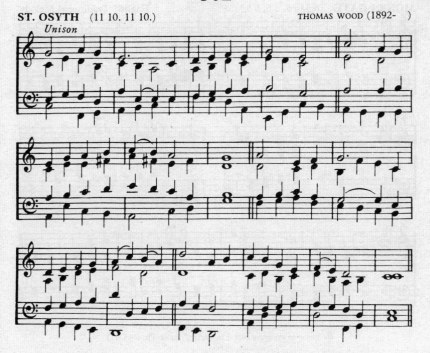

This hymn may also be sung to the tune O PERFECT LOVE, No. 301

With good will doing service, as to the Lord, and not to men (Ephesians vi. 7)

O LOVING Lord, who art for ever seeking
　Men of Thy mind, intent to do Thy will,
Strong in Thy strength, Thy power and grace bespeaking;
　Faithful to Thee, through good report and ill—

2 To Thee we come, and humbly make confession,
　Faithless so oft, in thought and word and deed,
Asking that we may have, in true possession,
　Thy free forgiveness in the hour of need.

3 In duties small, be Thou our inspiration,
　In large affairs endue us with Thy might;
Through faithful service cometh full salvation,
　So may we serve, Thy will our chief delight.

4 Not disobedient to the heavenly vision,
　Faithful in all things, seeking not reward,
Then, following Thee, may we fulfil our mission,
　True to ourselves, our brethren, and our Lord.

WILLIAM VAUGHAN JENKINS (1868-1920)

303

MONKS GATE   (6 5. 6 5. 6 6. 6 5.)   English Traditional Melody

Be strong in the grace that is in Christ Jesus (2 Timothy ii. 1)

HE who would valiant be
    'Gainst all disaster,
Let him in constancy
    Follow the Master.
There's no discouragement
Shall make him once relent
His first avowed intent
    To be a pilgrim.

2 Whoso beset him round
    With dismal stories,
Do but themselves confound;
    His strength the more is.
No foes shall stay his might,
Though he with giants fight,
He will make good his right
    To be a pilgrim.

3 Since, Lord, thou dost defend
    Us with Thy Spirit,
We know we at the end
    Shall life inherit.
Then fancies flee away!
I'll fear not what men say,
I'll labour night and day
    To be a pilgrim.

After JOHN BUNYAN (1628-88).
PERCY DEARMER (1867-1936)

304

HEATHLANDS (7 7. 7 7. 7 7.)   HENRY SMART (1813-79)

This hymn may also be sung to the tune WELLS, No. 198

Glorify God in your body, and in your spirit, which are God's (1 Corinthians vi. 20)

JESUS, Master, whose I am,
　Purchased, Thine alone to be,
By Thy blood, O spotless Lamb,
　Shed so willingly for me,
Let my heart be all Thine own,
Let me live to Thee alone.

2 Other lords have long held sway;
　　Now, Thy name alone to bear,
Thy dear voice alone obey,
　　Is my daily, hourly prayer:
Whom have I in heaven but Thee?
Nothing else my joy can be.

3 Jesus, Master, whom I serve,
　　Though so feebly and so ill,
Strengthen hand and heart and nerve
　　All Thy bidding to fulfil;
Open Thou mine eyes to see
All the work Thou hast for me.

4 Jesus, Master, wilt Thou use
　　One who owes Thee more than all?
As Thou wilt! I would not choose;
　　Only let me hear Thy call.
Jesus, let me always be
In Thy service, glad and free.

FRANCES RIDLEY HAVERGAL (1836-79)

305

HERMAS (6 5. 6 5. *Ter.*) FRANCES RIDLEY HAVERGAL (1836-79)

The Lord our God will we serve, and his voice will we obey (Joshua xxiv. 24)

WHO is on the Lord's side?
　Who will serve the King?
Who will be His helpers
　Other lives to bring?
Who will leave the world's side?
　Who will face the foe?
Who is on the Lord's side?
　Who for Him will go?
　　By Thy call of mercy,
　　　By Thy grace divine,
　　We are on the Lord's side;
　　　Saviour, we are Thine.

2 Jesus, Thou hast bought us,
　Not with gold or gem,
But with Thine own life-blood,
　For Thy diadem.
With Thy blessing filling
　Each who comes to Thee,
Thou hast made us willing,
　Thou hast made us free.
　　By Thy grand redemption,
　　　By Thy grace divine,
　　We are on the Lord's side;
　　　Saviour, we are Thine.

3 Fierce may be the conflict,
    Strong may be the foe,
  But the King's own army
    None can overthrow.
  Round His standard ranging,
    Victory is secure,
  For His truth unchanging
    Makes the triumph sure.
      Joyfully enlisting,
        By Thy grace divine,
      We are on the Lord's side;
        Saviour, we are Thine.

4 Chosen to be soldiers
    In an alien land,
  Chosen, called, and faithful,
    For our Captain's band,
  In the service royal
    Let us not grow cold;
  Let us be right loyal,
    Noble, true, and bold.
      Master, Thou wilt keep us,
        By Thy grace divine,
      Always on the Lord's side,
        Saviour, always Thine.

FRANCES RIDLEY HAVERGAL (1836-79)

306

ST. BRIDE (S.M.)   SAMUEL HOWARD (1710-82)

This hymn may also be sung to the tune NARENZA, No. 312

Based on Leviticus viii. 35

A CHARGE to keep I have,
    A God to glorify,
  A never-dying soul to save,
    And fit it for the sky:

2 To serve the present age,
    My calling to fulfil:
  O may it all my powers engage,
    To do my Master's will!

3 Arm me with jealous care,
    As in Thy sight to live;
  And O, Thy servant, Lord, prepare
    A strict account to give.

4 Help me to watch and pray,
    And on Thyself rely,
  And let me ne'er my trust betray,
    But press to realms on high.

CHARLES WESLEY (1707-88)

307

ANGEL'S SONG (Song 34)   (L.M.)   ORLANDO GIBBONS (1583-1625)

This hymn may also be sung to the tune FULDA, No. 308

I have set the Lord always before me (Psalm xvi. 8)

FORTH in Thy name, O Lord, I go,
　My daily labour to pursue,
Thee, only Thee, resolved to know
　In all I think, or speak, or do.

2 The task Thy wisdom hath assigned
　　O let me cheerfully fulfil,
　In all my works Thy presence find,
　　And prove Thy good and perfect will.

3 Thee may I set at my right hand,
　　Whose eyes my inmost substance see,
　And labour on at Thy command,
　　And offer all my works to Thee.

4 Give me to bear Thy easy yoke,
　　And every moment watch and pray,
　And still to things eternal look,
　　And hasten to Thy glorious day;

5 For Thee delightfully employ
　　Whate'er Thy bounteous grace hath given,
　And run my course with even joy,
　　And closely walk with Thee to heaven.

CHARLES WESLEY (1707-88)

308

FULDA (L.M.)   GARDINER'S *Sacred Melodies* (1812)

This hymn may also be sung to the tune PHILIPPINE, No. 367

A vessel unto honour, sanctified, and meet for the master's use (2 Timothy ii. 21)

L ORD, speak to me, that I may speak
    In living echoes of Thy tone;
As Thou hast sought, so let me seek
    Thy erring children lost and lone.

2 O lead me, Lord, that I may lead
    The wandering and the wavering feet;
O feed me, Lord, that I may feed
    Thy hungering ones with manna sweet.

3 O strengthen me, that, while I stand
    Firm on the rock, and strong in Thee,
I may stretch out a loving hand
    To wrestlers with the troubled sea.

4 O teach me, Lord, that I may teach
    The precious things Thou dost impart;
And wing my words, that they may reach
    The hidden depths of many a heart.

5 O fill me with Thy fullness, Lord,
    Until my very heart o'erflow
In kindling thought and glowing word,
    Thy love to tell, Thy praise to show.

6 O use me, Lord, use even me,
    Just as Thou wilt, and when, and where,
Until Thy blessed face I see,
    Thy rest, Thy joy, Thy glory share.

FRANCES RIDLEY HAVERGAL (1836-79)

309

OLD 104TH (10. 10. 11. 11.)   RAVENSCROFT'S *Psalter* (1621)

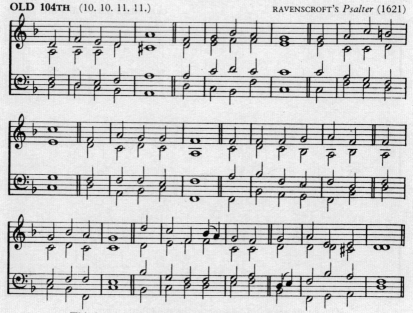

This hymn may also be sung to the tune HANOVER, No. 25

Based on SUPREME QUALIS ARBITER

We have this treasure in earthen vessels (2 Corinthians iv. 7)

DISPOSER supreme, and Judge of the earth,
Who choosest for Thine the weak and the poor;
To frail earthen vessels and things of no worth
Entrusting Thy riches which aye shall endure.

2 Those vessels soon fail, though full of Thy light,
And at Thy decree are broken and gone;
Then brightly appeareth Thy truth in its might,
As through the clouds riven the lightnings have shone.

3 Like clouds are they borne to do Thy great will,
And swift as the winds about the world go;
The Word with His wisdom their spirits doth fill,
They thunder, they lighten, the waters o'erflow.

4 Their sound goeth forth, ' Christ Jesus is Lord! '
Then Satan doth fear, his citadels fall:
As when the dread trumpets went forth at Thy word,
And one long blast shattered the Canaanites' wall.

5 Then loud be their trump, and stirring their sound,
To rouse us, O Lord, from slumber of sin;
The lights Thou hast kindled in darkness around,
O may they illumine our spirits within!

6 All honour and praise, dominion and might,
To Thee, Three in One, eternally be,
Who, shedding around us Thy marvellous light,
Dost call us from darkness Thy glory to see.

JEAN-BAPTISTE DE SANTEUIL (1630-97);
tr. ISAAC WILLIAMS (1802-65) and others.

310

VIGIL (6 4. 6 4. 6 7. 6 4.)   ARTHUR PATTON (d. 1892)

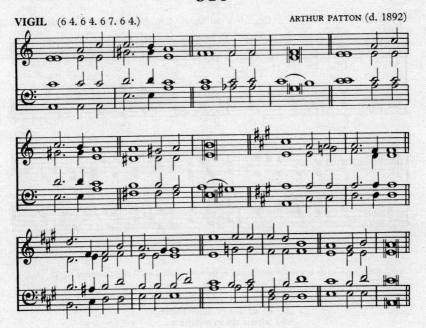

Let us not sleep, as do others; but let us watch and be sober (1 Thessalonians v. 6)

Hark, 'tis the watchman's cry:
   Wake, brethren, wake!
Jesus Himself is nigh:
   Wake, brethren, wake!
Sleep is for sons of night:
Ye are children of the light;
Yours is the glory bright;
   Wake, brethren, wake!

2 Call to each wakening band:
   Watch, brethren, watch!
Clear is our Lord's command:
   Watch, brethren, watch!
Be ye as men that wait
Always at their Master's gate,
E'en though He tarry late;
   Watch, brethren, watch!

3 Heed we the Master's call:
   Work, brethren, work!
There's room enough for all,
   Work, brethren, work!
This vineyard of the Lord
Constant labour will afford;
He will your work reward:
   Work, brethren, work!

4 Hear we the Saviour's voice:
   Pray, brethren, pray!
Would ye His heart rejoice,
   Pray, brethren, pray!
Sin calls for ceaseless fear,
Weakness needs the strong One near;
Long as ye struggle here,
   Pray, brethren, pray!

5 Sound now the final chord,
   Praise, brethren, praise!
Thrice holy is the Lord,
   Praise, brethren, praise!
What more befits the tongues
Soon to join the angels' songs?
Whilst heaven the note prolongs,
   Praise, brethren, praise!

ANON., from *The Revival* (1859)

311

SANDYS (S.M.)   English Traditional Carol from SANDYS' *Collection* (1833)

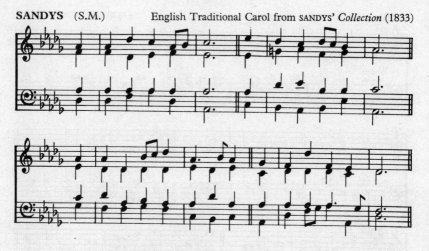

Whatsoever ye do in word or deed, do all in the name of the Lord Jesus (Colossians iii. 17

TEACH me, my God and King,
   In all things Thee to see,
And what I do in anything
   To do it as for Thee!

2 A man that looks on glass,
   On it may stay his eye;
Or if he pleaseth, through it pass,
   And then the heaven espy.

3 All may of Thee partake;
   Nothing can be so mean,
Which, with this tincture, ' for Thy sake,'
   Will not grow bright and clean.

4 A servant with this clause
   Makes drudgery divine:
Who sweeps a room, as for Thy laws,
   Makes that and the action fine.

5 This is the famous stone
   That turneth all to gold;
For that which God doth touch and own
   Cannot for less be told.

GEORGE HERBERT (1593-1633)

312

NARENZA (S.M.)

Cöln Gesangbuch (1619)
Adapted by WILLIAM HENRY HAVERGAL (1793-1870)

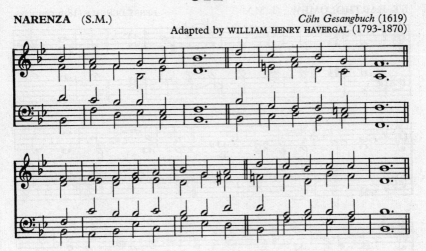

Blessed are those servants, whom the lord when he cometh shall find watching (Luke xii. 37)

YE servants of the Lord,
   Each in his office wait,
Observant of His heavenly word,
   And watchful at His gate.

2 Let all your lamps be bright,
   And trim the golden flame;
Gird up your loins, as in His sight,
   For holy in His name.

3 Watch: 'tis your Lord's command;
   And while we speak He's near;
Mark the first signal of His hand,
   And ready all appear.

4 O happy servant he,
   In such employment found!
He shall his Lord with rapture see,
   And be with honour crowned.

5 Christ shall the banquet spread
   With His own royal hand,
And raise that faithful servant's head
   Amid the angelic band.

PHILIP DODDRIDGE (1702-51)

313

ST. BARTHOLOMEW (L.M.)   HENRY DUNCALF (18th century)

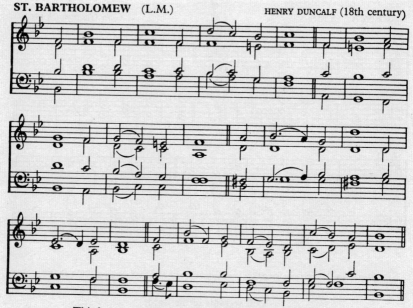

This hymn may also be sung to the tune BIRLING, No. 29

Ye know that your labour is not in vain in the Lord (1 Corinthians xv. 58)

GO, labour on; spend and be spent;
    Thy joy to do the Father's will;
It is the way the Master went:
    Should not the servant tread it still?

2 Go, labour on while it is day;
    The world's dark night is hastening on;
Speed, speed thy work; cast sloth away;
    It is not thus that souls are won.

3 Men die in darkness at thy side,
    Without a hope to cheer the tomb;
Take up the torch and wave it wide,
    The torch that lights time's thickest gloom.

4 Toil on, faint not, keep watch, and pray;
    Be wise the erring soul to win;
Go forth into the world's highway,
    Compel the wanderer to come in.

5 Toil on, and in thy toil rejoice;
    For toil comes rest, for exile home;
Soon shalt thou hear the Bridegroom's voice,
    The midnight peal, ' Behold, I come!'

HORATIUS BONAR (1808-89)

See also the section: THE CHURCH OF GOD: HOME AND OVERSEAS MISSIONS, Nos. 164-186.

The following hymns also refer to this theme:

336 O Jesus, I have promised   342 My glorious Victor, Prince divine

314

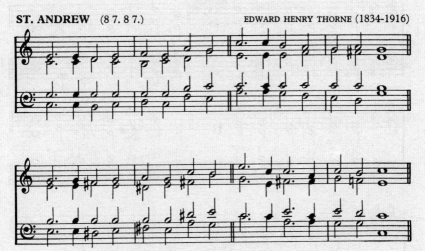

ST. ANDREW (8 7. 8 7.)   EDWARD HENRY THORNE (1834-1916)

This hymn may also be sung to the tune SHIPSTON, No. 252

He saith unto them, Follow me (Matthew iv. 19)

JESUS calls us! O'er the tumult
   Of our life's wild restless sea,
Day by day His sweet voice soundeth,
   Saying, ' Christian, follow Me.'

2 As, of old, apostles heard it
   By the Galilean lake,
Turned from home and toil and kindred,
   Leaving all for His dear sake.

3 Jesus calls us from the worship
   Of the vain world's golden store,
From each idol that would keep us,
   Saying, ' Christian, love Me more.'

4 In our joys and in our sorrows,
   Days of toil and hours of ease,
Still He calls, in cares and pleasures,
   ' Christian, love Me more than these.'

5 Jesus calls us! By Thy mercies,
   Saviour, make us hear Thy call,
Give our hearts to Thy obedience,
   Serve and love Thee best of all.

CECIL FRANCES ALEXANDER (1818-95)

315

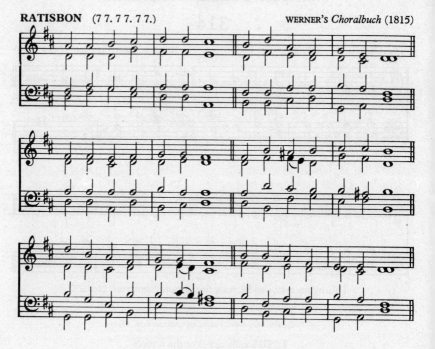

RATISBON (7 7. 7 7. 7 7.)   WERNER'S *Choralbuch* (1815)

Unto you that fear my name shall the Sun of righteousness arise (Malachi iv. 2)

CHRIST, whose glory fills the skies,
　　Christ, the true, the only light,
Sun of righteousness, arise,.
　　Triumph o'er the shades of night.
Dayspring from on high, be near;
Daystar, in my heart appear.

2 Dark and cheerless is the morn
　　Unaccompanied by Thee;
Joyless is the day's return,
　　Till Thy mercy's beams I see,
Till they inward light impart,
Glad my eyes, and warm my heart.

3 Visit, then, this soul of mine;
　　Pierce the gloom of sin and grief;
Fill me, radiancy divine;
　　Scatter all my unbelief;
More and more Thyself display,
Shining to the perfect day.

CHARLES WESLEY (1707-88)

316

WELLS (7 7. 7 7. 7 7.)

Melody by DMITRI STEPANOVITCH BORTNIANSKI (1752-1825)
Harmonized by ERIK ROUTLEY (1917-)

This hymn may also be sung to the tune RATISBON, No. 315

Yield yourselves unto God, as those that are alive from the dead (Romans vi. 13)

FATHER, Son, and Holy Ghost,
    One in Three, and Three in One,
As by the celestial host,
    Let Thy will on earth be done;
Praise by all to Thee be given,
Glorious Lord of earth and heaven.

2 If a sinner such as I
    May to Thy great glory live,
All my actions sanctify,
    All my words and thoughts receive;
Claim me for Thy service, claim
All I have, and all I am.

3 Take my soul and body's powers;
    Take my memory, mind, and will,
All my goods, and all my hours,
    All I know, and all I feel,
All I think, or speak, or do;
Take my heart;—but make it new!

4 O my God, Thine own I am,
    Let me give Thee back Thine own;
Freedom, friends, and health, and
    Consecrate to Thee alone; [fame,
Thine to live, thrice happy I;
Happier still if Thine I die.

5 Father, Son, and Holy Ghost,
    One in Three, and Three in One,
As by the celestial host,
    Let Thy will on earth be done;
Praise by all to Thee be given,
Glorious Lord of earth and heaven.

CHARLES WESLEY (1707-88)

317

Irish Traditional Melody

SLANE (10 10. 10 10. Irreg. Dactylic)   Harmonized by ERIK ROUTLEY (1917-)

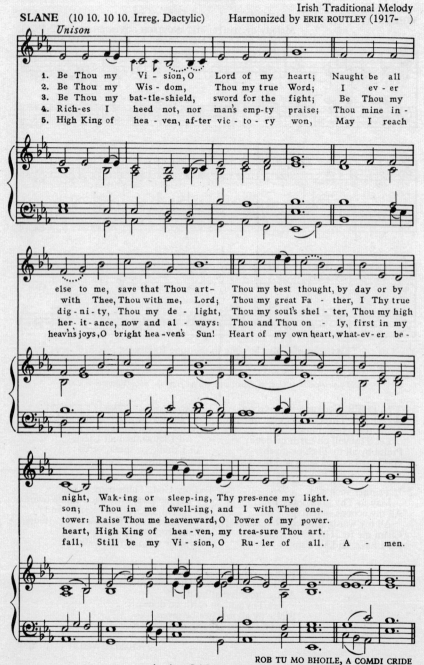

Unison

1. Be Thou my Vi - sion, O Lord of my heart; Naught be all
2. Be Thou my Wis - dom, Thou my true Word; I ev - er
3. Be Thou my bat-tle-shield, sword for the fight; Be Thou my
4. Rich - es I heed not, nor man's emp-ty praise; Thou mine in -
5. High King of hea - ven, af-ter vic-to-ry won, May I reach

else to me, save that Thou art— Thou my best thought, by day or by
with Thee, Thou with me, Lord; Thou my great Fa - ther, I Thy true
dig - ni - ty, Thou my de - light, Thou my soul's shel - ter, Thou my high
her- it-ance, now and al - ways: Thou and Thou on - ly, first in my
heav'ns joys, O bright hea-ven's Sun! Heart of my own heart, what-ev- er be-

night, Wak-ing or sleep-ing, Thy pres-ence my light.
son; Thou in me dwell-ing, and I with Thee one.
tower: Raise Thou me heavenward, O Power of my power.
heart, High King of hea - ven, my trea-sure Thou art.
fall, Still be my Vi - sion, O Ru - ler of all. A - men.

ROB TU MO BHOILE, A COMDI CRIDE
Ancient Irish; tr. ELEANOR HENRIETTA HULL, (1860-1935)
versified by MARY ELIZABETH BYRNE (1880-1931)

(Colossians i. 18)

318

FRANCONIA (S.M.)   WILLIAM HENRY HAVERGAL (1793-1870)
Founded on a melody in KÖNIG'S *Choralbuch* (1738)

ALTERNATIVE TUNE

PANIS VERE (S.M.)   BASIL HARWOOD (1859-1949)

Blessed are the pure in heart: for they shall see God (Matthew v. 8)

BLEST are the pure in heart,
For they shall see our God:
The secret of the Lord is theirs;
Their soul is Christ's abode.

2 The Lord, who left the heavens
Our life and peace to bring,
To dwell in lowliness with men,
Their pattern and their King,—

3 Still to the lowly soul
He doth Himself impart,
And for His dwelling and His throne.
Chooseth the pure in heart.

4 Lord, we Thy presence seek;
May ours this blessing be;
Give us a pure and lowly heart,
A temple meet for Thee.

JOHN KEBLE (1792-1866) and others

319

CARRICK   (7 6. 7 6. 7 7. 7 6.)   KENNETH GEORGE FINLAY (1882-　)

Small notes for organ are intended for final verse, the latter half of which should be sung in unison.

Be still, and know that I am God (Psalm xlvi. 10)

OPEN, Lord, my inward ear,
　And bid my heart rejoice;
Bid my quiet spirit hear
　Thy comfortable voice;
Never in the whirlwind found,
　Or where earthquakes rock the place,
Still and silent is the sound,
　The whisper of Thy grace.

2 From the world of sin, and noise,
　　And hurry I withdraw;
For the small and inward voice
　　I wait with humble awe;
Silent am I now and still,
　　Dare not in Thy presence move;
To my waiting soul reveal
　　The secret of Thy love.

*3 Thou didst undertake for me,
　　For me to death wast sold;
Wisdom in a mystery
　　Of bleeding love unfold;
Teach the lesson of Thy cross,
　　Let me die with Thee to reign;
All things let me count but loss,
　　So I may Thee regain.

4 Show me, as my soul can bear,
   The depth of inbred sin;
All the unbelief declare,
   The pride that lurks within;
Take me, whom Thyself hast bought,
   Bring into captivity
Every high aspiring thought
   That would not stoop to Thee.

5 Lord, my time is in Thy hand,
   My soul to Thee convert;
Thou canst make me understand,
   Though I am slow of heart;
Thine in whom I live and move,
   Thine the work, the praise is Thine;
Thou art wisdom, power, and love
   And all Thou art is mine.

CHARLES WESLEY (1707-88)

If desired, verse 3 may be omitted

320

AYRSHIRE (C.M.)   KENNETH GEORGE FINLAY (1882-)

The very God of peace sanctify you wholly (1 Thessalonians v. 23)

O DEAREST Lord, Thy sacred head
   With thorns was pierced for me;
O pour Thy blessing on my head
   That I may think for Thee.

2 O dearest Lord, Thy sacred hands
   With nails were pierced for me;
O shed Thy blessing on my hands
   That they may work for Thee.

3 O dearest Lord, Thy sacred feet
   With nails were pierced for me;
O pour Thy blessing on my feet
   That they may follow Thee.

4 O dearest Lord, Thy sacred heart
   With spear was pierced for me;
O pour Thy spirit in my heart
   That I may live for Thee.

HENRY ERNEST HARDY (1869-1946)

321

ST. PETER (C.M.)   ALEXANDER ROBERT REINAGLE (1799-1877)

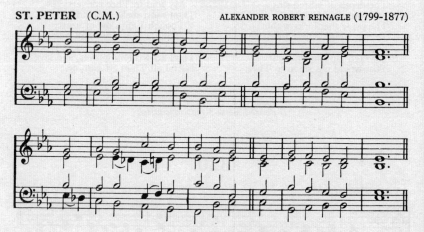

Thou shalt love the Lord thy God with all thy heart (Luke x. 27)

MY God, accept my heart this day,
And make it always Thine,
That I from Thee no more may stray,
No more from Thee decline.

2 Before the cross of Him who died,
Behold, I prostrate fall;
Let every sin be crucified,
And Christ be all in all.

3 Anoint me with Thy heavenly grace,
And seal me for Thine own;
That I may see Thy glorious face,
And worship near Thy throne.

4 Let every thought, and work, and word
To Thee be ever given:
Then life shall be Thy service, Lord,
And death the gate of heaven.

MATTHEW BRIDGES (1800-94)

322

BEATITUDO (C.M.)   JOHN BACCHUS DYKES (1823-76)

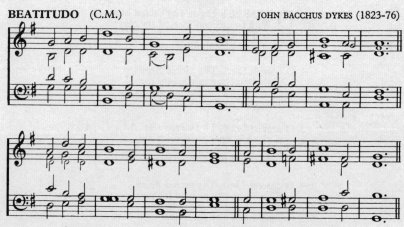

This hymn may also be sung to the tune CAITHNESS, No. 323

Oh that I were as in months past, as in the days when God preserved me (Job xxix. 2)

O FOR a closer walk with God
   A calm and heavenly frame,
A light to shine upon the road
   That leads me to the Lamb!

2 Where is the blessedness I knew
   When first I saw the Lord?
Where is the soul-refreshing view
   Of Jesus and His word?

3 What peaceful hours I once enjoyed!
   How sweet their memory still!
But they have left an aching void
   The world can never fill.

4 Return, O holy Dove! return,
   Sweet messenger of rest!
I hate the sins that made Thee mourn,
   And drove Thee from my breast.

5 The dearest idol I have known,
   Whate'er that idol be,
Help me to tear it from Thy throne,
   And worship only Thee.

6 So shall my walk be close with God,
   Calm and serene my frame;
So purer light shall mark the road
   That leads me to the Lamb.

WILLIAM COWPER (1731-1800)

323

CAITHNESS (C.M.)   *Scottish Psalter (1635)*

This hymn may also be sung to the tune ST. FLAVIAN, No. 354

Search me, O God, and know my heart (Psalm cxxxix. 23)

SEARCH me, O God! my actions try,
   And let my life appear
As seen by Thine all-searching eye;
   To mine my ways make clear.

2 Search all my sense, and know my
     heart,
   Who only canst make known,
And let the deep, the hidden part
   To me be fully shown.

3 Throw light into the darkened cells,
   Where passion reigns within;
Quicken my conscience till it feels
   The loathsomeness of sin.

4 Search, till Thy fiery glance has cast
   Its holy light through all,
And I by grace am brought at last
   Before Thy face to fall.

5 Thus prostrate I shall learn of Thee,
   What now I feebly prove,
That God alone in Christ can be
   Unutterable love!

FRANCIS BOTTOME (1823-94)

324

ST. GEORGE (S.M.)   HENRY JOHN GAUNTLETT (1805-76)

When he saw the multitudes, he was moved with compassion (Matthew ix. 36)

JESUS, I fain would find
    Thy zeal for God in me,
Thy yearning pity for mankind,
    Thy burning charity.

2 In me Thy Spirit dwell;
    In me Thy mercies move:
So shall the fervour of my zeal
    Be the pure flame of love.

CHARLES WESLEY (1707-88)

325

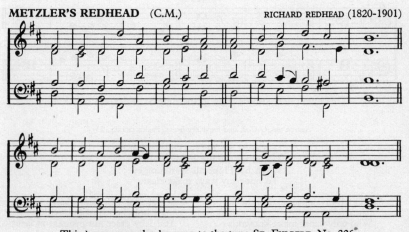

METZLER'S REDHEAD (C.M.)   RICHARD REDHEAD (1820-1901)

This hymn may also be sung to the tune ST. FULBERT, No. 326

The love of God is shed abroad in our hearts by the Holy Ghost which is given unto us (Romans v. 5)

* MY God! I know, I feel Thee mine,
    And will not quit my claim,
Till all I have is lost in Thine
And all renewed I am.

*2 I hold Thee with a trembling hand,
    But will not let Thee go,
Till steadfastly by faith I stand
And all Thy goodness know.

3 Jesus, Thine all-victorious love
    Shed in my heart abroad;
    Then shall my feet no longer rove,
      Rooted and fixed in God.

4 O that in me the sacred fire
    Might now begin to glow,
    Burn up the dross of base desire,
      And make the mountains flow!

5 O that it now from heaven might fall,
    And all my sins consume!
    Come, Holy Ghost, for Thee I call,
      Spirit of burning, come!

6 Refining fire, go through my heart,
    Illuminate my soul;
    Scatter Thy life through every part,
      And sanctify the whole.

CHARLES WESLEY (1707-88)

If desired, verses 1 and 2 may be omitted

326

ST. FULBERT (C.M.)   HENRY JOHN GAUNTLETT (1805-76)

O JESUS CHRISTUS, WACHS' IN MIR

Grow in grace, and in the knowledge of our Lord and Saviour Jesus Christ (2 Peter iii. 18)

O JESUS Christ, grow Thou in me,
    And all things else recede;
My heart be daily nearer Thee,
    From sin be daily freed.

2 Each day let Thy supporting might
    My weakness still embrace;
My darkness vanish in Thy light,
    Thy life my death efface.

3 In Thy bright beams which on me fall,
    Fade every evil thought;
That I am nothing, Thou art all,
    I would be daily taught.

4 More of Thy glory let me see,
    Thou Holy, Wise, and True!
I would Thy living image be,
    In joy and sorrow too.

5 Fill me with gladness from above,
    Hold me by strength divine!
Lord, let the glow of Thy great love
    Through my whole being shine.

6 Make this poor self grow less and less,
    Be Thou my life and aim;
O make me daily, through Thy grace,
    More meet to bear Thy name!

JOHANN CASPAR LAVATER (1741-1801);
tr. ELIZABETH LEE SMITH (1817-98)

327

INNSBRUCK NEW   (8 8 6. D.)   Based on HEINRICH ISAAK (*c.* 1455-*c.*1527)

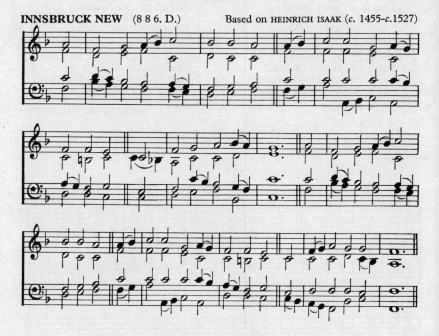

Casting all your care upon him; for he careth for you (1 Peter v. 7)

O LORD, how happy should we be
  If we could cast our care on Thee,
    If we from self could rest,
And feel at heart that One above,
In perfect wisdom, perfect love,
    Is working for the best.

2 How far from this our daily life,
  Ever disturbed by anxious strife,
    By sudden wild alarms.
O, could we but relinquish all
Our earthly props, and simply fall
    On Thine almighty arms.

3 Could we but kneel, and cast our load,
  E'en while we pray, upon our God,
    Then rise with lightened cheer,
Sure that the Father, who is nigh
To still the famished raven's cry,
    Will hear, in that we fear.

4 Lord, make these faithless hearts of ours
  Thy lessons learn from birds and flowers:
    Make them from self to cease,
Leave all things to a Father's will,
And taste, before Him lying still,
    E'en in affliction, peace.

JOSEPH ANSTICE (1808-36)

328

MAGDALEN COLLEGE (8 8 6. D.)   WILLIAM HAYES (1706-77)

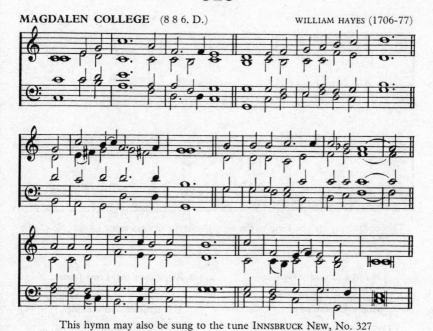

This hymn may also be sung to the tune INNSBRUCK NEW, No. 327

The love of Christ, which passeth knowledge (Ephesians iii. 19)

O LOVE divine, how sweet thou art!
　　When shall I find my longing heart
　　　All taken up by thee?
I thirst, I faint, I die to prove
The greatness of redeeming love,
　　　The love of Christ to me.

2 Stronger His love than death or hell;
　　Its riches are unsearchable;
　　　The first-born sons of light
Desire in vain its depth to see;
They cannot reach the mystery,
　　　The length, and breadth, and height.

3 God only knows the love of God;
　　O that it now were shed abroad
　　　In this poor stony heart!
For love I sigh, for love I pine;
This only portion, Lord, be mine,
　　　Be mine this better part.

4 O that I could for ever sit
　　Like Mary at the Master's feet!
　　　Be this my happy choice:
My only care, delight, and bliss,
My joy, my heaven on earth, be this,
　　　To hear the Bridegroom's voice.

CHARLES WESLEY (1707-88)

M   341

329

ST. ALPHEGE   (7 6. 7 6.)   HENRY JOHN GAUNTLETT (1805-76)

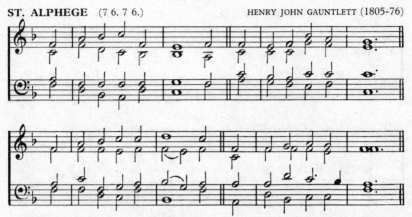

This hymn may also be sung to the tune CHRISTUS DER IST MEIN LEBEN, No. 330

Yield yourselves unto God, as those that are alive from the dead (Romans vi. 13)

IN full and glad surrender
   I give myself to Thee;
Thine utterly, and only,
   And evermore to be.

2 O Son of God, who lov'st me,
   I will be Thine alone;
And all I have, and all I am,
   Shall henceforth be Thine own.

3 Reign over me, Lord Jesus;
   O make my heart Thy throne:
It shall be Thine, my Saviour,
   It shall be Thine alone.

4 O come and reign, Lord Jesus,
   Rule over everything;
And keep me always loyal
   And true to Thee, my King.

FRANCES RIDLEY HAVERGAL (1836-79)

330

CHRISTUS DER IST MEIN LEBEN (7 6. 7 6.)

Melody by MELCHIOR VULPIUS (*c.* 1560-1616)
Adapted and harmonized by JOHANN SEBASTIAN BACH (1658-1750)

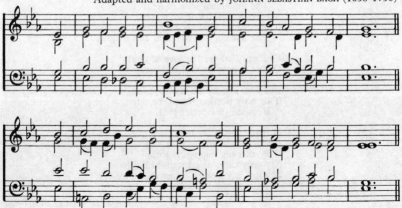

Deliver me, O Lord, from mine enemies: I flee unto thee to hide me (Psalm cxliii. 9)

O LAMB of God, still keep me
  Close to Thy piercèd side;
'Tis only there in safety
  And peace I can abide.

2 What foes and snares surround me,
    What lusts and fears within!
  The grace that sought and found me,
    Alone can keep me clean.

3 'Tis only in Thee hiding
    I feel myself secure;
  Only in Thee abiding,
    The conflict can endure.

4 Thine arm the victory gaineth
    O'er every hateful foe;
  Thy love my heart sustaineth
    In all its cares and woe.

5 Soon shall my eyes behold Thee
    With rapture face to face;
  One half hath not been told me
    Of all Thy power and grace;

6 Thy beauty, Lord, and glory,
    The wonders of Thy love,
  Shall be the endless story
    Of all Thy saints above.

JAMES GEORGE DECK (1802-84)

331

EWHURST   (8 8 8. 7.)   CECIL J. ALLEN (1886-)

Christ Jesus came into the world to save sinners (1 Timothy i. 15)

I AM not skilled to understand
  What God hath willed, what God hath planned;
I only know at His right hand
  Stands One who is my Saviour.

2 I take Him at His word and deed:
  'Christ died to save me,' this I read;
  And in my heart I find a need
    Of Him to be my Saviour.

3 That He should leave His place on
      high
  And come for sinful man to die,
  You count it strange? So once did I,
    Before I knew my Saviour.

4 And O, that He fulfilled may see
  The travail of His soul in me,
  And with His work contented be,
    As I with my dear Saviour!

5 Yea, living, dying, let me bring
  My strength, my solace, from this
      spring,
  That He who lives to be my King
    Once died to be my Saviour.

DORA GREENWELL (1821-82)

343

332

DINBYCH (D.S.M.)   Abridged from JOSEPH PARRY (1841-1903)

ALTERNATIVE TUNE

ICH HALTE TREULICH STILL (D.S.M.)   JOHANN SEBASTIAN BACH (1685-1750)

This hymn may also be sung to the tunes DIADEMATA, No. 72, and LEOMINSTER, No. 333

Christ Jesus, who of God is made unto us . . . sanctification (1 Corinthians i. 30)

JESUS, my strength, my hope,
  On Thee I cast my care,
With humble confidence look up,
  And know Thou hear'st my prayer.
Give me on Thee to wait,
  Till I can all things do,
On Thee, almighty to create,
  Almighty to renew.

2 I want a godly fear,
    A quick-discerning eye
  That looks to Thee when sin is near,
    And sees the tempter fly:
  A spirit still prepared,
    And armed with jealous care,
  For ever standing on its guard
    And watching unto prayer.

3 I want a true regard,
    A single, steady aim,
  Unmoved by threatening or reward,
    To Thee and Thy great name;
  A jealous, just concern
    For Thine immortal praise;
  A pure desire that all may learn
    And glorify Thy grace.

4 I rest upon Thy word;
    The promise is for me;
  My succour and salvation, Lord,
    Shall surely come from Thee:
  But let me still abide,
    Nor from my hope remove,
  Till Thou my patient spirit guide
    Into Thy perfect love.

CHARLES WESLEY (1707-88)

333

LEOMINSTER (D.S.M.)

GEORGE WILLIAM MARTIN (1828-81)
Arranged by ARTHUR SEYMOUR SULLIVAN (1842-1900)

This hymn may also be sung to the tune DINBYCH, No. 332 (i)

One is your Master, even Christ (Matthew xxiii. 8)

MAKE me a captive, Lord,
And then I shall be free;
Force me to render up my sword,
And I shall conqueror be.
I sink in life's alarms
When by myself I stand;
Imprison me within Thine arms,
And strong shall be my hand.

2 My heart is weak and poor
Until it master find;
It has no spring of action sure,
It varies with the wind;
It cannot freely move,
Till Thou hast wrought its chain;
Enslave it with Thy matchless love,
And deathless it shall reign.

3 My power is faint and low
Till I have learned to serve;
It wants the needed fire to glow,
It wants the breeze to nerve;
It cannot drive the world,
Until itself be driven;
Its flag can only be unfurled
When Thou shalt breathe from
heaven.

4 My will is not my own
Till Thou hast made it Thine;
If it would reach a monarch's throne
It must its crown resign;
It only stands unbent,
Amid the clashing strife,
When on Thy bosom it has leant
And found in Thee its life.

GEORGE MATHESON (1842-1906)

334

EVERLASTING LOVE (7 7. 7 7. D.)   JAMES MOUNTAIN (1843-1933)

We love him, because he first loved us (1 John iv. 19)

L OVED with everlasting love,
  Led by grace that love to know;
Spirit, breathing from above,
  Thou hast taught me it is so.
O this full and perfect peace!
  O this transport all divine!
In a love which cannot cease
  I am His, and He is mine.

2 Heaven above is softer blue,
  Earth around is sweeter green;
Something lives in every hue,
  Christless eyes have never seen:
Birds with gladder songs o'erflow,
  Flowers with deeper beauties shine,
Since I know, as now I know,
  I am His, and He is mine.

3 His for ever, only His:
  Who the Lord and me shall part?
Ah, with what a rest of bliss
  Christ can fill the loving heart!
Heaven and earth may fade and flee,
  First-born light in gloom decline;
But, while God and I shall be,
  I am His, and He is mine.

GEORGE WADE ROBINSON (1838-77)

335

ABBOT'S LEIGH　(8 7. 8 7. D.)　　　　　CYRIL V. TAYLOR (1907-　)

This hymn may also be sung to the tunes BLAENWERN, No. 271, and BETHANY, No. 75

ALTERNATIVE TUNE

ADORATION　(8 7. 8 7.)　　　　　J. ERIC HUNT (1903-　)

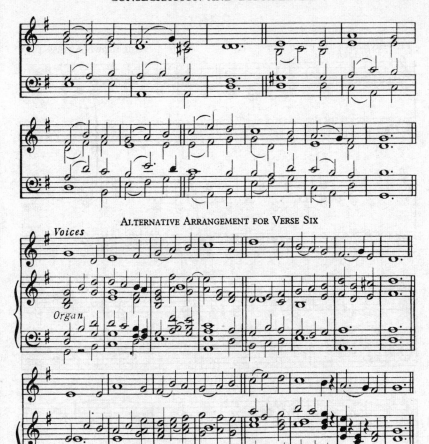

ALTERNATIVE ARRANGEMENT FOR VERSE SIX

Remember me, O Lord . . . : O visit me with thy salvation (Psalm cvi. 4)

LOVE divine, all loves excelling,
    Joy of heaven, to earth come down,
Fix in us Thy humble dwelling,
    All Thy faithful mercies crown.

2 Jesus, Thou art all compassion,
    Pure, unbounded love Thou art;
Visit us with Thy salvation,
    Enter every longing heart.

3 Come, almighty to deliver,
    Let us all Thy life receive;
Suddenly return, and never,
    Never more Thy temples leave.

4 Thee we would be always blessing,
    Serve Thee as Thy hosts above,
Pray, and praise Thee, without
    Glory in Thy perfect love. [ceasing,

5 Finish then Thy new creation:
    Pure and spotless may we be;
Let us see Thy great salvation,
    Perfectly restored in Thee.

6 Changed from glory into glory,
    Till in heaven we take our place,
Till we cast our crowns before Thee,
    Lost in wonder, love, and praise.

CHARLES WESLEY (1707-88)

336

THORNBURY (7 6. 7 6. D.)   BASIL HARWOOD (1859-1949)

Thou Guar - dian of my soul, of my soul.

This hymn may also be sung to the tune WOLVERCOTE, No. 112

If any man serve me, let him follow me (John xii. 26)

O JESUS, I have promised
    To serve Thee to the end;
Be Thou for ever near me,
    My Master and my Friend:
I shall not fear the battle
    If Thou art by my side,
Nor wander from the pathway
    If Thou wilt be my Guide.

2 O let me feel Thee near me:
    The world is ever near;
I see the sights that dazzle,
    The tempting sounds I hear;
My foes are ever near me,
    Around me and within;
But, Jesus, draw Thou nearer,
    And shield my soul from sin.

3 O let me hear Thee speaking
    In accents clear and still,
Above the storms of passion,
    The murmurs of self-will;
O speak to reassure me,
    To hasten or control;
O speak and make me listen,
    Thou Guardian of my soul.

4 O Jesus, Thou hast promised,
    To all who follow Thee,
That where Thou art in glory
    There shall Thy servant be;
And, Jesus, I have promised
    To serve Thee to the end;
O give me grace to follow,
    My Master and my Friend.

JOHN ERNEST BODE (1816-74)

337

ST. MATTHIAS (8 8. 8 8. 8 8.)   WILLIAM HENRY MONK (1823-89)

This hymn may also be sung to the tunes VATER UNSER, No. 114 (i), and STELLA, No. 114 (ii)

VERBORGNE GOTTESLIEBE DU

God is love; and he that dwelleth in love dwelleth in God, and God in him (1 John iv. 16)

THOU hidden love of God, whose height,
  Whose depth unfathomed, no man knows
I see from far Thy beauteous light,
  Inly I sigh for Thy repose;
My heart is pained, nor can it be
At rest, till it finds rest in Thee.

2 Thy secret voice invites me still
  The sweetness of Thy yoke to prove;
And fain I would; but though my will
  Seems fixed, yet wide my passions rove;
Yet hindrances strew all the way;
I aim at Thee, yet from Thee stray.

3 'Tis mercy all, that Thou hast brought
  My mind to seek her peace in Thee;
Yet, while I seek but find Thee not,
  No peace my wandering soul shall see.
O when shall all my wanderings end,
And all my steps to Thee-ward tend?

4 Is there a thing beneath the sun
  That strives with Thee my heart to share?
Ah! tear it thence, and reign alone,
  The Lord of every motion there;
Then shall my heart from earth be free,
When it hath found repose in Thee.

5 Each moment draw from earth away
  My heart, that lowly waits Thy call;
Speak to my inmost soul, and say,
  ' I am thy Love, thy God, thy All!'
To feel Thy power, to hear Thy voice,
To taste Thy love, be all my choice.

GERHARD TERSTEEGEN (1697-1769);
tr. JOHN WESLEY (1703-91)

338

DAVID'S HARP (8 8. 8 8. 8 8.)   ROBERT KING (*c.* 1684-1711)

This hymn may also be sung to the tune PATER OMNIUM No. 275 (ii)

O JESU CHRIST, MEIN SCHÖNSTES LICHT

We have known and believed the love that God hath to us (1 John iv. 16)

JESU, Thy boundless love to me
  No thought can reach, no tongue declare;
O knit my thankful heart to Thee,
  And reign without a rival there:
Thine wholly, Thine alone, I am;
Lord, with Thy love my heart inflame.

2 O grant that nothing in my soul
    May dwell, but Thy pure love alone;
  O may Thy love possess me whole,
    My joy, my treasure, and my crown:
  All coldness from my heart remove;
  May every act, word, thought, be love.

3 O Love, how cheering is Thy ray!
    All pain before Thy presence flies;
  Care, anguish, sorrow, melt away,
    Where'er Thy healing beams arise;
  O Jesus, nothing may I see,
  Nothing desire, or seek, but Thee.

4 In suffering, be Thy love my peace;
    In weakness, be Thy love my power;
  And, when the storms of life shall cease,
    Jesus, in that tremendous hour,
  In death, as life, be Thou my Guide,
  And save me, who for me hast died.

PAUL GERHARDT (1607-76);
tr. JOHN WESLEY (1703-91)

339

REPTON (8 6. 8 8 6.)   CHARLES HUBERT HASTINGS PARRY (1848-1918)

Rest in the Lord (Psalm xxxvii. 7)

DEAR Lord and Father of mankind,
  Forgive our foolish ways;
Reclothe us in our rightful mind;
In purer lives Thy service find,
  In deeper reverence, praise.

2 In simple trust like theirs who heard,
  Beside the Syrian sea,
The gracious calling of the Lord,
Let us, like them, without a word
  Rise up and follow Thee.

3 O Sabbath rest by Galilee!
  O calm of hills above,
Where Jesus knelt to share with Thee
The silence of eternity,
  Interpreted by love!

*4 With that deep hush subduing all
  Our words and works that drown
The tender whisper of Thy call,
As noiseless let Thy blessing fall
  As fell Thy manna down.

5 Drop Thy still dews of quietness,
  Till all our strivings cease;
Take from our souls the strain and
  stress,
And let our ordered lives confess
  The beauty of Thy peace.

6 Breathe through the heats of our desire
  Thy coolness and Thy balm;
Let sense be dumb, let flesh retire;
Speak through the earthquake, wind,
  and fire,
  O still small voice of calm!

JOHN GREENLEAF WHITTIER (1807-92)

If desired, verse 4 may be omitted

Harmony (verses 2 and 5) to be accompanied by the version opposite

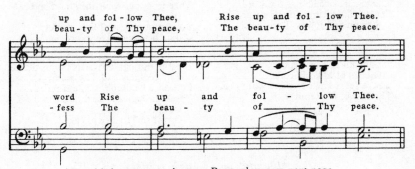

For this hymn set to the tune REST, please see next page

339

REST   (8 6. 8 8 6.)   FREDERICK CHARLES MAKER (1844-1927)

For this hymn set to the tune REPTON, please see previous page

Rest in the Lord (Psalm xxxvii. 7)

DEAR Lord and Father of mankind, *4
  Forgive our foolish ways;
Reclothe us in our rightful mind;
In purer lives Thy service find,
  In deeper reverence, praise.

2 In simple trust like theirs who heard,
  Beside the Syrian sea,
The gracious calling of the Lord,
Let us, like them, without a word
  Rise up and follow Thee.

3 O Sabbath rest by Galilee!
  O calm of hills above,
Where Jesus knelt to share with Thee
The silence of eternity,
  Interpreted by love!

4 With that deep hush subduing all
  Our words and works that drown
The tender whisper of Thy call,
As noiseless let Thy blessing fall
  As fell Thy manna down.

5 Drop Thy still dews of quietness,
  Till all our strivings cease;
Take from our souls the strain and
  stress,
And let our ordered lives confess
  The beauty of Thy peace.

6 Breathe through the heats of our desire
  Thy coolness and Thy balm;
Let sense be dumb, let flesh retire;
Speak through the earthquake, wind,
  and fire,
  O still small voice of calm!

JOHN GREENLEAF WHITTIER (1807-92)

*If desired, verse 4 may be omitted

340

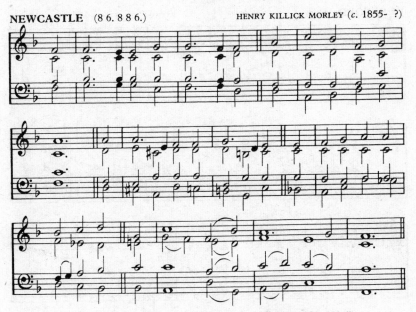

This hymn may also be sung to the tune REPTON, No. 339 (i)

God is light, and in him is no darkness at all (1 John i. 5)

ETERNAL Light! eternal Light!
　How pure the soul must be,
When, placed within Thy searching light,
It shrinks not, but with calm delight
　Can live, and look on Thee!

2 The spirits that surround Thy throne
　　May bear the burning bliss;
　But that is surely theirs alone,
　Since they have never, never known
　　A fallen world like this.

3 O, how shall I, whose native sphere
　　Is dark, whose mind is dim,
　Before the Ineffable appear,
　And on my naked spirit bear
　　The uncreated beam?

4 There is a way for man to rise
　　To that sublime abode;
　An offering and a sacrifice,
　A Holy Spirit's energies,
　　An Advocate with God:

5 These, these prepare us for the sight
　　Of holiness above;
　The sons of ignorance and night
　May dwell in the eternal Light,
　　Through the eternal Love.

THOMAS BINNEY (1798-1874)

341

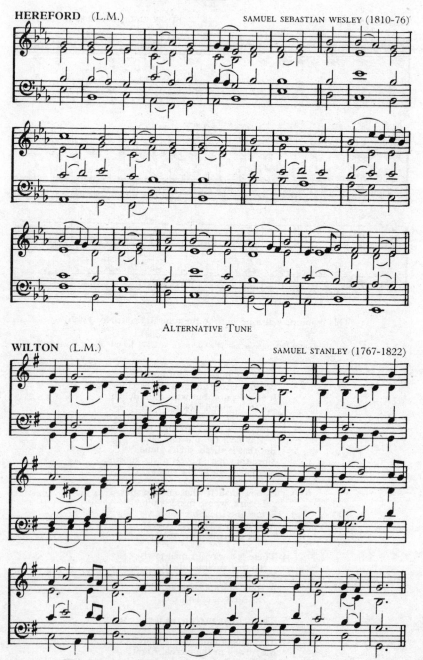

HEREFORD (L.M.)   SAMUEL SEBASTIAN WESLEY (1810-76)

ALTERNATIVE TUNE

WILTON (L.M.)   SAMUEL STANLEY (1767-1822)

This hymn may also be sung to the tune EISENACH, No. 131

He shall baptize you with the Holy Ghost and with fire (Luke iii. 16)

O THOU who camest from above,
   The pure celestial fire to impart,
Kindle a flame of sacred love
On the mean altar of my heart.

2 There let it for Thy glory burn
   With inextinguishable blaze,
And trembling to its source return
   In humble prayer and fervent praise.

3 Jesus, confirm my heart's desire
   To work, and speak, and think for
Still let me guard the holy fire, [Thee;
   And still stir up Thy gift in me;

4 Ready for all Thy perfect will,
   My acts of faith and love repeat,
Till death Thy endless mercies seal,
   And make the sacrifice complete.

CHARLES WESLEY (1707-88)

342

BODMIN   (L.M.)   ALFRED SCOTT-GATTY (1847-1918)

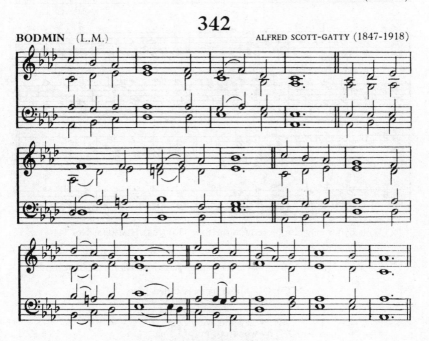

Based on Exodus xxi. 2-6

MY glorious Victor, Prince divine,
   Clasp these surrendered hands in Thine;
At length my will is all Thine own,
Glad vassal of a Saviour's throne.

2 My Master, lead me to Thy door;
   Pierce this now willing ear once more:
Thy bonds are freedom; let me stay
With Thee, to toil, endure, obey.

3 Yes, ear and hand, and thought and will,
   Use all in Thy dear slavery still!
Self's weary liberties I cast
Beneath Thy feet; there keep them fast.

4 Tread them still down; and then I know
   These hands shall with Thy gifts o'erflow;
And piercèd ears shall hear the tone
Which tells me Thou and I are one.

HANDLEY CARR GLYN MOULE (1841-1920)

343

REQUIEM   (8 7. 8 7. 7 7.)   WILHELM AUGUST FERDINAND SCHULTHES (1816-79)

This hymn may also be sung to the tune GOTT DES HIMMELS, No. 344

Thou shalt call his name JESUS: for he shall save his people from their sins (Matthew i. 21)

THOU whose name is callèd Jesus,
   Risen Lord of life and power,
O what joy it is to trust Thee
   Every day and every hour!
Of Thy wondrous grace I sing,
Saviour, Counsellor, and King.

2 Thou canst keep my feet from falling,
   Even my poor wayward feet,
Thou who dost present me faultless,
   In Thy righteousness complete;
Jesus, Lord, in knowing Thee,
O what strength and victory!

3 Make my life a bright outshining
   Of Thy life, that all may see
Thine own resurrection power
   Mightily put forth in me;
Ever let my heart become
Yet more consciously Thy home.

JEAN SOPHIA PIGOTT†

344

GOTT DES HIMMELS (8 7. 8 7. 7 7.) HEINRICH ALBERT (1604-51)

A shorter form of this melody (8 7. 8 7.) will be found under the title WALTHAM No. 144
This hymn may also be sung to the tune REQUIEM, No. 343

Speak, Lord; for thy servant heareth (1 Samuel iii. 9)

MASTER, speak! Thy servant heareth,
Waiting for Thy gracious word,
Longing for Thy voice that cheereth;
Master, let it now be heard.
I am listening, Lord, for Thee;
What hast Thou to say to me?

2 Speak to me by name, O Master,
Let me know it is to me;
Speak, that I may follow faster,
With a step more firm and free,
Where the Shepherd leads the flock
In the shadow of the Rock.

3 Master, speak! Though least and lowest,
Let me not unheard depart;
Master, speak! For O Thou knowest
All the yearning of my heart,
Knowest all its truest need;
Speak, and make me blest indeed.

4 Master, speak: and make me ready,
When Thy voice is truly heard,
With obedience glad and steady
Still to follow every word.
I am listening, Lord, for Thee;
Master, speak! O speak to me!

FRANCES RIDLEY HAVERGAL (1836-79)

345

ST. KEVERNE　(10 10. 10 10 4.)　　　　ARTHUR HENRY BROWN (1830-1926)

ALTERNATIVE TUNE

IT PASSETH KNOWLEDGE　(10 10. 10 10 4.)　　IRA DAVID SANKEY (1830-1908)

The love of Christ, which passeth knowledge (Ephesians iii. 19)

IT passeth knowledge, that dear love of Thine,
　My Saviour, Jesus! Yet this soul of mine
Would of Thy love, in all its breadth and length,
Its height and depth, and everlasting strength,
　Know more and more.

2 It passeth telling, that dear love of Thine,
   My Saviour, Jesus! Yet these lips of mine
   Would fain proclaim to sinners far and near
   A love which can remove all guilty fear,
      And love beget.

3 It passeth praises, that dear love of Thine,
   My Saviour, Jesus! Yet this heart of mine
   Would sing that love, so full, so rich, so free,
   Which brings a rebel sinner, such as me,
      Nigh unto God.

4 O fill me, Saviour, Jesus, with Thy love!
   Lead, lead me to the living fount above;
   Thither may I, in simple faith, draw nigh,
   And never to another fountain fly,
      But unto Thee.

5 And then, Lord Jesus, when Thy face I see,
   When at Thy lofty throne I bow the knee,
   Then of Thy love, in all its breadth and length,
   Its height and depth, its everlasting strength,
      My soul shall sing.

                              MARY SHEKLETON (1827-83)†

346

ST. STEPHEN   (C.M.)   WILLIAM JONES (1726-1800)

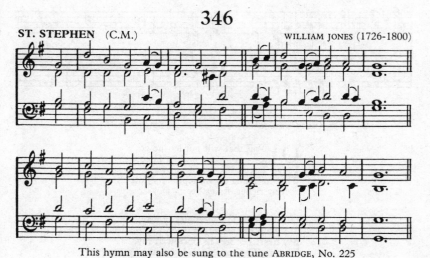

This hymn may also be sung to the tune ABRIDGE, No. 225

Let your heart therefore be perfect with the Lord our God (1 Kings viii. 61)

O FOR a heart to praise my God,
    A heart from sin set free;
A heart that always feels Thy blood
    So freely shed for me;

2 A heart resigned, submissive, meek,
    My dear Redeemer's throne;
Where only Christ is heard to speak,
Where Jesus reigns alone;

3 A humble, lowly, contrite heart,
    Believing, true, and clean,
Which neither life nor death can part
From Him that dwells within;

4 A heart in every thought renewed
    And filled with love divine,
Perfect and right and pure and good;
    A copy, Lord, of Thine.

5 Thy nature, gracious Lord, impart;
    Come quickly from above;
Write Thy new name upon my heart,
    Thy new, best name of love.

                              CHARLES WESLEY (1707-88)

347

ST. MARGARET (8 8. 8 8. 6.)   ALBERT LISTER PEACE (1844-1912)

If we be dead with Christ, we believe that we shall also live with him (Romans vi. 8)

O LOVE that wilt not let me go,
   I rest my weary soul in Thee:
I give Thee back the life I owe,
That in Thine ocean depths its flow
   May richer, fuller be.

2 O Light that followest all my way,
   I yield my flickering torch to Thee:
My heart restores its borrowed ray,
That in Thy sunshine's blaze its day
   May brighter, fairer be.

3 O Joy that seekest me through pain,
   I cannot close my heart to Thee:
I trace the rainbow through the rain,
And feel the promise is not vain,
   That morn shall tearless be.

4 O Cross that liftest up my head,
   I dare not ask to fly from Thee:
I lay in dust life's glory dead,
And from the ground there blossoms red
   Life that shall endless be.

GEORGE MATHESON (1842-1906)

348

ST. LEONARDS (8 7. 8 5.)   A. CYRIL BARHAM-GOULD (1891-1953)

Let this mind be in you, which was also in Christ Jesus (Philippians ii. 5)

MAY the mind of Christ my Saviour
    Live in me from day to day,
By His love and power controlling
    All I do and say.

2 May the Word of God dwell richly
    In my heart from hour to hour,
So that all may see I triumph
    Only through His power.

3 May the peace of God my Father
    Rule my life in everything,
That I may be calm to comfort
    Sick and sorrowing.

4 May the love of Jesus fill me,
    As the waters fill the sea;
Him exalting, self abasing,
    This is victory.

5 May I run the race before me,
    Strong and brave to face the foe,
Looking only unto Jesus
    As I onward go.

6 May His beauty rest upon me
    As I seek the lost to win,
And may they forget the channel,
    Seeing only Him.

KATE BARCLAY WILKINSON

349

LYDBROOK (8 7. 8 8. 7.)   PEGGY SPENCER PALMER

For me to live is Christ (Philippians i. 21)

O THE bitter shame and sorrow,
   That a time could ever be
When I let the Saviour's pity
Plead in vain, and proudly answered:
   All of self, and none of Thee!

2 Yet He found me. I beheld Him
   Bleeding on the accursèd tree,
Heard Him pray: Forgive them, Father!
And my wistful heart said faintly:
   Some of self, and some of Thee!

3 Day by day His tender mercy,
   Healing, helping, full and free,
Sweet and strong, and, ah! so patient,
Brought me lower, while I whispered:
   Less of self, and more of Thee!

4 Higher than the highest heaven,
   Deeper than the deepest sea,
Lord, Thy love at last hath conquered;
Grant me now my supplication:
   None of self, and all of Thee!

THEODORE MONOD (1836-1921)

350

LÜBECK   (7 7. 7 7.)   FREYLINGHAUSEN'S *Gesangbuch* (1704)

This hymn may also be sung to the tune NEWINGTON, No. 259

A living sacrifice, holy, acceptable unto God (Romans xii. 1)

TAKE my life, and let it be
Consecrated, Lord, to Thee.
Take my moments and my days;
Let them flow in ceaseless praise.

2 Take my hands, and let them move
At the impulse of Thy love.
Take my feet, and let them be
Swift and beautiful for Thee.

3 Take my voice, and let me sing
Always, only, for my King.
Take my lips, and let them be
Filled with messages from Thee.

4 Take my silver and my gold;
Not a mite would I withhold.
Take my intellect, and use
Every power as Thou shalt choose.

5 Take my will, and make it Thine;
It shall be no longer mine.
Take my heart, it is Thine own;
It shall be Thy royal throne.

6 Take my love; my Lord, I pour
At Thy feet its treasure-store.
Take myself, and I will be
Ever, only, all for Thee.

FRANCES RIDLEY HAVERGAL (1836-79)

351

OLD 120TH (6 6. 6 6. 6 6.)   Melody from *Este's Psalter* (1592).

ALTERNATIVE TUNE

BACA (6 6. 6 6. 6 6.)   WILLIAM HENRY HAVERGAL (1793-1870)

What shall I render unto the Lord for all his benefits toward me ? (Psalm cxvi. 12)

THY life was given for me,
   Thy blood, O Lord, was shed,
That I might ransomed be,
   And quickened from the dead:
Thy life was given for me;
What have I given for Thee ?

2 Long years were spent for me
   In weariness and woe,
That through eternity
   Thy glory I might know:
Long years were spent for me;
Have I spent one for Thee ?

*3 Thy Father's home of light,
   Thy rainbow-circled throne,
Were left for earthly night,
   For wanderings sad and lone:
Yea, all was left for me;
Have I left aught for Thee ?

4 Thou, Lord, hast borne for me
   More than my tongue can tell
Of bitterest agony,
   To rescue me from hell:
Thou sufferedst all for me;
What have I borne for Thee ?

*5 And Thou hast brought to me
   Down from Thy home above
Salvation full and free,
   Thy pardon and Thy love:
Great gifts Thou broughtest me;
What have I brought to Thee ?

6 O let my life be given,
   My years for Thee be spent,
World-fetters all be riven,
   And joy with suffering blent:
Thou gav'st Thyself for me;
I give myself to Thee.

FRANCES RIDLEY HAVERGAL (1836-79)

If desired, verses 3 and 5 may be omitted

352

COLESHILL (C.M.) Later version of melody first found in BARTON'S *Psalms* (1644)

This hymn may also be sung to the tune DUNDEE, No. 136

Create in me a clean heart, O God; and renew a right spirit within me (Psalm li. 10)

I WANT a principle within
   Of jealous, godly fear,
A sensibility of sin,
   A pain to feel it near.

2 I want the first approach to feel
   Of pride or fond desire,
To catch the wandering of my will,
   And quench the kindling fire.

3 That I from Thee no more may part,
   No more Thy goodness grieve,
The filial awe, the fleshly heart,
   The tender conscience, give.

4 Quick as the apple of an eye,
   O God, my conscience make;
Awake my soul when sin is nigh,
   And keep it still awake.

5 O may the least omission pain
   My well instructed soul,
And drive me to the blood again
   Which makes the wounded whole.

CHARLES WESLEY (1707-88)

353

CAMACHA (6 4. 6 4. 6 6. 6 4.)   B. MANSELL RAMSEY (1849-1923)

Teach me thy way, O Lord, and lead me in a plain path (Psalm xxvii. 11)

TEACH me Thy way, O Lord,
   Teach me Thy way!
Thy gracious aid afford,
   Teach me Thy way!
Help me to walk aright,
More by faith, less by sight;
Lead me with heavenly light:
   Teach me Thy way!

2 When doubts and fears arise,
   Teach me Thy way!
When storms o'erspread the skies,
   Teach me Thy way!
Shine through the cloud and rain,
Through sorrow, toil, and pain;
Make Thou my pathway plain:
   Teach me Thy way!

3 Long as my life shall last,
   Teach me Thy way!
Where'er my lot be cast,
   Teach me Thy way!
Until the race is run,
Until the journey's done,
Until the crown is won,
   Teach me Thy way!

B. MANSELL RAMSEY (1849-1923)

See also the section: THE MAN OF GOD: PENITENCE AND FAITH, Nos. 201-230

MORNING AND EVENING
354

DAY'S *Psalter* (1562)

Whatsoever ye do, do all to the glory of God (1 Corinthians x. 31)

MY Father, for another night
Of quiet sleep and rest,
For all the joy of morning light,
Thy holy name be blest.

2 Now with the new-born day I give
Myself anew to Thee,
That as Thou willest I may live,
And what Thou willest be.

3 Whate'er I do, things great or small,
Whate'er I speak or frame,
Thy glory may I seek in all,
Do all in Jesus' name.

4 My Father, for His sake, I pray,
Thy child accept and bless;
And lead me by Thy grace today
In paths of righteousness.

HENRY WILLIAMS BAKER (1821-77)

355

MORNING HYMN (L.M.) FRANÇOIS HIPPOLYTE BARTHÉLÉMON (1741-1808)

Walk as children of light (Ephesians v. 8)

A WAKE, my soul, and with the sun
Thy daily stage of duty run;
Shake off dull sloth, and joyful rise,
To pay thy morning sacrifice.

*2 Thy precious time misspent redeem;
Each present day thy last esteem;
Improve thy talent with due care;
For the great day thyself prepare.

3 In conversation be sincere;
Keep conscience as the noontide clear;
Think how all-seeing God thy ways
And all thy secret thoughts surveys.

4 Wake, and lift up thyself, my heart,
And with the angels bear thy part,
Who all night long unwearied sing
High praise to the eternal King.

*5 All praise to Thee who safe hast kept,
And hast refreshed me while I slept!
Grant, Lord, when I from death shall
wake,
I may of endless light partake.

6 Lord, I my vows to Thee renew;
Disperse my sins as morning dew;
Guard my first springs of thought and
will,
And with Thyself my spirit fill.

7 Direct, control, suggest, this day,
All I design, or do, or say,
That all my powers, with all their
might,
In Thy sole glory may unite.

8 Praise God, from whom all blessings flow;
Praise Him, all creatures here below;
Praise Him above, ye heavenly host;
Praise Father, Son, and Holy Ghost.

THOMAS KEN (1637-1711)

*If a shorter hymn is desired, either verses 2-4 or verses 5-7 may be omitted. For
verses 5-8 see also Hymn No. 358

356

MELCOMBE (L.M.)   SAMUEL WEBBE (1740-1816)

His compassions fail not (Lamentations iii. 22)

NEW every morning is the love
   Our wakening and uprising prove;
Through sleep and darkness safely brought,
Restored to life, and power, and thought.

2 New mercies, each returning day,
   Hover around us while we pray;
   New perils past, new sins forgiven,
   New thoughts of God, new hopes of heaven.

3 If on our daily course our mind
   Be set to hallow all we find,
   New treasures still, of countless price,
   God will provide for sacrifice.

4 The trivial round, the common task,
   Will furnish all we ought to ask,
   Room to deny ourselves, a road
   To bring us daily nearer God.

5 Only, O Lord, in thy dear love,
   Fit us for perfect rest above;
   And help us, this and every day,
   To live more nearly as we pray.

JOHN KEBLE (1792-1866)

N

357

ARFON (7 7. 7 7. 7 7.) Welsh Hymn Melody

This hymn may also be sung to the tune RATISBON, No. 315

The Lord is thy keeper (Psalm cxxi. 5)

AT Thy feet, O Christ, we lay
    Thine own gift of this new day;
Doubt of what it holds in store
Makes us crave Thine aid the more;
Lest it prove a time of loss,
Mark it, Saviour, with Thy cross.

2 If it flow on calm and bright,
Be Thyself our chief delight;
If it bring unknown distress,
Good is all that Thou canst bless;
Only, while its hours begin,
Pray we, keep them clear of sin.

3 We in part our weakness know,
And in part discern our foe;
Well for us, before Thine eyes
All our danger open lies;
Turn not from us, while we plead
Thy compassions and our need.

4 Fain would we Thy word embrace,
Live each moment on Thy grace,
All our selves to Thee consign,
Fold up all our wills in Thine,
Think, and speak, and do, and be
Simply that which pleases Thee.

5 Hear us, Lord, and that right soon;
Hear, and grant the choicest boon
That Thy love can e'er impart,
Loyal singleness of heart;
So shall this and all our days,
Christ our God, show forth Thy praise.

WILLIAM BRIGHT (1824-1901)

358

TALLIS' CANON (L.M.)   THOMAS TALLIS (*c.* 1510-85)

When I awake, I am still with thee (Psalm cxxxix. 18)

GLORY to Thee who safe hast kept,
And hast refreshed me while I
    slept;
Grant, Lord, when I from death shall
    wake,
I may of endless light partake.

2 Lord, I my vows to Thee renew;
Disperse my sins as morning dew;
Guard my first springs of thought and
    will,
And with Thyself my spirit fill.

3 Direct, control, suggest, this day,
All I design, or do, or say,
That all my powers, with all their
    might,
In Thy sole glory may unite.

4 Praise God, from whom all blessings
    flow;
Praise Him, all creatures here below;
Praise Him above, ye heavenly host;
Praise Father, Son, and Holy Ghost.

THOMAS KEN (1637-1711)

The following hymns also refer to this theme:
307   Forth in Thy name, O Lord, I go
109   When morning gilds the skies

359

I will both lay me down in peace, and sleep: for thou, Lord, only makest me dwell in safety (Psalm iv. 8)

GLORY to Thee, my God, this
    night
For all the blessings of the light;
Keep me, O keep me, King of kings,
Beneath Thine own almighty wings.

2 Forgive me, Lord, for Thy dear Son,
The ill that I this day have done,
That with the world, myself, and Thee,
I, ere I sleep, at peace may be.

3 Teach me to live, that I may dread
The grave as little as my bed;
Teach me to die, that so I may
Rise glorious at the aweful day.

4 O may my soul on Thee repose,
And may sweet sleep mine eyelids close,
Sleep that may me more vigorous make
To serve my God when I awake.

5 When in the night I sleepless lie,
My soul with heavenly thoughts supply;
Let no ill dreams disturb my rest,
No powers of darkness me molest.

6 Praise God, from whom all blessings
    flow;
Praise Him, all creatures here below;
Praise Him above, ye heavenly host;
Praise Father, Son, and Holy Ghost.

THOMAS KEN (1637-1711)

360

ANGELUS (L.M.)   *Cantica Spiritualia* (1847). Founded on a
melody by GEORG JOSEPH (*c.* 1657)

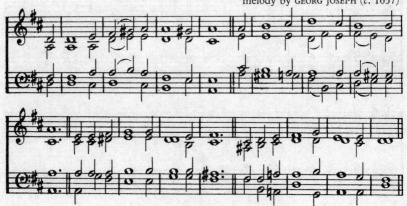

And at even, when the sun did set, they brought unto him all that were diseased. (Mark i. 32)

A T even, when the sun was set,
   The sick, O Lord, around Thee lay;
O in what divers pains they met!
   O with what joy they went away!

2 Once more 'tis eventide, and we,
   Oppressed with various ills draw near;
What if Thy form we cannot see,
   We know and feel that Thou art here.

3 O Saviour Christ, our woes dispel:
   For some are sick, and some are sad,
And some have never loved Thee well,
   And some have lost the love they had;

*4 And some are pressed with worldly care,
   And some are tried with sinful doubt;
And some such grievous passions tear,
   That only Thou canst cast them out;

*5 And some have found the world is vain,
   Yet from the world they break not free;
And some have friends who give them pain,
   Yet have not sought a friend in Thee;

6 And none, O Lord, have perfect rest,
   For none are wholly free from sin;
And they who fain would serve Thee best
   Are conscious most of wrong within.

7 O Saviour Christ, Thou too art Man;
   Thou hast been troubled, tempted, tried;
Thy kind but searching glance can scan
   The very wounds that shame would hide;

8 Thy touch has still its ancient power;
   No word from Thee can fruitless fall:
Hear in this solemn evening hour,
   And in Thy mercy heal us all.

HENRY TWELLS (1823-1900)

*If desired, verses 4 and 5 may be omitted

361

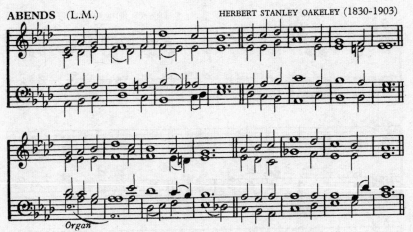

ABENDS (L.M.)   HERBERT STANLEY OAKELEY (1830-1903)

Organ

This hymn may also be sung to the tune BIRLING, No. 29

Abide with us (Luke xxiv. 29)

SUN of my soul, Thou Saviour dear,
It is not night if Thou be near;
O may no earth-born cloud arise
To hide Thee from Thy servant's eyes.

*2 When the soft dews of kindly sleep
My wearied eyelids gently steep,
Be my last thought, how sweet to rest
For ever on my Saviour's breast.

3 Abide with me from morn till eve,
For without Thee I cannot live;
Abide with me when night is nigh,
For without Thee I dare not die.

4 If some poor wandering child of Thine
Have spurned today the voice divine,
Now, Lord, the gracious work begin;
Let him no more lie down in sin.

*5 Watch by the sick; enrich the poor
With blessings from Thy boundless store;
Be every mourner's sleep tonight
Like infant's slumbers, pure and light.

6 Come near and bless us when we wake,
Ere through the world our way we take,
Till in the ocean of Thy love
We lose ourselves in heaven above.

JOHN KEBLE (1792-1866)

If desired, verses 2 and 5 may be omitted

362

ELLERS (10 10. 10 10.)   EDWARD JOHN HOPKINS (1818-1901)

ALTERNATIVE TUNE

JULIUS (10 10. 10 10.)   MARTIN SHAW (1875-)

Peace I leave with you, my peace I give unto you (John xiv. 27)

SAVIOUR, again to Thy dear name we raise
  With one accord our parting hymn of praise;
We stand to bless Thee ere our worship cease,
Then, lowly kneeling, wait Thy word of peace.

2 Grant us Thy peace upon our homeward way;
  With Thee began, with Thee shall end the day;
  Guard Thou the lips from sin, the hearts from shame,
  That in this house have called upon Thy name.

3 Grant us Thy peace, Lord, through the coming night,
  Turn Thou for us its darkness into light;
  From harm and danger keep Thy children free,
  For dark and light are both alike to Thee.

4 Grant us Thy peace throughout our earthly life,
  Our balm in sorrow, and our stay in strife;
  Then, when Thy voice shall bid our conflict cease,
  Call us, O Lord, to Thine eternal peace.

                              JOHN ELLERTON (1826-93)

363

THANET   (8. 3 3. 6.)   JOSEPH JOWETT (1784-1856)

What shall I render unto the Lord for all his benefits toward me? (Psalm cxvi. 12)

ERE I sleep, for every favour
  This day showed
  By my God,
I will bless my Saviour.

2 O my Lord, what shall I render
    To Thy name,
    Still the same,
  Gracious, good and tender?

3 Thou hast ordered all my goings
    In Thy way,
    Heard me pray,
  Sanctified my doings.

4 Leave me not, but ever love me;
    Let Thy peace
    Be my bliss,
  Till Thou hence remove me.

5 Thou my rock, my guard, my tower.
    Safely keep,
    While I sleep,
  Me, with all Thy power.

6 So, whene'er in death I slumber,
    Let me rise
    With the wise,
  Counted in their number.

                              JOHN CENNICK (1718-55)

364

ST. CLEMENT (9 8. 9 8.)   CLEMENT COTTERILL SCHOLEFIELD (1839-1904)

ALTERNATIVE TUNE

LES COMMANDEMENS DE DIEU (9 8. 9 8.)
Composed or adapted by LOUIS BOURGEOIS (1510-61) in *Genevan Psalter* (1551)

From the rising of the sun unto the going down of the same the Lord's name is to be praised (Psalm cxiii. 3)

THE day Thou gavest, Lord, is ended;
The darkness falls at Thy behest;
To Thee our morning hymns ascended,
Thy praise shall sanctify our rest.

2 We thank Thee that Thy Church
    unsleeping,
    While earth rolls onward into light,
Through all the world her watch is
    keeping,
    And rests not now by day or night.

3 As o'er each continent and island
    The dawn leads on another day,
The voice of prayer is never silent,
    Nor dies the strain of praise away.

4 The sun that bids us rest is waking
    Our brethren 'neath the western sky,
And hour by hour fresh lips are
    making
    Thy wondrous doings heard on high.

5 So be it, Lord! Thy throne shall never,
    Like earth's proud empires, pass
    away;
Thy kingdom stands, and grows for
    ever,
    Till all Thy creatures own Thy sway.

JOHN ELLERTON (1826-93)

365

SUNSET   (8 7. 8 7.)   GEORGE C. STEBBINS (1846-1945)

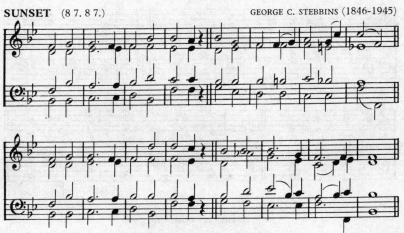

He that keepeth Israel shall neither slumber nor sleep (Psalm cxxi. 4)

SAVIOUR, breathe an evening blessing,
    Ere repose our spirits seal;
Sin and want we come confessing;
    Thou canst save, and Thou canst heal.

2 Though the night be dark and dreary,
    Darkness cannot hide from Thee;
Thou art He who, never weary,
    Watchest where Thy people be.

3 Though destruction walk around us,
    Though the arrow past us fly,
Angel-guards from Thee surround us,
    We are safe if Thou art nigh.

4 Blessed Spirit, brooding o'er us,
    Chase the darkness of our night,
Till the perfect day before us
    Breaks in everlasting light.

JAMES EDMESTON (1791-1867) and
EDWARD HENRY BICKERSTETH (1825-1906)

The following hymn also refers to this theme:
287 Abide with me: fast falls the eventide

N*

THE LORD'S DAY
366

CHURCH TRIUMPHANT (L.M.)   JAMES WILLIAM ELLIOTT (1833-1915)

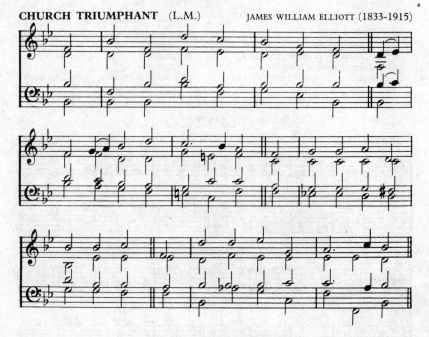

EN DIES EST DOMINICA

Because I live, ye shall live also (John xiv. 19)

AGAIN the Lord's own day is here,
The day to Christian people dear,
As, week by week, it bids them tell
How Jesus rose from death and hell.

2 For by His flock their Lord declared
His resurrection should be shared;
And we who trust in Him to save
With Him are risen from the grave.

3 We, one and all, of Him possessed,
Are with exceeding treasures blessed;
For all He did, and all He bare,
He gives us as our own to share.

4 Eternal glory, rest on high,
A blessèd immortality,
True peace and gladness, and a throne,
Are all His gifts, and all our own.

5 And therefore unto Thee we sing,
O Lord of peace, eternal King;
Thy love we praise, Thy name adore,
Both on this day and evermore.

Ascribed to THOMAS À KEMPIS (1379-1471);
tr. JOHN MASON NEALE (1818-66) and others

PHILIPPINE (L.M.)   ROBERT EDWIN ROBERTS (1878-1940)

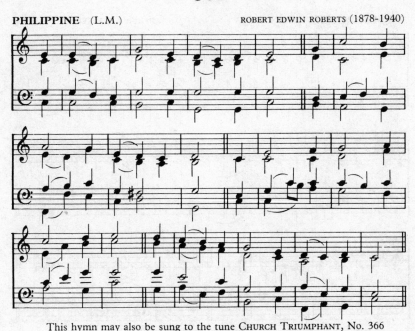

This hymn may also be sung to the tune CHURCH TRIUMPHANT, No. 366

Based on Malachi iv. 2

THOU glorious Sun of Righteousness,
  On this day risen to set no more,
Shine on us now, to heal and bless,
  With brighter beams than e'er before.

2 Shine on Thy pure eternal word,
  Its mysteries to our souls reveal;
And whether read, remembered, heard,
  O let it quicken, strengthen, heal.

3 Shine on the temples of Thy grace,
  In righteousness Thy priests be clad;
Unveil the brightness of Thy face,
  And make Thy chosen people glad.

4 Shine, till Thy glorious beams shall chase
  The brooding cloud from every eye;
Till every earthly dwelling place
  Shall hail the Dayspring from on high.

5 Shine on, shine on, eternal Sun!
  Pour richer floods of life and light,
Till that bright Sabbath be begun,
  That glorious day which knows no night.

CHARLOTTE ELLIOTT (1789-1871)

368

FARMBOROUGH   (8 8. 8 8. 8 8.)   ARTHUR S. WARRELL (1883-1939)

Organ

This is the day which the Lord hath made (Psalm cxviii. 24)

COME, let us with our Lord arise,
Our Lord, who made both earth and skies;
Who died to save the world He made,
And rose triumphant from the dead;
He rose, the Prince of life and peace,
And stamped the day for ever His.

2 This is the day the Lord hath made,
That all may see His love displayed,
May feel His resurrection's power,
And rise again to fall no more,
In perfect righteousness renewed,
And filled with all the life of God.

3 Then let us render Him His own,
With solemn prayer approach the throne,
With meekness hear the gospel word,
With thanks His dying love record;
Our joyful hearts and voices raise,
And fill His courts with songs of praise.

CHARLES WESLEY (1707-88)

369

NEW CALABAR   (7 7. 7 7.)   JOHN DOWNING FARRER (1829-1919)

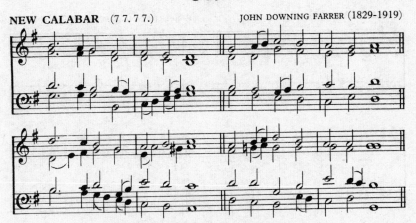

This hymn may also be sung to the tune CULBACH, No. 23

DIE PARENTE TEMPORUM

That same day . . . Jesus himself drew near, and went with them (Luke xxiv. 13, 15)

ON this day, the first of days,
   God the Father's name we praise;
Who, creation's Lord and Spring,
Did the world from darkness bring.

2 On this day the eternal Son
Over death His triumph won;
On this day the Spirit came
With His gifts of living flame.

3 O that fervent love today
May in every heart have sway,
Teaching us to praise aright
God the Source of life and light.

4 Father, who didst fashion me
Image of Thyself to be,
Fill me with Thy love divine,
Let my every thought be Thine.

5 Holy Jesus, may I be
Dead and buried here with Thee;
And, by love inflamed, arise
Unto Thee a sacrifice.

6 Thou who dost all gifts impart,
Shine, blessed Spirit, in my heart;
Best of gifts Thyself bestow;
Make me burn Thy love to know.

7 God, eternal Three in One,
Dwell within my heart alone;
Thou dost give Thyself to me,
May I give myself to Thee.

18th century; tr. HENRY WILLIAMS BAKER (1821-77)†

DOMINICA (S.M.)   HERBERT STANLEY OAKELEY (1830-1903)

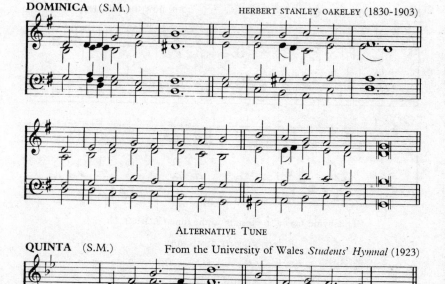

ALTERNATIVE TUNE

QUINTA (S.M.)   From the University of Wales *Students' Hymnal* (1923)

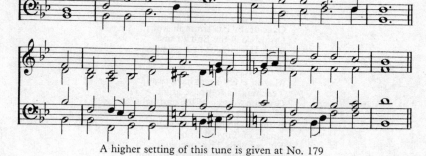

A higher setting of this tune is given at No. 179

I was in the Spirit on the Lord's day (Revelation i. 10)

THIS is the day of light:
Let there be light today;
O Dayspring, rise upon our night,
And chase its gloom away.

2 This is the day of rest:
Our failing strength renew;
On weary brain and troubled breast
Shed Thou Thy freshening dew.

3 This is the day of peace:
Thy peace our spirits fill;
Bid Thou the blasts of discord cease,
The waves of strife be still.

4 This is the day of prayer:
Let earth to heaven draw near;
Lift up our hearts to seek Thee there,
Come down to meet us here.

5 This is the first of days:
Send forth Thy quickening breath,
And wake dead souls to love and praise,
O Vanquisher of death!

JOHN ELLERTON (1826-93)

371

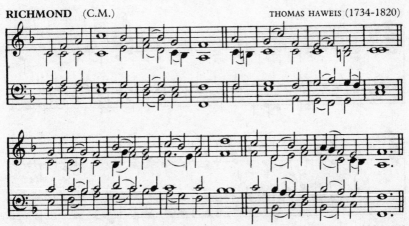

RICHMOND (C.M.)   THOMAS HAWEIS (1734-1820)

An alternative arrangement of this tune with Fa-burden will be found at No. 248

Based on Psalm cxviii

THIS is the day the Lord hath made,
   He calls the hours His own;
Let heaven rejoice, let earth be glad,
   And praise surround the throne.

2 This day He rose and left the dead,
   And Satan's empire fell;
This day the saints His triumphs spread,
   And all His wonders tell.

3 Hosanna to the anointed King,
   To David's holy Son!
O help us, Lord, descend and bring
   Salvation from Thy throne.

4 Blessed be the Lord, who comes to men
   With messages of grace;
Who comes, in God His Father's name,
   To save our sinful race.

5 Hosanna in the highest strains
   The Church on earth can raise;
The highest heavens in which He reigns
   Shall give Him nobler praise.

ISAAC WATTS (1674-1748)†

SOLOTHURN (L.M.)   Swiss Traditional Melody

This hymn may also be sung to the tune WARRINGTON, No. 260

Based on Psalm xcii

SWEET is the work, my God, my King,
To praise Thy Name, give thanks and sing;
To show Thy love by morning light,
And talk of all Thy truth at night.

2 Sweet is the day of sacred rest,
No mortal care shall seize my breast;
O may my heart in tune be found
Like David's harp of solemn sound.

3 My heart shall triumph in my Lord,
And bless His works and bless His word:
Thy works of grace, how bright they shine:
How deep Thy counsels, how divine!

4 Then shall I bear a glorious part,
When grace hath well refined my heart,
And fresh supplies of joy are shed,
Like holy oil to cheer my head.

5 Then shall I see and hear and know
All I desired or wished below;
And every power find sweet employ
In that eternal world of joy.

ISAAC WATTS (1674-1748)

373

DEDICATION (7 5. 7 5. D.)   GEORGE ALEXANDER MACFARREN (1813-87)

My times are in thy hand (Psalm xxxi. 15)

FATHER, let me dedicate
　All my times to Thee,
In whatever worldly state
　Thou wilt have me be;
Not from sorrow, pain, or care
　Freedom dare I claim;
This alone shall be my prayer,
　'Glorify Thy name!'

2 Can a child presume to choose
　Where or how to live?
Can a father's love refuse
　All the best to give?
More Thou givest every day
　Than the best can claim,
Nor withholdest aught that may
　Glorify Thy name.

3 If Thou callest to the cross,
　And its shadow come,
Turning all my gain to loss,
　Shrouding heart and home,
Let me think how Thy dear Son
　To His glory came,
And in deepest woe pray on,
　'Glorify Thy name!'

4 If in mercy Thou wilt spare
　Joys that yet are mine,
If on life, serene and fair,
　Brighter rays may shine,
Let me glad heart, while it sings,
　Thee in all proclaim,
And, whate'er the future brings,
　Glorify Thy name.

LAWRENCE TUTTIETT (1825-97)

374

ALLELUIA, DULCE CARMEN (8 7. 8 7. 8 7.) SAMUEL WEBBE (1740-1816)
From *Essay on the Church Plain Chant* (1782)

All these blessings shall come on thee . . . if thou shalt hearken unto the voice of the Lord thy God
(Deuteronomy xxviii. 2)

L ORD, behold us with Thy blessing
Once again assembled here:
Onward be our footsteps pressing
In Thy love and faith and fear;
Still protect us
By Thy presence ever near.

2 For Thy mercy we adore Thee,
For this rest upon our way;
Lord, again we bow before Thee,
Speed our labours day by day;
Mind and spirit
With Thy choicest gifts array.

3 Keep the spell of home affection
Still alive in every heart;
May its power, with mild direction,
Draw our love from self apart,
Till Thy children
Feel that Thou their Father art.

4 Break temptation's fatal power,
Shielding all with guardian care,
Safe in every careless hour,
Safe from sloth and sensual snare;
Thou, our Saviour,
Still our failing strength repair.

HENRY JAMES BUCKOLL (1803-71)

375

DISMISSAL (8 7. 8 7. 8 7.)   WILLIAM LETTON VINER (1790-1867)

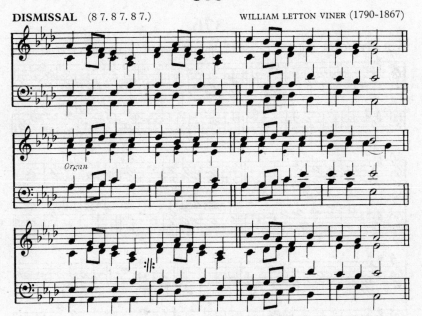

The Lord bless thee, and keep thee (Numbers vi. 24)

LORD, dismiss us with Thy blessing,
　　Thanks for mercies past receive;
Pardon all, their faults confessing;
　　Time that's lost may all retrieve;
　　　　May Thy children
　　Ne'er again Thy Spirit grieve.

2 Bless Thou all our days of leisure,
　　Help us selfish lures to flee;
Sanctify our every pleasure;
　　Pure and blameless may it be;
　　　　May our gladness
　　Draw us evermore to Thee.

3 By Thy kindly influence cherish
　　All the good we here have gained;
May all taint of evil perish
　　By Thy mightier power restrained;
　　　　Seek we ever
　　Knowledge pure and love unfeigned.

4 Let Thy Father-hand be shielding
　　All who here shall meet no more;
May their seed-time past be yielding
　　Year by year a richer store;
　　　　Those returning
　　Make more faithful than before.

HENRY JAMES BUCKOLL (1803-71)

376

WIR PFLÜGEN (76.76.D.66.84.) JOHANN ABRAHAM PETER SCHULTZ (1747-1800)

WIR PFLÜGEN UND WIR STREUEN

Every good gift . . . is from above (James i. 17)

WE plough the fields, and scatter
    The good seed on the land,
But it is fed and watered
    By God's almighty hand;
He sends the snow in winter,
    The warmth to swell the grain,
The breezes and the sunshine,
    And soft refreshing rain:

*All good gifts around us
    Are sent from heaven above;
Then thank the Lord, O thank the Lord,
    For all His love.*

2 He only is the Maker
    Of all things near and far;
He paints the wayside flower;
    He lights the evening star;

The winds and waves obey Him;
    By Him the birds are fed;
Much more to us, His children,
    He gives our daily bread:

3 We thank Thee then, O Father,
    For all things bright and good,
The seed-time and the harvest,
    Our life, our health, our food.
No gifts have we to offer
    For all Thy love imparts,
But that which Thou desirest,
    Our humble, thankful hearts:

MATTHIAS CLAUDIUS (1740-1815);
tr. JANE MONTGOMERY CAMPBELL (1817-78)

377

ST. GEORGE'S WINDSOR   (7 7. 7 7. D.)   GEORGE JOB ELVEY (1816-93)

Based on Matthew xiii. 36-43

COME, ye thankful people, come,
  Raise the song of harvest-home:
All is safely gathered in
Ere the winter storms begin;
God, our Maker, doth provide
For our wants to be supplied:
Come to God's own temple, come,
Raise the song of harvest-home.

2 All the world is God's own field,
Fruit unto His praise to yield;
Wheat and tares together sown,
Unto joy or sorrow grown;
First the blade, and then the ear,
Then the full corn shall appear:
Lord of harvest, grant that we
Wholesome grain and pure may be.

3 For the Lord our God shall come,
And shall take His harvest home,
From His field shall in that day
All offences purge away,
Give His angels charge at last
In the fire the tares to cast,
But the fruitful ears to store
In His garner evermore.

4 Even so, Lord, quickly come,
Bring Thy final harvest home;
Gather Thou Thy people in,
Free from sorrow, free from sin;
There, for ever purified,
In Thy garner to abide:
Come, with all Thine angels, come,
Raise the glorious harvest-home.

HENRY ALFORD (1810-71)

The following hymns also refer to this theme:

  12   Let us with a gladsome mind
  31   I sing the almighty power of God
  32   For the beauty of the earth
257   My God, I thank Thee, who hast made
258   O Lord of heaven and earth and sea

CANTICLES
378

TE DEUM

HENRY LAWES (1596-1662); arr. JOSEPH CORFE (1740-1820)

ROBERT COOKE (1768-1814)

EDWARD JOHN HOPKINS (1818-1901)

TE DEUM LAUDAMUS

For those who prefer a pointed version, the pointing as given in The Parish Psalter
is shown on the opposite page

We praise Thee, O God: we acknowledge Thee to be the Lord.
All the earth doth worship Thee: the Father everlasting.
To Thee all angels cry aloud: the heavens, and all the powers therein.
To Thee cherubin, and seraphin: continually do cry,
Holy, holy, holy: Lord God of Sabaoth;
Heaven and earth are full of the majesty: of Thy glory.
The glorious company of the apostles: praise Thee.
The goodly fellowship of the prophets: praise Thee.
The noble army of martyrs: praise Thee.
The holy Church throughout all the world: doth acknowledge Thee;
The Father: of an infinite majesty;
Thine honourable, true: and only Son;
Also the Holy Ghost: the Comforter.

Thou art the King of glory: O Christ.
Thou art the everlasting Son: of the Father.
When Thou tookest upon Thee to deliver man: Thou didst not abhor the Virgin's womb.
When Thou hadst overcome the sharpness of death: Thou didst open the kingdom of
    heaven to all believers.

Thou sittest at the right hand of God: in the glory of the Father.
We believe that Thou shalt come: to be our Judge.
We therefore pray Thee, help Thy servants: whom Thou hast redeemed with Thy precious blood.
Make them to be numbered with Thy saints: in glory everlasting.

O Lord save Thy people: and bless Thine heritage.
Govern them: and lift them up for ever.
Day by day: we magnify Thee;
And we worship Thy Name: ever world without end.
Vouchsafe, O Lord: to keep us this day without sin.
O Lord, have mercy upon us: have mercy upon us.
O Lord, let Thy mercy lighten upon us: as our trust is in Thee.
O Lord, in Thee have I trusted: let me never be confounded.

LATIN (*c*. 4th century)

TE DEUM LAUDAMUS

With pointing as given in The Parish Psalter

We praise ' Thee O ' God: we acknowledge ' Thee to ' be the ' Lord.
All the earth doth ' worship ' Thee: the ' Father ' ever ' lasting.
To Thee all angels ' cry a ' loud: the heavens and ' all the ' powers there ' in.
To Thee ' cherubin and ' seraphin: con ' tinual ' ly do ' cry,
Holy ' holy ' holy: Lord ' God of ' Saba ' oth;
†Heaven and ' earth are ' full: of the ' majesty ' of Thy ' glory.
The glorious company of the apostles ' praise ' Thee: the goodly fellowship of the ' prophets ' praise ' Thee:
The noble ' army of ' martyrs: praise ' — ' — ' Thee.
The holy Church throughout all the world doth ac ' knowledge ' Thee: the Father ' of an ' infinite ' majesty,
Thine honourable true and ' only ' Son: also the ' Holy ' Ghost the ' Comforter.

Thou art the King of ' glory O ' Christ: Thou art the ever ' lasting ' Son of the ' Father.
When Thou tookest upon Thee to de ' liver ' man: Thou didst not ab ' hor the ' Virgin's ' womb.
2nd When Thou hadst overcome the ' sharpness of ' death: Thou didst open the kingdom
Part of ' heaven to ' all be ' lievers.
Thou sittest at the right ' hand of ' God: in the ' glory ' of the ' Father.
*We be ' lieve that ' Thou ' shalt ' come to ' be our ' Judge.
We therefore pray Thee ' help Thy ' servants: whom Thou hast redeemed ' with Thy ' precious ' blood.
Make them to be numbered ' with Thy ' saints: in ' glory ' ever ' lasting.

O Lord save Thy people and ' bless Thine ' heritage: govern them and ' lift them ' up for ' ever.
Day by day we ' magnify ' Thee: and we worship Thy Name ' ever ' world without ' end.
Vouch ' safe O ' Lord: to keep us this ' day with ' out ' sin.
O Lord have ' mercy up ' on us: have ' mer ' cy up ' on us.
O Lord let Thy mercy ' lighten up ' on us: as our ' trust is ' in ' Thee.
O Lord in Thee ' have I ' trusted: let me ' never ' be con ' founded.

LATIN (*c*. 4th century)

†This verse may be sung without any break at the colon.
*Or: We believe that ' Thou shalt ' come: to ' be ' our ' Judge.

379

MAGNIFICAT

JAMES TURLE (1802-82)

ALTERNATIVE CHANT

SAMUEL SEBASTIAN WESLEY (1810-76)

ALTERNATIVE CHANT

THOMAS ATTWOOD (1765-1838)

MAGNIFICAT

For those who prefer a pointed version, the pointing as given in The Parish Psalter *is
shown on the opposite page.*

Luke i. 46-55

My soul doth magnify the Lord: and my spirit hath rejoiced in God my Saviour.
For He hath regarded: the lowliness of His hand-maiden.
For behold, from henceforth: all generations shall call me blessed.
For He that is mighty hath magnified me: and holy is His Name.
And His mercy is on them that fear Him: throughout all generations.
He hath shewed strength with His arm: He hath scattered the proud in the imagi-
nation of their hearts.
He hath put down the mighty from their seat: and hath exalted the humble and meek.
He hath filled the hungry with good things: and the rich He hath sent empty away.
He remembering His mercy hath holpen His servant Israel: as He promised to our
forefathers, Abraham and his seed for ever.
    Glory be to the Father, and to the Son: and to the Holy Ghost;
    As it was in the beginning, is now, and ever shall be: world without end. Amen.

MAGNIFICAT

With pointing as given in The Parish Psalter

Luke i. 46-55

My soul doth ′ magnify the ′ Lord: and my spirit hath re ′ joiced in ′ God my ′ Saviour.
For He ′ hath re ′ garded: the ′ lowliness ′ of His ′ hand-maiden.
For be ′ hold from ′ henceforth: all gene ′ rations shall ′ call me ′ blessed.
For He that is mighty hath ′ magnified ′ me: and ′ holy ′ is His ′ Name.
And His mercy is on ′ them that ′ fear Him: through ′ out all ′ gene ′ rations.
He hath shewed ′ strength with His ′ arm: He hath scattered the proud in the imagi ′ nation ′ of their ′ hearts.
He hath put down the mighty ′ from their ′ seat: and hath ex ′ alted the ′ humble and ′ meek.
He hath filled the hungry with ′ good ′ things: and the rich He ′ hath sent ′ empty a ′ way.
He re ′ membering His ′ mercy: hath ′ holpen His ′ servant ′ Israel.
As He promised ′ to our ′ forefathers: Abraham ′ and his ′ seed for ′ ever.
  Glory be to the Father, and ′ to the ′ Son: and ′ to the ′ Holy ′ Ghost;
  As it was in the beginning, is now and ′ ever ′ shall be: world without ′ end. ′
                                                                    A ′ men.

380

NUNC DIMITTIS   THOMAS KELWAY (*d.* 1740)

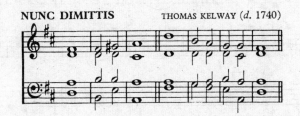

ALTERNATIVE CHANT

EDWIN GEORGE MONK (1819-1900)

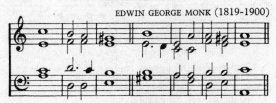

NUNC DIMITTIS

With pointing as given in The Parish Psalter

Luke ii. 29-32

Lord, now lettest Thou Thy servant de ′ part in ′ peace: ac ′ cording ′ to Thy ′ word.
For mine eyes have ′ seen Thy sal ′ vation: which Thou hast prepared before the ′ face of ′ all ′ people.
To be a light to ′ lighten the ′ Gentiles: and to be the ′ glory · of Thy ′ people ′ Israel.
  Glory be to the Father, and ′ to the ′ Son: and ′ to the ′ Holy ′ Ghost;
  As it was in the beginning, is now and ′ ever ′ shall be: world without ′ end ′.
                                                                    A ′ men

CHRISTMAS CAROLS
381

QUITTEZ, PASTEURS (11 10 11. 6 12.)

French Carol Melody. Arranged by MARJORIE THELMA RENTON

Unison (or Soprano only)   *Harmony*

QUITTEZ, PASTEURS

Unto you is born this day . . . a Saviour (Luke ii. 11)

O LEAVE your sheep, your lambs that follow after,
   O leave the brook, the pasture and the crook;
No longer weep; turn weeping into laughter,
   O shepherds seek your goal!
   Your Lord, your Lord, your Lord, who cometh to console!

2 You'll find Him laid within a simple stable,
   A babe new-born, in poverty forlorn,
In love arrayed, a love so deep 'tis able
   To search the night for you:
   'Tis He! 'tis He! 'tis He! 'tis He, the Shepherd true!

3 O kings so great! A light is streaming o'er you,
   More radiant far than diadem or star;
Forgo your state; a baby lies before you,
   Whose wonder shall be told:
   Bring myrrh, bring myrrh, bring myrrh, bring frankincense and gold!

French; tr. ALICE RALEIGH

382

THE BABE IN THE MANGER   (8 6. 8 6. 6.)

Melody from CORNER'S *Geistliche Nachtigall* (1649).
Harmonized by H. WALFORD DAVIES (1869-1941)

She brought forth her firstborn son . . . and laid him in a manger (Luke ii. 7)

*THE night is dark, the winds are still,
　One star is in the skies;
We follow over field and hill
　To where the Baby lies,
　The Hope of all men lies!

2 There is no glory in the place
　Save His who nestles there,
And that sweet light on Mary's face
　Whose look is like a prayer,
　A tender mother's prayer.

*3 No palace for a prince's birth,
　No glad exultant throng;
Yet all the listening skies and earth
　Have heard the angel's song,
　The glorious angel's song.

4 O holy Babe, our hearts are torn
　With woes that will not cease;
O let us greet Thee on this morn
　With songs of new-born peace,
　Of never ending peace.

ARTHUR L. SALMON (1865-1952)

The first and third verses may be sung unaccompanied by a single voice.

383

IN DULCI JUBILO   (Irregular.)   German Carol Melody (14th century)

Good tidings of great joy (Luke ii. 10)

GOOD Christian men, rejoice
With heart and soul and voice!
Give ye heed to what we say:
Jesus Christ is born today.
Ox and ass before Him bow,
And He is in the manger now.
Christ is born today.

2 Good Christian men, rejoice
With heart and soul and voice!
Now ye hear of endless bliss:
Jesus Christ was born for this.
He hath oped the heavenly door,
And man is blessed for evermore.
Christ was born for this.

3 Good Christian men, rejoice
With heart and soul and voice!
Now ye need not fear the grave:
Jesus Christ was born to save;
Calls you one, and calls you all,
To gain His everlasting hall.
Christ was born to save.

JOHN MASON NEALE (1818-66)†

384

ES IST EIN' ROS' ENTSPRUNGEN (7 6. 7 6. 6 7 6.)   Ancient German Melody.
Harmony chiefly from MICHAEL PRAETORIUS (1571-1621)

ES IST EIN' ROS' ENTSPRUNGEN

*There shall come forth a rod out of the stem of Jesse, and a Branch shall grow
out of his roots (Isaiah xi. 1)*

FROM Jesse's stock up-springing,
    On tender root has grown:
A rose by Prophet's singing
    To all the world made known.
The rose 'midst winter's cold,
    A lovely blossom bearing,
In former days foretold.

2 This rose then of my story
    Isaiah did proclaim.
What God ordained in glory,
    By blessed Mary came.
The Child the Virgin bore,
    The world's salvation bringing
Through Him for evermore.

3 The rose-bud small and tender
    Gives fragrance every day.
And by its brilliant splendour
    Makes darkness pass away.
True God, true Man we pray,
    Help us in every sorrow,
And guard us on our way.

German; tr. MARY E. BUTLER (1841-1916)

385

THE INFANT KING (4. 9 4 8. 9 9. 4.)   From an old Basque Noël.
Arranged by EDGAR PETTMAN (1865-1943)

They saw the young child . . . and worshipped him (Matthew ii. 11)

S ING lullaby!
Lullaby baby, now reclining,
Sing lullaby!
Hush, do not wake the Infant King.
Angels are watching, stars are shining
Over the place where He is lying:
Sing lullaby!

2   Sing lullaby!
Lullaby baby, now a-sleeping,
Sing lullaby!
Hush, do not wake the Infant King.
Soon will come sorrow with the morning,
Soon will come bitter grief and weeping:
Sing lullaby!

3   Sing lullaby!
    Lullaby baby, now a-dozing,
      Sing lullaby!
    Hush, do not wake the Infant King.
    Soon comes the cross, the nails, the piercing,
    Then in the grave at last reposing:
      Sing lullaby!

4   Sing lullaby!
    Lullaby! is the babe a-waking?
      Sing lullaby!
    Hush, do not stir the Infant King.
    Dreaming of Easter, gladsome morning.
    Conquering Death, its bondage breaking:
      Sing lullaby!

SABINE BARING-GOULD (1834-1924)

386

German Carol Melody.
PUER NOBIS   (7 6. 7 7. Irregular.)   Arranged by GEOFFREY SHAW (1879-1943)

PUER NOBIS NASCITUR

When the fulness of the time was come, God sent forth his Son (Galatians iv. 4)

UNTO us a boy is born!
   King of all creation,
Came He to a world forlorn,
   The Lord of every nation.

2 Cradled in a stall was He
   With sleepy cows and asses;
But the very beasts could see
   That He all men surpasses.

3 Herod then with fear was filled:
   'A prince', he said, ' in Jewry!'
All the little boys he killed
   At Bethlem in his fury.

4 Now may Mary's son, who came
   So long ago to love us,
Lead us all with hearts aflame
   Unto the joys above us.

5 Alpha and Omega He!
   Let the organ thunder,
While the choir with peals of glee
   Doth rend the air asunder!

German (15th century); tr. PERCY DEARMER (1867-1936)

387

OLWEN (6 6 8. 6 6 8. *Ter.*)   Welsh Carol. Arranged by ERIK ROUTLEY (1917-)

O DEUED POB CRISTION

They came with haste, and found . . . the babe lying in a manger (Luke ii. 16)

ALL poor men and humble,
   All lame men who stumble,
Come haste ye, nor feel ye afraid;
For Jesus, our treasure,
With love past all measure,
In lowly poor manger was laid.

2 Though wise men who found Him
   Laid rich gifts around Him,
Yet oxen they gave Him their hay:
And Jesus in beauty
Accepted their duty;
Contented in manger He lay.

3 Then haste we to show Him
   The praises we owe Him;
Our service He ne'er can despise:
Whose love still is able
To show us that stable
Where softly in manger He lies.

Welsh; tr. KATHERINE EMILY ROBERTS (1877-)

388

QUEM PASTORES LAUDAVERE   (8 8 8. 7.)

German Carol Melody (14th century)

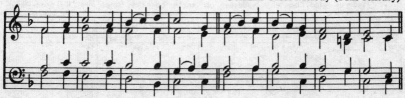

QUEM PASTORES LAUDAVERE

Sing praises unto our King, sing praises (Psalm xlvii. 6)

SHEPHERDS came, their praises bringing,
   Who had heard the angels singing,
' Far from you be fear unruly,
   Christ is King of Glory born.'

2 Sages, whom a star had guided,
   Incense, gold, and myrrh provided,
· Made their sacrifices duly
   To the King of Glory born.

3 Jesus, born the King of heaven,
   Unto us in mercy given,
Be unto Thy merit truly
   Honour, praise, and glory done.

Latin (14th century); tr. GEORGE BRADFORD CAIRD (1917-)

389

SUSSEX CAROL (8 8. 8 8. 8 8.)   English Traditional Carol.
Collected and arranged by RALPH VAUGHAN WILLIAMS (1872-)

1 On Christ-mas night all Chris-tians sing, To hear the news the
   why should men on earth be sad, Since our Re-deem-er

an-gels bring. On Christ-mas night all Chris-tians sing, To hear the news the
made us glad. Then why should men on earth be sad, Since our Re-deem-er

an-gels bring; News of great joy_ news of_ great mirth,
made us glad, When from our sin_ He set_ us free,

News of our mer-ci-ful_ King's birth ___
All for to gain our lib-er-   2 Then -ty. ___

For verse 4 turn to next page

4 All out of dark-ness we have light, Which made the an-gels sing this night. All out of dark-ness we have light, Which made the an-gels sing this night:— 'Glo - ry to God and peace to men, Now and for ev - er-more. A-men.'

rall. *a tempo*

colla voce

rall.

390

FRAGRANCE (9 8. 9 8. 9 8.)

Old French Carol Melody.
Harmonized and arranged by CHARLES HERBERT KITSON (1874-1944)

p Thou who wast rich beyond all splen - dour, All for love's sake be - cam - est poor; *mf* Thrones for a man - ger didst sur - ren - der, Sap-phire paved courts for sta - ble floor. Thou who wast rich be - yond all splen - dour, All for love's sake *dim. e rall.* be - cam - est poor.

For verses 2 and 3 turn to next page

(Philippians ii. 8)

FRANK HOUGHTON (1894-)

391

HUMILITY   (7 7. 7 7. and refrain.)   JOHN GOSS (1800-80)

Solo or Unison

REFRAIN *Harmony*

Though he was rich, yet for your sakes he became poor (2 Corinthians viii. 9)

SEE, amid the winter's snow,
Born for us on earth below,
See, the tender Lamb appears,
Promised from eternal years.

    Hail, thou ever-blessèd morn!
    Hail, redemption's happy dawn!
    Sing through all Jerusalem:
    Christ is born in Bethlehem!

2 Lo, within a manger lies
He who built the starry skies,
He who, throned in height sublime,
Sits amid the cherubim.

*3 Say, ye holy shepherds, say,
What your joyful news today;
Wherefore have ye left your sheep
On the lonely mountain steep?

*4 'As we watched at dead of night,
Lo, we saw a wondrous light:
Angels, singing peace on earth,
Told us of the Saviour's birth.'

5 Sacred Infant, all divine,
What a tender love was Thine,
Thus to come from highest bliss
Down to such a world as this!

    6 Teach, O teach us, holy Child,
    By Thy face so meek and mild,
    Teach us to resemble Thee
    In Thy sweet humility.

EDWARD CASWALL (1814-78)

If desired, verses 3 and 4 may be omitted

Descant for verses 4 and 6 by HERBERT ARTHUR CHAMBERS (1880-)

Hail, thou ev-er blessed morn! Hail, re-demption's happy dawn!

Hail, thou ev - er bless - ed morn! Hail, redemption's hap - py dawn!

Sing thro' all Je - ru-sa-lem, Christ is born in Bethlehem.

Sing thro' all Je - ru - sa-lem, Christ is born in Bethle - hem.

392

CHRISTMAS CAROL (D.C.M. Irregular.)   WALFORD DAVIES (1869-1941)

This carol may also be sung to the tune FOREST GREEN, No. 202 (i)

Immanuel . . . God with us (Matthew i. 23)

O LITTLE town of Bethlehem,
  How still we see thee lie!
Above thy deep and dreamless sleep
  The silent stars go by:
Yet in thy dark streets shineth
  The everlasting Light;
The hopes and fears of all the years
  Are met in thee tonight.

2 O morning stars, together
  Proclaim the holy birth,
And praises sing to God the King,
  And peace to men on earth;
For Christ is born of Mary;
  And, gathered all above,
While mortals sleep, the angels keep
  Their watch of wondering love.

3 How silently, how silently,
  The wondrous gift is given!
So God imparts to human hearts
  The blessings of His heaven.
No ear may hear His coming;
  But in this world of sin,
Where meek souls will receive Him, still
  The dear Christ enters in.

4 O holy Child of Bethlehem,
  Descend to us, we pray;
Cast out our sin, and enter in;
  Be born in us today.
We hear the Christmas angels
  The great glad tidings tell;
O come to us, abide with us,
  Our Lord Immanuel.

PHILLIPS BROOKS (1835-93)

393

BONN (8. 3 3. 6. D.)   JOHANN GEORG EBELING (1637-76)

FRÖHLICH SOLL MEIN HERZE SPRINGEN

They rejoiced with exceeding great joy (Matthew ii. 10)

ALL my heart this night rejoices,
As I hear, far and near,
    Sweetest angel voices;
' Christ is born! ', their choirs are singing,
Till the air, everywhere,
    Now with joy is ringing.

2 Hark! a voice from yonder manger,
    Soft and sweet, doth entreat:
        ' Flee from woe and danger;
    Brethren, come: from all doth grieve you
    You are freed; all you need
        I will surely give you.'

3 Come, then, let us hasten yonder;
    Here let all, great and small,
        Kneel in awe and wonder;
    Love Him who with love is yearning;
    Hail the star that from far,
        Bright with hope is burning.

4 Thee, O Lord, with heed I'll cherish,
    Live to Thee, and with Thee
        Dying, shall not perish,
    But shall dwell with Thee for ever
    Far on high, in the joy
        That can alter never.

PAUL GERHARDT (1607-76);
tr. CATHERINE WINKWORTH (1829-78)

394

THE FIRST NOWELL   (Irregular.)   English Traditional Carol

We have seen his star in the east, and are come to worship him (Matthew ii. 2)

THE first Nowell the angel did say
Was to certain poor shepherds in fields as they lay;
In fields where they lay keeping their sheep,
On a cold winter's night that was so deep.

Nowell, Nowell, Nowell, Nowell,
Born is the King of Israel.

2 They lookèd up and saw a star
Shining in the east, beyond them far,
And to the earth it gave great light,
And so it continued both day and night.

3 And by the light of that same star,
Three wise men came from country far;
To seek for a King was their intent,
And to follow the star wherever it went.

4 This star drew nigh to the north-west;
O'er Bethlehem it took its rest,
And there it did both stop and stay
Right over the place where Jesus lay.

5 Then entered in those wise men three
Full reverently upon their knee,
And offered there in His presence
Their gold, and myrrh, and
frankincense.

6 Then let us all with one accord
Sing praises to our heavenly Lord,
That hath made heaven and earth of nought,
And with His blood mankind hath bought.

TRADITIONAL

Descant for verses 2, 4, and 6 by JOHN E. WEST (1863-1928)

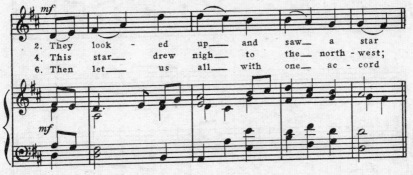

2. They look — ed up and saw a star
4. This star drew nigh to the north - west;
6. Then let us all with one ac - cord

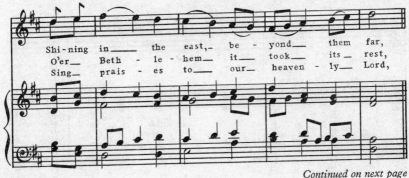

Shi - ning in the east,— be - yond them far,
O'er Beth - le - hem— it took— its rest,
Sing— prais - es to— our heaven - ly Lord,

Continued on next page

And to___ the earth___ it gave___ great light,
And there___ it did___ both stop___ and stay
That hath___ made heaven and earth of nought,

And so it con-tin-ued both day___ and night.
Right o-ver the place___ where Je___ sus lay.
And with___ His blood___ man-kind___ hath bought.

REFRAIN

Now - ell, Now - ell, Now - ell,____ Now - ell,____

Born is the King___ of Is - ra - el.

395

BUNESSAN (5 5. 5 3. D.)

Old Gaelic Melody.
Harmonized and arranged by F. DEREK KIDNER (1913-   )

*The small notes indicate optional accompaniment. Tenors and Altos omit the first two lines of words;
Basses the first four. Verse 2 should be sung in unison, or by unaccompanied solo voice.

LEAHABH AN AIGH

God also hath highly exalted him (Philippians ii. 9)

CHILD in the manger,
    Infant of Mary;
Outcast and stranger,
    Lord of all!
Child who inherits
    All our transgressions,
All our demerits
    On Him fall.

2 Once the most holy
    Child of salvation
Gently and lowly
    Lived below;
Now as our glorious
    Mighty Redeemer,
See Him victorious
    O'er each foe.

3 Prophets foretold Him,
    Infant of wonder;
Angels behold Him
    On His throne;
Worthy our Saviour
    Of all their praises;
Happy for ever
    Are His own.

MARY MACDONALD (1817-*c*. 1890); tr. LACHLAN MACBEAN (1853-1931)

396

MYN LYKING (Irregular.) English Traditional Carol (14th century).
Collected and arranged by RICHARD RUNCIMAN TERRY (1865-1938)

cresc. e rall.   *dim. rall.*

Lul - lay my dere   herte, myn own dere der - ling.

p

Lul - lay my dere   herte, myn own dere der - ling.

Lul - lay my dere   herte, myn own dere der - ling.

Lul - lay,   myn own dere der - ling.

rall.   *p*

mf a tempo   *Fine*

2. That same Lord is He that made al - lé thing   Of

mf

cresc.   *rall.*   D.S. 𝄋 *al Fine*

al - lé lord - es He is Lord, of al - lé kyng - es Kyng.

cresc.   *rall.*

For verses 3 and 4 turn to next page

3. There was mick-le mel-o-dy at that chyl-de's birth.

cresc. molto rall.   D.S. 𝄋 al Fine

All that were in heav'n-ly bliss, they made mick-le mirth.

4. An-gels bright sang their song to that chyld; Blyss-

cresc. molto rit.   D.S. 𝄋 al Fine

-id be Thou, and so be she, so meek and so mild.

(Luke ii. 11)   TRADITIONAL (14th century)

397

CRANHAM (6 5. 6 5. D. Irregular.)   GUSTAV HOLST (1874-1934)

The metre of this hymn is irregular. The music as printed is that of the first verse, and it can easily be adapted to the others. Verse 2 runs as follows:

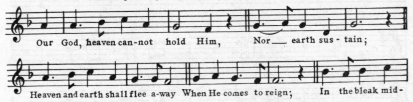

Our God, heaven can-not hold Him,   Nor____ earth sus - tain;

Heaven and earth shall flee a-way When He comes to reign;   In the bleak mid-

They presented unto him gifts (Matthew ii. 11)

IN the bleak mid-winter,
    Frosty wind made moan,
Earth stood hard as iron,
    Water like a stone;
Snow had fallen, snow on snow,
    Snow on snow,
In the bleak mid-winter,
    Long ago.

2 Our God, heaven cannot hold Him,
    Nor earth sustain;
Heaven and earth shall flee away
    When He comes to reign:
In the bleak mid-winter
    A stable-place sufficed
The Lord God Almighty,
    Jesus Christ.

3 Angels and archangels
    May have gathered there,
Cherubim and seraphim
    Thronged the air;
But His mother only,
    In her maiden bliss,
Worshipped the Belovèd
    With a kiss.

4 What can I give Him,
    Poor as I am?
If I were a shepherd,
    I would bring a lamb;
If I were a wise man,
    I would do my part;
Yet what I can I give Him—
    Give my heart.

CHRISTINA GEORGINA ROSSETTI (1830-94)

398

GOD REST YOU MERRY, GENTLEMEN (8 6. 8 6. 8 6. and refrain.)

English Traditional Carol
Descant for verses 4 and 7 by F. DEREK KIDNER (1913-)

Good tidings of great joy (Luke ii. 10)

GOD rest you merry, gentlemen,
Let nothing you dismay,
For Jesus Christ our Saviour
Was born upon this day;
To save us all from Satan's power
When we were gone astray.
O tidings of comfort and joy!

2 In Bethlehem in Jewry
This blessèd Babe was born,
And laid within a manger
Upon this blessèd morn;
The which His mother Mary
Did nothing take in scorn.

3 From God our heavenly Father
A blessèd angel came,
And unto certain shepherds
Brought tidings of the same,
How that in Bethlehem was born
The Son of God by name.

4 'Fear not,' then said the angel,
'Let nothing you affright,
This day is born a Saviour
Of a pure virgin bright,
To free all those who trust in Him
From Satan's power and might.'

5 The shepherds at those tidings
Rejoicèd much in mind,
And left their flocks a-feeding
In tempest, storm, and wind,
And went to Bethlehem straightway,
This blessèd Babe to find.

6 And when to Bethlehem they came,
Whereat this Infant lay,
They found Him in a manger
Where oxen feed on hay;
His mother Mary kneeling
Unto the Lord did pray.

7 Now to the Lord sing praises,
All you within this place,
And with true love and brotherhood
Each other now embrace;
This holy tide of Christmas
All anger should efface.

TRADITIONAL

399

BESIDE THY CRADLE (8 7. 8 7. 8 8 7.) Chorale from *The Christmas Oratorio*, by JOHANN SEBASTIAN BACH (1685-1750)

Be - side Thy cra - dle here I stand, O

Thou that e - ver liv - est, And bring Thee with a

will - ing hand The ver - y gifts Thou giv - est.

Ac - cept me; 'tis my mind and heart,

My soul, my strength, my ev - 'ry part,

That Thou from me re - qui - rest.

(Matthew xxii. 37)   From *The Christmas Oratorio*

See also the section: THE SON OF GOD: HIS INCARNATION, NOS. 34-44

427

DOXOLOGIES

400

LASST UNS ERFREUEN (8 8. 4 4. 8 8. and Hallelujahs.)

Melody from *Geistliche Kirchengesang* (Cologne, 1623)

Based on Psalm cxvii

FROM all that dwell below the skies
Let the Creator's praise arise:
Hallelujah!
Let the Redeemer's name be sung
Through every land, by every tongue.
Hallelujah!

2 Eternal are Thy mercies, Lord;
Eternal truth attends Thy word:
Hallelujah!
Thy praise shall sound from shore to shore,
Till suns shall rise and set no more.
Hallelujah!

ISAAC WATTS (1674-1748)

428

401

OLD 100TH (L.M.)   From the *Genevan Psalter* (1551)

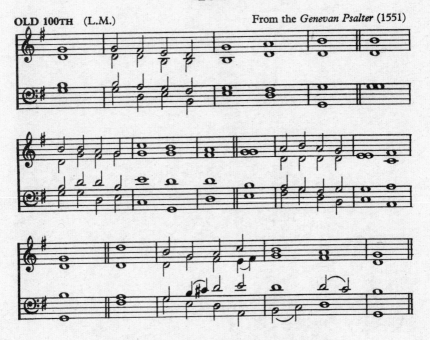

This Doxology may also be sung with Hallelujahs
to the tune LASST UNS ERFREUEN, No. 400

My mouth shall speak the praise of the Lord (Psalm cxlv. 21)

PRAISE God, from whom all blessings flow,
    Praise Him, all creatures here below,
Praise Him above, ye heavenly host,
Praise Father, Son, and Holy Ghost.

THOMAS KEN (1637-1711)

INDEX OF PARAPHRASES AND SCRIPTURE PASSAGES ON WHICH HYMNS ARE BASED

See also Index of Scripture References below

INDEX OF SCRIPTURE REFERENCES

INDEX OF SCRIPTURE REFERENCES

INDEX OF ORIGINAL FIRST LINES
OF TRANSLATED HYMNS

INDEX OF AUTHORS, TRANSLATORS
AND SOURCES OF WORDS

ALPHABETICAL INDEX OF TUNES

Numbers within brackets indicate hymns where a cross-reference to the tune is given. An asterisk indicates the provision of a Descant, Fa-burden or alternative harmonization.

Abbot's Leigh, 143, 335 (i)
Abends, 361
Aberystwyth, 208 (ii)
Abingdon, 235 (i)
Abridge, (137), 225, (346)
Ach Gott und Herr, 162 (i)
Adeste Fideles, 40*
Adoration, 335 (ii)*
Adoro Te, 153
Aescendune, 200
Alberta, 242
Alford, 150
Alleluia, 151
Alleluia, dulce carmen, 285 (i), 374
All for Jesus, 64, (252)
All Saints, 110
Almsgiving, 258 (i)
Andernach, 3
Angel's Song (Song 34), 132, 307
Angelus, 360
Angel-voices, 17
Antwerp, 28 (i), (132), (159), 205
Arfon, 357
Arnstadt, 290
Ascension, 70
Attwood, 127 (ii)
Aurelia, 141, (175), 182
Austria, 20, (143)
Ayrshire, 320

Baca, 351 (ii)
Ballerma, 245
Bangor, 156
Beatitudo, (84), 267, 322
Beeding, 295 (i)
Belmont, 214, (282)
Beside Thy Cradle, 399
Bethany, (47), 75, (335)
Beverley, 163
Binchester, 286
Birling, 29, (167), (313), (361)
Bishopgarth, 172
Bishopthorpe, 48, (244)
Blaenwern, 271, (335)
Bodley, 54
Bodmin, 206, 342
Bonn, 393
Bremen (Munich), 135, 183
Breslau, (78), 288
Bristol, 34 (i)
Bryn Calfaria, 196
Bunessan, 395

Cairnbrook, (149), 222

Caithness, (322), 323
Camacha, 353
Cannock, 167, 284
Capetown, 129
Carlisle, 1*, (178), (199)
Carrick, 319
Cassel, 161
Caswall, 56
Celeste, 92, (230)
Charity, 128
Chorus Angelorum, (7), 101
Christchurch, (107), 108
Christe Sanctorum, 22
Christmas Carol, 392
Christus der ist mein Leben, (329), 330
Church Triumphant, (54), 74 (ii), (166), 366, (367)
Cloisters, 145
Coleshill, 352
Constance, 117
Contemplation, 246
Corde Natus, 35
Cotswold, (235), 236
Cranham, 397
Crediton, 223
Crieff, 140 (i)
Crimond, 279
Cross of Jesus, 85, 187
Crüger, 82, (238), (255)
Cuddesdon, 93 (ii)
Culbach, 23, (94), (369)
Cwm Rhondda, 283 (ii)

Darwall's 148th, 19*, (107)
Das neugeborne Kindelein, 275 (i)
David's Harp (L.M.), 254
David's Harp (88.88.88.), 338
Day of Praise, 121
Dedication, 373
Deus Tuorum Militum, 291 (i)
Diademata, 72, (332)
Dinbych, 332 (i), (333)
Dismissal, 375
Dix, 44
Dolomite Chant, 157 (ii)
Dominica, 370 (i)
Dominus regit me, 162 (ii), 277 (ii)
Down Ampney, 118
Duke Street, 293 (ii)
Dulcis Memoria, 103 (ii)
Dundee (French), 136, (352)
Dunfermline, 31, (136)

Easter Hymn, 65
Ebenezer (Ton-Y-Botel), 116, (171)
Eisenach, 131, (341)
Ein' feste Burg, 232, 233
Ellacombe, 292
Ellasgarth, 106*
Ellers, 212, 362 (i)
Engelberg, 91
Epiphany, 43 (i)
Es ist ein' Ros' entsprungen, 384
Es ist kein Tag, 258 (ii)
Eudoxia, 209 (i), (269)
Evelyns, 93 (i)
Eventide, 287
Everlasting Love, 334
Everton, 170
Ewhurst, 331
Ewing, 194

Fareham, 179 (ii)
Farley Castle, 289
Farmborough, 237, 368
Farrant, 139 (i)
Festus, 76, 227
Forest Green, (188), 202 (i), (392)
Fort William, 43 (ii)
Franconia, (121), 318 (i)
Fragrance, 89, 390*
(French) see Dundee, 136
From Strength to Strength, 299 (ii)
Fulda, 207, (307), 308

Galilee, 81 (ii)
Garelochside, 5
Gerontius, 7
Gideon, 53 (ii)
Glasgow, 83
Glenpark, 281 (ii)
God rest you merry, Gentlemen, 398*
Gonfalon Royal, 148 (i)
Gopsal, 80
Goshen, 217
Gott des Himmels, (343), 344
Grafton, (196), 197
Gwalchmai, 14

Hanover, 25*, (100), (309)
Harewood, 107
Harts, 94, 176
Heathlands, (32), 169, 304
Heinlein, (155), 210
Helmsley, 88

METRICAL INDEX OF TUNES

An asterisk indicates the provision of a Descant, Fa-burden, or alternative harmonization.

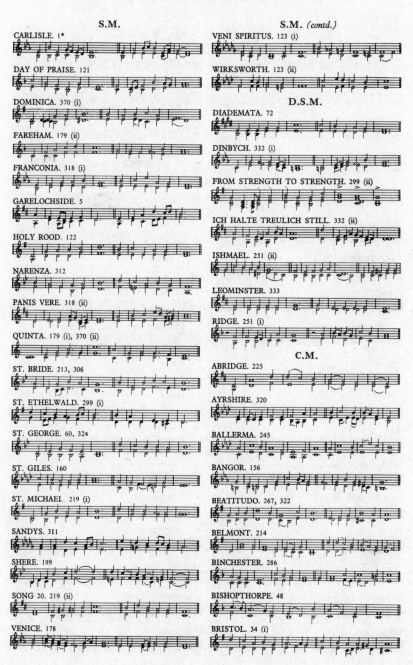

S.M.

CARLISLE. 1*

DAY OF PRAISE. 121

DOMINICA. 370 (i)

FAREHAM. 179 (ii)

FRANCONIA. 318 (i)

GARELOCHSIDE. 5

HOLY ROOD. 122

NARENZA. 312

PANIS VERE. 318 (ii)

QUINTA. 179 (i), 370 (ii)

ST. BRIDE. 213, 306

ST. ETHELWALD. 299 (i)

ST. GEORGE. 60, 324

ST. GILES. 160

ST. MICHAEL. 219 (i)

SANDYS. 311

SHERE. 199

SONG 20. 219 (ii)

VENICE. 178

S.M. *(contd.)*

VENI SPIRITUS. 123 (i)

WIRKSWORTH. 123 (ii)

D.S.M.

DIADEMATA. 72

DINBYCH. 332 (i)

FROM STRENGTH TO STRENGTH. 299 (ii)

ICH HALTE TREULICH STILL. 332 (ii)

ISHMAEL. 251 (ii)

LEOMINSTER. 333

RIDGE. 251 (i)

C.M.

ABRIDGE. 225

AYRSHIRE. 320

BALLERMA. 245

BANGOR. 156

BEATITUDO. 267, 322

BELMONT. 214

BINCHESTER. 286

BISHOPTHORPE. 48

BRISTOL. 34 (i)

C.M. *(contd.)*

CAITHNESS. 323

CHORUS ANGELORUM. 101

COLESHILL. 352

CONTEMPLATION. 246

CREDITON. 223

CRIMOND. 279

DUNDEE. 136

DUNFERMLINE. 31

FARRANT. 139 (i)

GERONTIUS. 7

GLASGOW. 83

HORSLEY. 57 (i)

IRISH. 125, 298

KILMARNOCK. 224

LONDON NEW. 30

LYDIA. 102

MARTYRDOM. 282

METZLER'S REDHEAD. 113, 325

MILES LANE. 90 (i)

C.M. *(contd.)*

NATIVITY. 98

NUN DANKET ALL. 96

RICHMOND. 248*, 371

ST. AGNES. 97

ST. ANNE. 27

ST. BERNARD. 79

ST. BOTOLPH. 193

ST. FLAVIAN. 354

ST. FRANCIS XAVIER. 265

ST. FULBERT. 326

ST. HUGH. 263

ST. JAMES. 105

ST. MAGNUS. 104

ST. PETER. 99, 321

ST. SAVIOUR. 142

ST. STEPHEN. 244, 346

SENNEN COVE. 84

SOUTHWELL. 139 (ii)

STÖRL. 130

C.M. *(contd.)*

STRACATHRO. 124, 262

STROUDWATER. 137

TALLIS' ORDINAL. 264

THIS ENDRIS NYGHT. 57 (ii), 266

UNIVERSITY. 247 (ii)

WALSALL. 58

WEST BURN. 34 (ii)

WESTMINSTER. 6

WILTSHIRE. 247 (i)

WINCHESTER OLD. 37*

D.C.M.

CHRISTMAS CAROL (Irregular). 392

ELLACOMBE. 292

FOREST GREEN. 202 (i)

KINGSFOLD. 202 (ii)

LADYWELL. 90 (ii)

PETERSHAM. 188

ST. MATTHEW. 115

L.M.

ABENDS. 361

L.M. *(contd.)*

ANDERNACH. 3

ANGEL'S SONG. 132, 307

ANGELUS. 360

ANTWERP. 28 (i), 205

BIRLING. 29

BODLEY. 54

BODMIN. 206, 342

BRESLAU. 288

CANNOCK. 167, 284

CHURCH TRIUMPHANT. 74 (ii), 366

DAVID'S HARP. 254

DEUS TUORUM MILITUM. 291 (i)

DUKE STREET. 293 (ii)

DULCIS MEMORIA. 103 (ii)

EISENACH. 131

FESTUS. 76, 227

FULDA. 207, 308

GALILEE. 81 (ii)

GIDEON. 53 (ii)

L.M. (contd.)

GONFALON ROYAL. 148 (i)

HEREFORD. 341 (i)

HERONGATE. 53 (i)

MAINZER. 166

MARYTON. 103 (i)

MELCOMBE. 356

MORNING HYMN. 355

O AMOR QUAM EXSTATICUS. 78

OLD 100th. 2*, 401

OMBERSLEY. 191, 280

PHILIPPINE. 74 (i), 367

RIMINGTON. 28 (ii)

RIVAULX. 216

ROCKINGHAM. 55

RUSHFORD. 293 (i)

ST. BARTHOLOMEW. 313

ST. DROSTANE. 50

ST. LAWRENCE. 159

SAMSON. 291 (ii)

L.M. (contd.)

SOLOTHURN. 372

TALLIS' CANON. 358, 359

TRURO. 81 (i), 294

VENI CREATOR. 127 (i)

WAREHAM. 148 (ii)

WARRINGTON. 260

WILTON. 341 (ii)

WINCHESTER NEW. 77, 190

4.9 4 8.9 9.4.

THE INFANT KING. 385

55.53.D.

BUNESSAN. 395

55.55.65.65.

(See also under 10.10.11.11.)

HANOVER. 25*

HOUGHTON. 240

LAUDATE DOMINUM. 9

PADERBORN. 100

55.88.55.

ARNSTADT. 290

64.64.D.

(See also under 10. 10. and 10 10. 10 10.)

LATHBURY. 140 (ii)

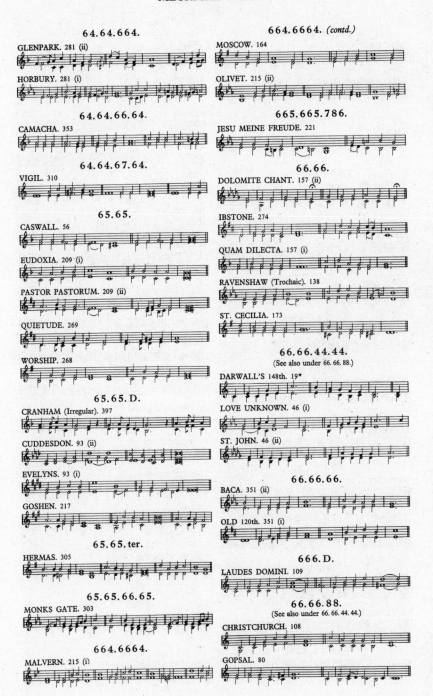

64.64.664.

GLENPARK. 281 (ii)

HORBURY. 281 (i)

64.64.66.64.

CAMACHA. 353

64.64.67.64.

VIGIL. 310

65.65.

CASWALL. 56

EUDOXIA. 209 (i)

PASTOR PASTORUM. 209 (ii)

QUIETUDE. 269

WORSHIP. 268

65.65.D.

CRANHAM (Irregular). 397

CUDDESDON. 93 (ii)

EVELYNS. 93 (i)

GOSHEN. 217

65.65.ter.

HERMAS. 305

65.65.66.65.

MONKS GATE. 303

664.6664.

MALVERN. 215 (i)

664.6664. (contd.)

MOSCOW. 164

OLIVET. 215 (ii)

665.665.786.

JESU MEINE FREUDE. 221

66.66.

DOLOMITE CHANT. 157 (ii)

IBSTONE. 274

QUAM DILECTA. 157 (i)

RAVENSHAW (Trochaic). 138

ST. CECILIA. 173

66.66.44.44.
(See also under 66.66.88.)

DARWALL'S 148th. 19*

LOVE UNKNOWN. 46 (i)

ST. JOHN. 46 (ii)

66.66.66.

BACA. 351 (ii)

OLD 120th. 351 (i)

666.D.

LAUDES DOMINI. 109

66.66.88.
(See also under 66.66.44.44.)

CHRISTCHURCH. 108

GOPSAL. 80

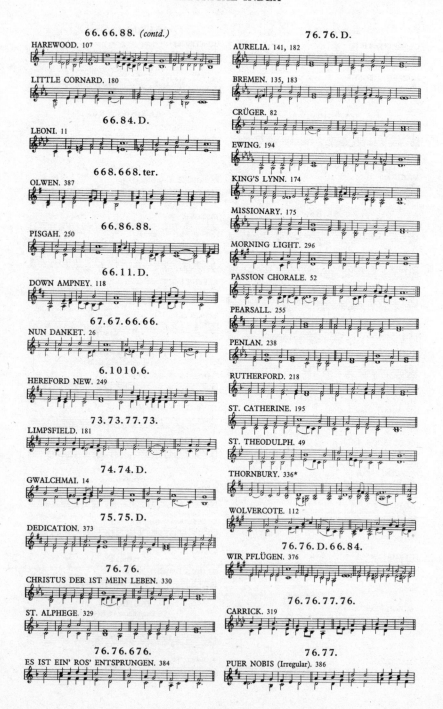

66.66.88. (contd.)
HAREWOOD. 107

LITTLE CORNARD. 180

66.84.D.
LEONI. 11

668.668.ter.
OLWEN. 387

66.86.88.
PISGAH. 250

66.11.D.
DOWN AMPNEY. 118

67.67.66.66.
NUN DANKET. 26

6.1010.6.
HEREFORD NEW. 249

73.73.77.73.
LIMPSFIELD. 181

74.74.D.
GWALCHMAI. 14

75.75.D.
DEDICATION. 373

76.76.
CHRISTUS DER IST MEIN LEBEN. 330

ST. ALPHEGE. 329

76.76.676.
ES IST EIN' ROS' ENTSPRUNGEN. 384

76.76.D.
AURELIA. 141, 182

BREMEN. 135, 183

CRÜGER. 82

EWING. 194

KING'S LYNN. 174

MISSIONARY. 175

MORNING LIGHT. 296

PASSION CHORALE. 52

PEARSALL. 255

PENLAN. 238

RUTHERFORD. 218

ST. CATHERINE. 195

ST. THEODULPH. 49

THORNBURY. 336*

WOLVERCOTE. 112

76.76.D.66.84.
WIR PFLÜGEN. 376

76.76.77.76.
CARRICK. 319

76.77.
PUER NOBIS (Irregular). 386

76.86.D.

ALFORD. 150

76.86.86.86.

ST. CHRISTOPHER. 59

776.778.

INNSBRUCK. 220

777.

ST. PHILIP. 261 (ii)

TYHOLLAND. 261 (i)

777.3.

BEEDING. 295 (i)

VIGILATE. 295 (ii)

777.5.

CAPETOWN. 129

CHARITY. 128

777.6.

WORSHIP. 15

77.77.

ASCENSION (and Hallelujahs). 70

CULBACH. 23

EASTER HYMN (and Hallelujahs). 65

HARTS. 94, 176

HEINLEIN. 210

LÜBECK. 120, 155, 350

77.77. *(contd.)*

MELLING. 256

MONKLAND. 12

NEW CALABAR. 369

NEWINGTON. 259

ORIENTIS PARTIBUS. 177

RENFREWSHIRE. 192 (i)

ST. BEES. 192 (ii)

SONG 13. 154

UNIVERSITY COLLEGE. 297

VIENNA. 95, 270

77.77. (and refrain)

HUMILITY. 391*

77.77.4.

ORIENTIS PARTIBUS. 69

77.77.77.

ARFON. 357

CASSEL. 161

DIX. 44

HEATHLANDS. 169, 304

NORICUM. 32

PETRA. 211

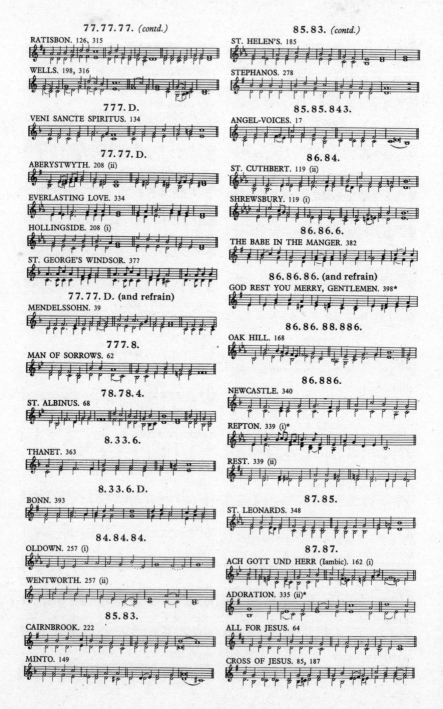

77.77.77. *(contd.)*

RATISBON. 126, 315

777.D.

VENI SANCTE SPIRITUS. 134

77.77.D.

ABERYSTWYTH. 208 (ii)

EVERLASTING LOVE. 334

HOLLINGSIDE. 208 (i)

ST. GEORGE'S WINDSOR. 377

77.77. D. (and refrain)

MENDELSSOHN. 39

777.8.

MAN OF SORROWS. 62

78.78.4.

ST. ALBINUS. 68

8.33.6.

THANET. 363

8.33.6.D.

BONN. 393

84.84.84.

OLDOWN. 257 (i)

WENTWORTH. 257 (ii)

85.83.

CAIRNBROOK. 222

MINTO. 149

WELLS. 198, 316

85.83. *(contd.)*

ST. HELEN'S. 185

STEPHANOS. 278

85.85.843.

ANGEL-VOICES. 17

86.84.

ST. CUTHBERT. 119 (ii)

SHREWSBURY. 119 (i)

86.86.6.

THE BABE IN THE MANGER. 382

86.86.86. (and refrain)

GOD REST YOU MERRY, GENTLEMEN. 398*

86.86. 88.886.

OAK HILL. 168

86.886.

NEWCASTLE. 340

REPTON. 339 (i)*

REST. 339 (ii)

87.85.

ST. LEONARDS. 348

87.87.

ACH GOTT UND HERR (Iambic). 162 (i)

ADORATION. 335 (ii)*

ALL FOR JESUS. 64

CROSS OF JESUS. 85, 187

87.87. *(contd.)*

DOMINUS REGIT ME (Iambic). 162 (ii), 277 (ii)

LAUS DEO. 18

MARCHING. 272

ST. ANDREW. 314

ST. COLUMBA (Iambic). 277 (i)

SHIPSTON. 252, 273 (ii)

STUTTGART. 42

SUNSET. 365

SUSSEX. 273 (i)

WALTHAM. 144

87.87. (and refrain)

IRIS. 38

87.87.66.667.

EIN' FESTE BURG. 232, 233

87.87.77.

ALL SAINTS. 110

GOTT DES HIMMELS. 344

IRBY. 41*

REQUIEM. 343

87.87.$\frac{4}{8}$7.

ALLELUIA, DULCE CARMEN. 285 (i), 374

87.87.$\frac{4}{8}$7. *(contd.)*

BRYN CALFARIA. 196

CWM RHONDDA. 283 (ii)

DISMISSAL. 375

GRAFTON. 197

HELMSLEY. 88

MANNHEIM. 285 (ii)

MIDHURST. 111 (ii)

NEANDER. 186

ORIEL. 111 (i)

PICARDY. 165

PRAISE, MY SOUL. 8*

REGENT SQUARE. 63

RHUDDLAN. 229

ST. HELEN. 283 (i)

TRIUMPH. 73

87.87.877.

CORDE NATUS. 35

87.87.D.

ABBOT'S LEIGH. 143, 335 (i)

ALLELUIA. 151

87.87.D. *(contd.)*

AUSTRIA. 20

BETHANY. 75

BISHOPGARTH (Iambic). 172

BLAENWERN. 271

CONSTANCE (Iambic). 117

EBENEZER. 116

EVERTON. 170

HYFRYDOL. 171, 253

LUX EOI. 66

PLEADING SAVIOUR. 36

ST. AUDREY NEW. 47

87.87.887.

BESIDE THY CRADLE. 399

87.88.7.

LYDBROOK. 349

87.887.77.77.

BEVERLEY. 163

88.44.88 (and Hallelujahs)

LASST UNS ERFREUEN. 4, 400

886.D.

INNSBRUCK NEW. 327

MAGDALEN COLLEGE. 328

888.

KEYNSHAM. 300

888.3.

AESCENDUNE (Trochaic). 200

ST. AËLRED (Iambic). 276

888.4.

ALMSGIVING. 258 (i)

ES IST KEIN TAG. 258 (ii)

VICTORY. 67 (i)

VULPIUS. 67 (ii)

888.6.

MISERICORDIA. 204

SAFFRON WALDEN. 203

888.7.

EWHURST. 331

QUEM PASTORES LAUDAVERE. 388

88.88. Anapaestic

CELESTE. 92

88.88.6.

ST. MARGARET. 347

88.88.88.

ABINGDON. 235 (i)

ATTWOOD. 127 (ii)

COTSWOLD. 236

88.88.88. (contd.)

DAS NEUGEBORNE KINDELEIN. 275 (i)

DAVID'S HARP. 338

FARMBOROUGH. 237, 368

MELITA. 226

PATER OMNIUM. 275 (ii)

SAGINA. 235 (ii)

ST. CATHERINE. 228

ST. MATTHIAS. 337

STELLA. 114 (ii)

SURREY. 189

SUSSEX CAROL. 389*

VATER UNSER. 114 (i)

VENI IMMANUEL. 86

WOKING. 184

WYCH CROSS. 243

888. D.

MONMOUTH. 13

88.88. D. Anapaestic

LLANGRISTIOLUS. 230

TREWEN. 231

810.10.4.

ELLASGARTH. 106*

98.98.

LES COMMANDEMENS DE DIEU. 364 (ii)

ST. CLEMENT. 364 (i)

SPIRITUS VITAE. 133

98.98.98.

FRAGRANCE. 89, 390*

98.98. D.

RENDEZ À DIEU. 158

104.66.66.104.

LUCKINGTON. 10 (i)

WILTON. 10 (ii)

104.104.1010

ALBERTA. 242

10.10.

CRIEFF. 140 (i)

SONG 46. 234

1010 10.4.

ENGELBERG. 91

SINE NOMINE. 147

1010.1010.

ADORO TE. 153

ELLERS. 212, 362 (i)

10 10. 10 10. *(contd.)*

EVENTIDE. 287

FARLEY CASTLE. 289

JULIUS. 362 (ii)

OLD 124th. 201

ST. AGNES. 152 (ii)

SLANE (Dactylic: Irregular). 317

SONG 22. 152 (i)

WOODLANDS. 16

10 10. 10 10 4.

IT PASSETH KNOWLEDGE. 345 (ii)

ST. KEVERNE. 345 (i)

10 10. 10 10. 10 10.

SONG 1. 146

UNDE ET MEMORES. 239

10. 10. 11. 11.
(See also under 55. 55. 65. 65)

OLD 104th. 309

10 11. 11 11 (and refrain)

MACCABAEUS. 71

11 10 11. 6 12.

QUITTEZ, PASTEURS. 381

11 10. 11 10.

EPIPHANY (Dactylic). 43 (i)

11 10. 11 10. *(contd.)*

FORT WILLIAM (Dactylic). 43 (ii)

O PERFECT LOVE. 301

ST. OSYTH. 302

11 10. 11 10. D.

LONDONDERRY AIR. 87*

11 11 11. 5.

CHRISTE SANCTORUM. 22

CLOISTERS. 145

HERZLIEBSTER JESU. 51

11 11. 11 11.

ST. DENIO. 33, 241

11 12. 12 10.

NICAEA. 21

14 14. 4. 7. 8.

LOBE DEN HERREN. 24

Irregular

ADESTE FIDELES. 40*

THE FIRST NOWELL. 394*

IN DULCI JUBILO. 383

MARGARET. 45

MYN LYKING. 396

O MAKE ME UNDERSTAND IT. 61

INDEX OF FIRST LINES WITH METRES AND TUNES

Tunes within brackets are those to which cross reference is made. An asterisk indicates the provision of a Descant, Fa-burden or alternative harmonization. To enable hymns to be found quickly their numbers are printed at the top right or left-hand corners of the pages as well as above the music.

No.	First Line	Metre	Name of Tune
306	A charge to keep I have	S.M.	St. Bride (*Narenza*)
230	A debtor to mercy alone	8 8. 8 8. D. Anapaestic	Llangristiolus (*Trewen & Celeste*)
232	A safe stronghold	8 7. 8 7. 6 6. 6 6 7.	Ein' feste Burg
231	A sovereign Protector I have	8 8. 8 8. D. Anapaestic	Trewen
287	Abide with me	10 10. 10 10.	Eventide
366	Again the Lord's own day is here	L.M.	Church Triumphant
51	Ah, holy Jesu, how hast Thou offended	11 11. 11 5.	Herzliebster Jesu
58	Alas! and did my Saviour bleed?	C.M.	Walsall (*St. Falvian*)
4	All creatures of our God	8 8. 4 4. 8 8. and Hallelujahs	Lasst uns erfreuen
49	All glory, laud and honour	7 6. 7 6. D.	St. Theodulph
90	All hail the power of Jesus' name!	C.M. D.C.M.	i. Miles Lane ii. Ladywell (*Lydia*)
393	All my heart this night rejoices	8. 3 3. 6. D.	Bonn
2	All people that on earth	L.M.	Old 100th*
387	All poor men and humble	6 6 8. 6 6 8. *Ter.*	Olwen
91	All praise to Thee, for Thou, O King divine	10 10 10. 4.	Engelberg (*Sine Nomine*)
235	And can it be, that I should gain	8 8. 8 8. 8 8.	i. Abingdon ii. Sagina
17	Angel voices, ever singing	8 5. 8 5. 8 4 3.	Angel-voices
38	Angels from the realms of glory	8 7. 8 7. and refrain	Iris (*Regent Square*)
266	Approach, my soul, the mercy-seat	C.M.	This endris nyght (*Stracathro*)
294	Arm of the Lord, awake	L.M.	Truro
278	Art thou weary, heavy-laden	8 5. 8 3.	Stephanos
225	As pants the hart	C.M.	Abridge (*Martyrdom*)
44	As with gladness men of old	7 7. 7 7. 7 7.	Dix
360	At even, when the sun was set	L.M.	Angelus
93	At the name of Jesus	6 5. 6 5. D.	i. Evelyns ii. Cuddesdon
357	At Thy feet, O Christ, we lay	7 7. 7 7. 7 7.	Arfon (*Ratisbon*)
355	Awake, my soul, and with the sun	L.M.	Morning Hymn
291	Awake, our souls! away our fears!	L.M.	i. Deus Tuorum Militum ii. Samson (*St. Bartholomew*)
239	Be still, my soul: the Lord is on thy side	10 10. 10 10. 10 10.	Unde et memores (*Song 1*)
317	Be Thou my Vision	10 10. 10 10. (Irreg.) Dactylic	Slane
3	Before Jehovah's aweful throne	L.M.	Andernach
76	Before the throne of God above	L.M.	Festus
240	Begone, unbelief	5 5. 5 5. 6 5. 6 5.	Houghton
190	Behold a Stranger at the door!	L.M.	Winchester New
245	Behold the amazing gift of love	C.M.	Ballerma (*St. Stephen*)
189	Behold, the Lamb of God, who bears	8 8. 8 8. 8 8.	Surrey
83	Behold! the mountain of the Lord	C.M.	Glasgow
264	Behold us, Lord, a little space	C.M.	Tallis' Ordinal
59	Beneath the cross of Jesus	7 6. 8 6. 8 6. 8 6.	St. Christopher
399	Beside Thy cradle here I stand	8 7. 8 7. 8 8 7.	Beside Thy Cradle
249	Blessèd be God, our God	6. 10. 10. 6.	Hereford New

No.	First Line	Metre	Name of Tune
318	Blest are the pure in heart	S.M.	i. Franconia
			ii. Panis Vere
244	Blest be the everlasting God	C.M.	St. Stephen
			(*Bishopthorpe*)
161	Bread of heaven, on Thee I feed	7 7. 7 7. 7 7.	Cassel
158	Bread of the world in mercy broken	9 8. 9 8. D.	Rendez à Dieu
140	Break Thou the bread of life	10. 10.	i. Crieff
		6 4. 6 4. D.	ii. Lathbury
123	Breathe on me, Breath of God	S.M.	i. Veni Spiritus
			ii. Wirksworth
94	Brethren, let us join to bless	7 7. 7 7.	Harts (*Culbach*)
18	Bright the vision that delighted	8 7. 8 7.	Laus Deo
43	Brightest and best	11 10. 11 10.	i. Epiphany
		Dactylic	ii. Fort William
395	Child in the manger	5 5. 5 3. D.	Bunessan
256	Children of the heavenly King	7 7. 7 7.	Melling (*Monkland*)
315	Christ, whose glory fills the skies	7 7. 7 7. 7 7.	Ratisbon
295	Christian, seek not yet repose	7 7 7. 3.	i. Beeding
			ii. Vigilate
118	Come down, O Love divine	6 6. 11. D.	Down Ampney
131	Come, gracious Spirit, heavenly dove	L.M.	Eisenach (*Wareham*)
124	Come, Holy Ghost, our hearts inspire	C.M.	Stracathro
127	Come, Holy Ghost, our souls inspire	L.M.	i. Veni Creator
		8 8. 8 8. 8 8.	ii. Attwood
121	Come, Holy Spirit, come	S.M.	Day of Praise (*Franconia*)
98	Come, let us join our cheerful songs	C.M.	Nativity
224	Come, let us to the Lord our God	C.M.	Kilmarnock
368	Come, let us with our Lord arise	8 8. 8 8. 8 8.	Farmborough
270	Come, my soul, thy suit prepare	7 7. 7 7.	Vienna (*Song* 13)
252	Come, Thou fount of every blessing	8 7. 8 7.	Shipston (*All for Jesus & Lux Eoi*)
134	Come, Thou Holy Spirit, come	7 7 7. D.	Veni Sancte Spiritus
85	Come, Thou long-expected Jesus	8 7. 8 7.	Cross of Jesus (*Laus Deo*)
129	Come to our poor nature's night	7 7 7. 5.	Capetown
194	'Come unto me, ye weary'	7 6. 7 6. D.	Ewing
196	Come, ye sinners, poor and needy	8 7. 8 7. 4 7.	Bryn Calfaria (*Grafton*)
197	Come, ye souls by sin afflicted	8 7. 8 7. 4 7.	Grafton
377	Come, ye thankful people, come	7 7. 7 7. D.	St. George's, Windsor
251	Come, ye that love the Lord	D.S.M.	i. Ridge
			ii. Ishmael (*Ich halte treulich still*)
152	Come ye yourselves apart	10 10. 10 10.	i. Song 22
			ii. St. Agnes
199	Commit thou all	S.M.	Shere (*Carlisle*)
95	Conquering kings their titles take	7 7. 7 7.	Vienna
36	Cradled in a manger, meanly	8 7. 8 7. D.	Pleading Saviour
72	Crown Him with many crowns	D.S.M.	Diademata
339	Dear Lord and Father of mankind	8 6. 8 8 6.	i. Repton*
			ii. Rest
210	Depth of mercy! can there be	7 7. 7 7.	Heinlein (*Song* 13)
309	Disposer supreme, and Judge of the earth	10. 10. 11. 11.	Old 104th (*Hanover*)
42	Earth has many a noble city	8 7. 8 7.	Stuttgart
193	Enthrone thy God within thy heart	C.M.	St. Botolph

No.	First Line	Metre	Name of Tune
363	Ere I sleep, for every favour	8. 3 3. 6.	Thanet
340	Eternal Light! eternal Light!	8 6. 8 8 6.	Newcastle (*Repton*)
146	Eternal Ruler of the ceaseless round	10 10. 10 10. 10 10.	Song 1
182	Facing a task unfinished	7 6. 7 6. D.	Aurelia
273	Father, hear the prayer we offer	8 7. 8 7.	i. Sussex
			ii. Shipston
373	Father, let me dedicate	7 5. 7 5. D.	Dedication
22	Father most holy, merciful and loving	11 11 11. 5.	Christe Sanctorum
216	Father of heaven, whose love profound	L.M.	Rivaulx
139	Father of mercies, in Thy Word	C.M.	i. Farrant
			ii. Southwell
316	Father, Son, and Holy Ghost	7 7. 7 7. 7 7.	Wells (*Ratisbon*)
276	Fierce raged the tempest	8 8 8. 3. Iambic	St. Aëlred
293	Fight the good fight	L.M.	i. Rushford
			ii. Duke Street
248	Fill Thou my life, O Lord my God	C.M.	Richmond* (*West Burn*)
147	For all the saints	10 10 10. 4.	Sine Nomine
265	For mercies, countless as the sands	C.M.	St. Francis Xavier
172	'For My sake and the gospel's, go'	8 7. 8 7. D. Iambic	Bishopgarth
32	For the beauty of the earth	7 7. 7 7. 7 7.	Noricum (*Heathlands*)
307	Forth in Thy name, O Lord, I go	L.M.	Angel's Song (*Fulda*)
400	From all that dwell below the skies	8 8. 4 4. 8 8. and Hallelujahs	Lasst uns erfreuen
175	From Greenland's icy mountains	7 6. 7 6. D.	Missionary (*Aurelia*)
384	From Jesse's stock up-springing	7 6. 7 6. 6 7 6.	Es ist ein' Ros' entsprungen
171	From the depths of sin and failure	8 7. 8 7. D.	Hyfrydol (*Ebenezer*)
61	Give me a sight, O Saviour	Irregular	O make me understand it
142	Give me the wings of faith	C.M.	St. Saviour
28	Give to our God immortal praise	L.M.	i. Antwerp
			ii. Rimington
143	Glorious things of thee are spoken	8 7. 8 7. D.	Abbot's Leigh (*Austria*)
56	Glory be to Jesus	6 5. 6 5.	Caswall
359	Glory to Thee, my God, this night	L.M.	Tallis' Canon
358	Glory to Thee who safe hast kept	L.M.	Tallis' Canon
313	Go, labour on	L.M.	St. Bartholomew (*Birling*)
191	God calling yet! Shall I not hear?	L.M.	Ombersley
212	God made me for Himself	10 10. 10 10.	Ellers
30	God moves in a mysterious way	C.M.	London New (*Irish*)
169	God of mercy, God of grace	7 7. 7 7. 7 7.	Heathlands
398	God rest you merry, gentlemen	8 6. 8 6. 8 6. and refrain	God rest you merry, Gentlemen
383	Good Christian men, rejoice	Irregular	In dulci jubilo
15	Gracious God, we worship Thee	7 7 7. 6.	Worship
126	Gracious Spirit, dwell with me!	7 7. 7 7. 7 7.	Ratisbon (*Wells*)
128	Gracious Spirit, Holy Ghost	7 7 7. 5.	Charity
262	Great Shepherd of Thy people, hear	C.M.	Stracathro
283	Guide me, O Thou great Jehovah	8 7. 8 7. 4 7.	i. St. Helen
			ii. Cwm Rhondda
70	Hail the day that sees Him rise	7 7. 7 7. and Hallelujahs	Ascension
75	Hail, Thou once despisèd Jesus!	8 7. 8 7. D.	Bethany

FIRST LINES WITH METRES AND TUNES

No.	First Line	Metre	Name of Tune
82	Hail to the Lord's Anointed	7 6. 7 6. D.	Crüger
66	Hallelujah! Hallelujah!	8 7. 8 7. D.	Lux Eoi (*Hyfrydol*)
151	Hallelujah! sing to Jesus!	8 7. 8 7. D.	Alleluia (*Hyfrydol*)
192	Hark, my soul! it is the Lord	7 7. 7 7.	i. Renfrewshire
			ii. St. Bees (*Song* 13)
34	Hark, the glad sound, the Saviour comes	C.M.	i. Bristol
			ii. West Burn
39	Hark, the herald angels sing	7 7. 7 7. D. and refrain	Mendelssohn
63	Hark! the voice of love and mercy	8 7. 8 7. 4 7.	Regent Square
310	Hark, 'tis the watchman's cry	6 4. 6 4. 6 7. 6 4.	Vigil
185	He expecteth, He expecteth!	8 5. 8 3.	St. Helen's
148	He wants not friends that hath Thy love	L.M.	i. Gonfalon Royal
			ii. Wareham
303	He who would valiant be	6 5. 6 5. 6 6. 6 5.	Monks Gate
153	Here, O my Lord, I see Thee	10 10. 10 10.	Adoro te (*St. Agnes*)
180	Hills of the North, rejoice	6 6. 6 6. 8 8.	Little Cornard
149	Holy Father, in Thy mercy	8 5. 8 3.	Minto (*Cairnbrook*)
21	Holy, holy, holy, Lord God Almighty!	11. 12. 12. 10.	Nicaea
120	Holy Spirit, truth divine	7 7. 7 7.	Lübeck
254	How blest is life if lived for Thee	L.M.	David's Harp
84	How bright these glorious spirits shine!	C.M.	Sennen Cove (*Beatitudo & Irish*)
241	How firm a foundation	11 11. 11 11.	St. Denio
92	How good is the God we adore	8 8. 8 8. Anapaestic	Celeste (*Llangristiolus*)
99	How sweet the name of Jesus sounds	C.M.	St. Peter
331	I am not skilled to understand	8 8 8. 7.	Ewhurst
156	I am not worthy, holy Lord	C.M.	Bangor (*Nun danket all*)
222	I am trusting Thee, Lord Jesus	8 5. 8 3.	Cairnbrook
87	I cannot tell why He, whom angels worship	11 10. 11 10. D.	Londonderry Air*
219	I hear the words of love	S.M.	i. St. Michael
			ii. Song 20
202	I heard the voice of Jesus say	D.C.M.	i. Forest Green
			ii. Kingsfold
157	I hunger and I thirst	6 6. 6 6.	i. Quam Dilecta
			ii. Dolomite Chant
74	I know that my Redeemer lives	L.M.	i. Philippine
			ii. Church Triumphant (*Lasst uns erfreuen*)
396	I saw a fair mayden syttin and sing	Irregular	Myn Lyking
31	I sing the almighty power of God	C.M.	Dunfermline (*Sennen Cove*)
289	I take Thy promise, Lord	10 10. 10 10.	Farley Castle (*Woodlands*)
352	I want a principle within	C.M.	Coleshill (*Dundee*)
253	I will sing the wondrous story	8 7. 8 7. D.	Hyfrydol
13	I'll praise my Maker while I've breath	8 8 8. D.	Monmouth
223	I'm not ashamed to own my Lord	C.M.	Crediton (*Martyrdom*)
33	Immortal, invisible, God only wise	11 11. 11 11.	St. Denio
48	Immortal love, for ever full	C.M.	Bishopthorpe
329	In full and glad surrender	7 6. 7 6.	St. Alphege (*Christus der ist mein Leben*)
238	In heavenly love abiding	7 6. 7 6. D.	Penlan (*Crüger*)
397	In the bleak mid-winter	6 5. 6 5. D. Irregular	Cranham
64	In the cross of Christ I glory	8 7. 8 7.	All for Jesus (*Stuttgart*)

460

No.	First Line	Metre	Name of Tune
53	It is a thing most wonderful	L.M.	i. Herongate
			ii. Gideon
345	It passeth knowledge, that dear love of Thine	10 10. 10 10 4.	i. St. Keverne
			ii. It passeth knowledge
117	I've found a Friend; O such a Friend!	8 7. 8 7. D. Iambic	Constance
314	Jesus calls us! O'er the tumult	8 7. 8 7.	St. Andrew (Shipston)
65	Jesus Christ is risen today	7 7. 7 7. and Hallelujahs	Easter Hymn
324	Jesus, I fain would find	S.M.	St. George
217	Jesus, I will trust Thee	6 5. 6 5. D.	Goshen
68	Jesus lives! thy terrors now	7 8. 7 8. 4.	St. Albinus
229	Jesus, Lord of life and glory	8 7. 8 7. 4 7.	Rhuddlan
208	Jesu, Lover of my soul	7 7. 7 7. D.	i. Hollingside
			ii. Aberystwyth
304	Jesus, Master, whose I am	7 7. 7 7. 7 7.	Heathlands (Wells)
228	Jesu, my Lord, my God, my All	8 8. 8 8. 8 8.	St. Catherine
332	Jesus, my strength, my hope	D.S.M.	i. Dinbych
			ii. Ich halte treulich still (Diademata & Leominster)
221	Jesu, priceless treasure	6 6 5. 6 6 5. 7 8 6.	Jesu meine Freude
81	Jesus shall reign where'er the sun	L.M.	i. Truro
			ii. Galilee (Rimington)
268	Jesus, stand among us	6 5. 6 5.	Worship (Quietude)
290	Jesus, still lead on	5 5. 8 8. 5 5.	Arnstadt
102	Jesus! the name high over all	C.M.	Lydia (Richmond)
205	Jesus, the sinner's Friend, to Thee	L.M.	Antwerp
97	Jesu, the very thought of Thee	C.M.	St. Agnes (Nun danket all)
96	Jesus, these eyes have never seen	C.M.	Nun danket all (Southwell)
325	Jesus Thine all-victorious love	C.M.	Metzler's Redhead (St. Fulbert)
103	Jesu, Thou joy of loving hearts	L.M.	i. Maryton
			ii. Dulcis Memoria
207	Jesu, Thy blood and righteousness	L.M.	Fulda
338	Jesu, Thy boundless love to me	8 8. 8 8. 8 8.	David's Harp (Pater Omnium)
160	Jesus, we thus obey	S.M.	St. Giles (St. Michael)
154	Jesus, we Thy promise claim	7 7. 7 7.	Song 13
260	Jesus, where'er Thy people meet	L.M.	Warrington
107	Join all the glorious names	6 6. 6 6. 8 8.	Harewood (Christchurch & Darwall's 148th)
165	Judge eternal, throned in splendour	8 7. 8 7. 8 7.	Picardy (Rhuddlan)
204	Just as I am, without one plea	8 8 8. 6.	Misericordia (Saffron Walden)
14	King of glory, King of peace	7 4. 7 4. D.	Gwalchmai
136	Lamp of our feet, whereby we trace	C.M.	Dundee (Dunfermline)
285	Lead us, heavenly Father	8 7. 8 7. 8 7.	i. Alleluia, dulce carmen
			ii. Mannheim
275	Leader of faithful souls, and guide	8 8. 8 8. 8 8.	i. Das neugeborne Kindelein
			ii. Pater Omnium
10	Let all the world in every corner sing	10 4. 6 6. 6 6. 10 4.	i. Luckington
			ii. Wilton
110	Let us love, and sing, and wonder	8 7. 8 7. 7 7.	All Saints
12	Let us with a gladsome mind	7 7. 7 7.	Monkland

No.	First Line	Metre	Name of Tune
16	' Lift up your hearts! ' We lift them, Lord, to Thee	10 10. 10 10.	Woodlands (*Julius*)
88	Lo! He comes, with clouds descending	8 7. 8 7. 4 7.	Helmsley
73	Look, ye saints! the sight is glorious	8 7. 8 7. 4 7.	Triumph (*Neander & Regent Square*)
374	Lord, behold us with Thy blessing	8 7. 8 7. 4 7.	Alleluia, dulce carmen
375	Lord, dismiss us with Thy blessing	8 7. 8 7. 4 7.	Dismissal
122	Lord God the Holy Ghost	S.M.	Holy Rood (*St. Bride*)
170	Lord, her watch Thy Church is keeping	8 7. 8 7. D.	Everton
206	Lord, I was blind: I could not see	L.M.	Bodmin (*Ombersley*)
168	Lord Jesus Christ, the work is Thine	8 6. 8 6. 8 8. 8 8 6.	Oak Hill
159	Lord Jesus Christ, we seek Thy face	L.M.	St. Lawrence (*Antwerp*)
29	Lord of all being, throned afar	L.M.	Birling (*Ombersley*)
145	Lord of our life, and God of our salvation	11 11 11. 5.	Cloisters
183	Lord of the living harvest	7 6. 7 6. D.	Bremen
308	Lord, speak to me, that I may speak	L.M.	Fulda (*Philippine*)
263	Lord, teach us how to pray aright	C.M.	St. Hugh (*Stracathro*)
138	Lord, Thy word abideth	6 6. 6 6. Trochaic	Ravenshaw
335	Love divine, all loves excelling	8 7. 8 7. D. 8 7. 8 7.	i. Abbot's Leigh ii. Adoration★ (*Blaenwern & Bethany*)
334	Loved with everlasting love	7 7. 7 7. D.	Everlasting Love
69	Love's redeeming work is done	7 7. 7 7. 4.	Orientis Partibus
379	Magnificat		
333	Make me a captive, Lord	D.S.M.	Leominster (*Dinbych*)
62	Man of Sorrows! what a name	7 7 7. 8.	Man of Sorrows
344	Master, speak! Thy servant heareth	8 7. 8 7. 7 7.	Gott des Himmels (*Requiem*)
144	May the grace of Christ our Saviour	8 7. 8 7.	Waltham
348	May the mind of Christ my Saviour	8 7. 8 5.	St. Leonard's
215	My faith looks up to Thee	6 6 4. 6 6 6 4.	i. Malvern ii. Olivet
354	My Father, for another night	C.M.	St. Flavian
342	My glorious Victor, Prince divine	L.M.	Bodmin
321	My God, accept my heart this day	C.M.	St. Peter
6	My God, how wonderful Thou art	C.M.	Westminster (*St. Fulbert*)
325	My God! I know, I feel Thee mine	C.M.	Metzler's Redhead (*St. Fulbert*)
257	My God, I thank Thee, who hast made	8 4. 8 4. 8 4.	i. Oldown ii. Wentworth
236	My hope is built on nothing less	8 8. 8 8. 8 8.	Cotswold (*Surrey*)
46	My song is love unknown	6 6. 6 6. 4 4. 4 4.	i. Love Unknown ii. St. John
281	Nearer, my God, to Thee	6 4. 6 4. 6 6 4.	i. Horbury ii. Glenpark
155	Never further than Thy cross	7 7. 7 7.	Lübeck (*Heinlein & Song* 13)
356	New every morning is the love	L.M.	Melcombe
106	None other Lamb, none other Name	8 10. 10 4.	Ellasgarth★
60	Not all the blood of beasts	S.M.	St. George
213	Not what these hands have done	S.M.	St. Bride
237	Now I have found the ground wherein	8 8. 8 8. 8 8.	Farmborough (*Melita*)
26	Now thank we all our God	6 7. 6 7. 6 6. 6 6.	Nun danket

No.	First Line	Metre	Name of Tune
41	Once in royal David's city	8 7. 8 7. 7 7.	Irby*
319	Open, Lord, my inward ear	7 6. 7 6. 7 7. 7 6.	Carrick
119	Our blest Redeemer, ere He breathed	8 6. 8 4.	i. Shrewsbury ii. St. Cuthbert
234	Peace, perfect peace, in this dark world of sin?	10. 10.	Song 46
401	Praise God, from whom all blessings flow	L.M.	Old 100th (*Lasst uns erfreuen*)
8	Praise, my soul, the King of heaven	8 7. 8 7. 4 7.	Praise, my soul*
20	Praise the Lord! ye heavens, adore Him	8 7. 8 7. D.	Austria
7	Praise to the Holiest in the height	C.M.	Gerontius (*Chorus Angelorum & Richmond*)
24	Praise to the Lord, the Almighty	14 14. 4. 7. 8.	Lobe den Herren
267	Prayer is the soul's sincere desire	C.M.	Beatitudo
261	Present with the two or three	7 7 7.	i. Tyholland ii. St. Philip
199	Put thou thy trust in God	S.M.	Shere (*Carlisle*)
80	Rejoice, the Lord is King!	6 6. 6 6. 8 8.	Gopsal
233	Rejoice today with one accord	8 7. 8 7. 6 6. 6 6 7.	Ein' feste Burg
178	Revive Thy work, O Lord	S.M.	Venice (*Carlisle*)
50	Ride on! ride on in majesty!	L.M.	St. Drostane (*Winchester New*)
211	Rock of ages, cleft for me	7 7. 7 7. 7 7.	Petra (*Wells*)
362	Saviour, again to Thy dear name we raise	10 10. 10 10.	i. Ellers ii. Julius
365	Saviour, breathe an evening blessing	8 7. 8 7.	Sunset
323	Search me, O God! my actions try	C.M.	Caithness (*St. Flavian*)
391	See, amid the winter's snow	7 7. 7 7. and refrain	Humility*
200	Seek ye first, not earthly pleasure	8 8 8. 3. Trochaic	Aescendune
167	Send forth the gospel! Let it run	L.M.	Cannock (*Birling & Ombersley*)
388	Shepherds came, their praises bringing	8 8 8. 7.	Quem Pastores Laudavere
385	Sing lullaby!	4. 9 4 8. 9 9. 4.	The Infant King
198	Sinners Jesus will receive	7 7. 7 7. 7 7.	Wells
299	Soldiers of Christ, arise	S.M. D.S.M.	i. St. Ethelwald ii. From Strength to Strength
177	Soldiers of the cross, arise!	7 7. 7 7.	Orientis Partibus
255	Sometimes a light surprises	7 6. 7 6. D.	Pearsall (*Crüger*)
23	Songs of praise the angels sang	7 7. 7 7.	Culbach
187	Souls of men! why will ye scatter	8 7. 8 7.	Cross of Jesus
179	Sow in the morn thy seed	S.M.	i. Quinta ii. Fareham
269	Speak, Lord, in the stillness	6 5. 6 5.	Quietude (*Eudoxia*)
186	Speed Thy servants, Saviour, speed them	8 7. 8 7. 4 7.	Neander
130	Spirit divine, attend our prayers	C.M.	Störl (*Richmond*)
176	Spread, O spread, thou mighty word	7 7. 7 7.	Harts (*Vienna*)
1	Stand up, and bless the Lord	S.M.	Carlisle* (*Quinta*)
296	Stand up, stand up for Jesus	7 6. 7 6. D.	Morning Light
162	Strengthen for service, Lord, the hands	8 7. 8 7. Iambic	i. Ach Gott und Herr ii. Dominus regit me
361	Sun of my soul, Thou Saviour dear	L.M.	Abends (*Birling*)
372	Sweet is the work, my God, my King	L.M.	Solothurn (*Warrington*)

No.	First Line	Metre	Name of Tune
350	Take my life, and let it be	7 7. 7 7.	Lübeck (*Newington*)
288	'Take up thy cross,' the Saviour said	L.M.	Breslau
378	Te Deum		
311	Teach me, my God and King	S.M.	Sandys
353	Teach me Thy way, O Lord	6 4. 6 4. 6 6. 6 4.	Camacha
150	Ten thousand times ten thousand	7 6. 8 6. D.	Alford
141	The Church's one foundation	7 6. 7 6. D.	Aurelia
364	The day Thou gavest, Lord, is ended	9 8. 9 8.	i. St. Clement
			ii. Les Commande-mens de Dieu
394	The first Nowell the angel did say	Irregular	The First Nowell*
11	The God of Abraham praise	6 6. 8 4. D.	Leoni
104	The head that once was crowned with thorns	C.M.	St. Magnus
277	The King of love my Shepherd is	8 7. 8 7. Iambic	i. St. Columba
			ii. Dominus regit me
188	The Lord is rich and merciful	D.C.M.	Petersham (*Forest Green*)
279	The Lord's my Shepherd, I'll not want	C.M.	Crimond (*University*)
184	The Master comes! He calls for thee	8 8. 8 8. 8 8.	Woking (*Wych Cross*)
382	The night is dark, the winds are still	8 6. 8 6. 6.	The Babe in the Manger
292	The Son of God goes forth to war	D.C.M.	Ellacombe (*Ladywell*)
137	The Spirit breathes upon the Word	C.M.	Stroudwater (*Abridge*)
67	The strife is o'er, the battle done	8 8 8. 4.	i. Victory
			ii. Vulpius
243	Thee will I love, my strength, my tower	8 8. 8 8. 8 8.	Wych Cross (*Pater Omnium*)
214	There is a fountain filled with blood	C.M.	Belmont (*Wiltshire*)
57	There is a green hill far away	C.M.	i. Horsley
			ii. This endris nyght
71	Thine be the glory, risen, conquering Son	10 11. 11 11. and refrain	Maccabaeus
259	Thine for ever! God of love	7 7. 7 7.	Newington
370	This is the day of light	S.M.	i. Dominica
			ii. Quinta
371	This is the day the Lord hath made	C.M.	Richmond
163	Thou art coming, O my Saviour	8 7. 8 8 7. 7 7. 7 7.	Beverley
105	Thou art the Way; to Thee alone	C.M.	St. James
45	Thou didst leave Thy throne	Irregular	Margaret
367	Thou glorious Sun of Righteousness	L.M.	Philippine (*Church Triumphant*)
337	Thou hidden love of God, whose height	8 8. 8 8. 8 8.	St. Matthias (*Vater Unser & Stella*)
114	Thou hidden source of calm repose	8 8. 8 8. 8 8.	i. Vater Unser
			ii. Stella
89 390 }	Thou who wast rich	9 8. 9 8. 9 8.	Fragrance*
164	Thou whose almighty word	6 6 4. 6 6 6 4.	Moscow
343	Thou whose name is callèd Jesus	8 7. 8 7. 7 7	Requiem (*Gott des Himmels*)
247	Through all the changing scenes of life	C.M.	i. Wiltshire
			ii. University
272	Through the night of doubt and sorrow	8 7. 8 7.	Marching
173	Thy kingdom come, O God	6 6. 6 6.	St. Cecilia
351	Thy life was given for me	6 6. 6 6. 6 6.	i. Old 120th
			ii. Baca
274	Thy way, not mine, O Lord	6 6. 6 6.	Ibstone
111	To the name of our salvation	8 7. 8 7. 8 7.	i. Oriel
			ii. Midhurst

No.	First Line	Metre	Name of Tune
115	To Thee, and to Thy Christ, O God	D.C.M.	St. Matthew
242	Unto the hills around do I lift up	10 4. 10 4. 10 10.	Alberta
386	Unto us a boy is born!	7 6. 7 7. Irregular	Puer Nobis
286	Walk in the light: so shalt thou know	C.M.	Binchester (St. Agnes)
108	We come, O Christ, to Thee	6 6. 6 6. 8 8.	Christchurch
181	We have heard the joyful sound	7 3. 7 3. 7 7. 7 3.	Limpsfield
226	We have not known Thee as we ought	8 8. 8 8. 8 8.	Melita (Surrey)
376	We plough the fields, and scatter	7 6. 7 6. D. 6 6. 8 4.	Wir pflügen
301	'We rest on Thee,' our shield and our defender	11 10. 11 10.	O Perfect Love (St. Osyth)
54	We sing the praise of Him who died	L.M.	Bodley (Church Triumphant)
201	Weary of self and laden with my sin	10 10. 10 10.	Old 124th
271	What a Friend we have in Jesus	8 7. 8 7. D.	Blaenwern
246	When all Thy mercies, O my God	C.M.	Contemplation
55	When I survey the wondrous cross	L.M.	Rockingham
109	When morning gilds the skies	6 6 6. D.	Laudes Domini
77	Where high the heavenly temple stands	L.M.	Winchester New
78	Wherewith, O God, shall I draw near	L.M.	O Amor quam exstaticus (Breslau)
37	While shepherds watched their flocks by night	C.M.	Winchester Old★
305	Who is on the Lord's side?	6 5. 6 5. Ter.	Hermas
47	Who is this, so weak and helpless?	8 7. 8 7. D.	St. Audrey New (Bethany)
79	With joy we meditate the grace	C.M.	St. Bernard
300	Why should I fear the darkest hour	8 8 8.	Keynsham
19	Ye holy angels bright	6 6. 6 6. 4 4. 4 4.	Darwall's 148th★
100	Ye servants of God	5 5. 5 5. 6 5. 6 5.	Paderborn (Hanover)
312	Ye servants of the Lord	S.M.	Narenza

NATIONAL ANTHEM

GOD save our gracious Queen,
Long live our noble Queen,
  God save the Queen!
Send her victorious,
Happy and glorious,
Long to reign over us;
  God save the Queen!

2 Thy choicest gifts in store
On her be pleased to pour,
  Long may she reign!
May she defend our laws,
And ever give us cause
To sing with heart and voice
  God save the Queen!